Here's What Other
Good Morning I Love You,
Maintaining Sanity & Humor Amidst
Widowhood, Caregiving and Alzheimer's

Vicki Veasey's *Good Morning I Love You* is one of my favorite books in guiding families through the trials and tribulations of being a caregiver for a senior loved one afflicted with Alzheimer's Disease. The subtitle and blurb *Maintaining Sanity & Humor Amidst Widowhood, Caregiving, and Alzheimer's* certainly lends credibility to Veasey's message, as readers not only will entrust her advice, but they will trust that they too are not alone on this journey.

—**Linda M. McKenna, Owner & Senior Care Advocate Golden Rule Senior Placement Services, LLC**

Many of us have first-hand knowledge of Alzheimer's/dementia through family or friends affected by this insidious disease. Those of us who have been in the position of caregiver, know and relate to the cycle of pain, love, humor, disbelief, and forgiveness; we all experience on our journey of "doing our best," yet lamenting our shortcomings. In *Good Morning I Love You, Maintaining Sanity & Humor Amidst Widowhood, Caregiving and Alzheimer's*, author Vicki Veasey takes us on an unfettered pilgrimage through not only the caregiving experience but the heartache and joys of the rest of life that continue unabated along-side our adventure as caretaker to our loved one(s). Along the way, she graciously and vulnerably shares sage advice and tips she's acquired along the way. *Good Morning I Love You* is an honest account of the challenges in the day to day life of dealing with Alzheimer's/dementia. It is a worthwhile read for anyone feeling isolated in their position. Vicki reminds us we are not alone.

—**Dianne Osmun, Author of**
Finding Mom in the Midst of Alzheimer's:
A Daughter's Journey of Healing,
Reconciliation and Acceptance

Vicki has written a raw, honest, and compassionate account of what caregiving of Alzheimer's patients is like. Folk who have been through this will most certainly identify, and those who are beginning this process have a helpful and clear vision of what is ahead. This book is a must-read for caregivers, pastors, and anyone else involved in the care of those suffering from dementia and Alzheimer's.

—**Reverend Robin A. DeAngelis**

As I scrolled through the Table of Contents, I was captivated by the chapter titles such as, "Where's the Nearest Bathroom?" "Only Mom Would Have Understood," and "If Only I Had Stood My Ground." These and other chapters enticed me to read further. Reading the Introduction and finding the statements of "when will this end," and "when will I have the opportunity to have fun and live life to its fullest" made me realize that as a caregiver, I had the same feelings as Vicki and even the same sense of guilt for even thinking them. I knew then that this story would be as promised: a truly honest story of Caregiving. A definite read for anyone caring for those they love.

—**Karen Kline, BSN, RN**
Former Coordinator of Memory Lane Respite
and Support Group
First United Methodist Church
Homosassa, Florida

In *Good Morning I Love You, Maintaining Sanity & Humor Amidst Widowhood, Caregiving and Alzheimer's* Vicki Veasey's un-censored account of the daily life of being a caregiver for both parents with Alzheimer's and dementia will bring you to laughter and/or tears. Out of her experience using raw language, she has written a much-needed resource for those facing difficult times with loved ones diagnosed with Alzheimer's. My stepfather's last years were spent with this debilitating disease and I had no resources like Vicki's book. I have also worked for years with hospice patients, including Alzheimer's and dementia patients. I have trained hundreds of volunteers on how to respond and interact with those in mental and cognitive decline and have visited many patients within Alzheimer's facilities and floors. I have also witnessed the wear and tear on the families trying to be the sole caregivers for their loved ones. *Good Morning I Love You, Maintaining Sanity & Humor Amidst Widowhood, Caregiving and Alzheimer's* should become a book every home health care, hospice, and Alzheimer's non-profit organization or nursing home provides for their clients' families.

—Marian Poeppelmeyer, Speaker, Coach, Author of *Finding My Father*; former Hospice Volunteer Director for ten counties and former Hospice Community Liaison

Vicki writes from the heart. As the granddaughter of an Alzheimer's victim, I wish Vicki's tips had been around then. The book is insightful and has wonderful tips if your loved one has this awful disease. I would recommend it to anyone whose loved one has any form of dementia.

—Rebecka Vigus, The Writer Whisperer, award winning author of *Crossing the Line*

Vicki is faced with caring for both her parents while dealing with the declining health and loss of her husband. Like many who have a rough time, she learned a lot about caring for folks with differing dementia symptoms. Thankfully for us she shares what she learns in neat little tips scattered throughout her book. If you are now facing the prospect of dealing with a loved one with dementia, read this book and several books to help guide you!

—**Susan Straley, Author of the Trippin Series starting with** *Alzheimer's Trippin' with George* **and** *The Journey Continues Alzheimer's Trippin' with George*

Good Morning I Love You

Maintaining Sanity & Humor Amidst
Widowhood, Caregiving and Alzheimer's

VICKI VEASEY

Based on a True Story

AUTHOR ACADEMY elite

Published by Author Academy Elite
PO Box 43, Powell, OH 43035
www.AuthorAcademyElite.com

Identifiers:
Library of Congress Control Number: 2020908188
Paperback ISBN: 978-1-64746-266-6
Hardcover ISBN: 978-1-64746-267-3
E-Book ISBN: 978-1-64746-268-0

Available in hardback, paperback, e-book, and audiobook

Any Internet addresses (websites, blogs, etc.) and telephone numbers
printed in this book are offered as a resource. They are not intended in any
way to be or imply an endorsement by Author Academy Elite, nor does
Author Academy Elite vouch for the content of these sites and
numbers for the life of this book.

Everyone in this memoir is a real person who graced my life in
some capacity, no composite characters. The dialogues and events are
true to my memory. Most individuals have retained their own names with
the exception of several, whose names have been changed to
protect their privacy.

Cover design by Debbie O'Byrne

Dedicated...

In loving memory to my husband, Matthew J. Veasey, Jr. and my parents, Paul and Phyllis Heltunen.

To caregivers, past, present, and future, keep your faith in God—He will guide you and give you strength as you face the daily challenges of caring for your loved one with Alzheimer's or dementia.

And most importantly, to God for guiding me on this journey called life. I couldn't have survived the two most crucial years of my life if it weren't for God's love and grace.

Table of Contents

Part 2—A Door Opens

Part 3—Acceptance, Moving Forward

Foreword

I'd like to introduce myself. As the former primary care physician for Paul and Phyllis Heltunen, I was a direct eyewitness to the story you are about to read. Their story was not a unique one; there are similar stories of other families in the United States, and even worldwide, who have been affected by dementia and Alzheimer's. The real story is how dementia, especially Alzheimer's, becomes an unwilling member of family dynamics. When Vicki first mentioned she was writing a book, I asked if I could contribute. She was delighted. I strongly felt a physician's perspective on dementia, especially Alzheimer's, was warranted.

I am board certified as a geriatrics and internal medicine physician. I've treated many patients with dementia, and I anticipate the percentage of dementia patients I will treat in the future will increase as the baby-boomer generation continues to age. When you are a physician who cares for dementia patients, you not only learn about your patient but also their caregiver. I've looked many caregivers in the eye and became adept at reading their untold stories as reflected in their weary facial expressions, tired and dejected eyes, and physically exhausted body language.

After a while, you can recognize a caregiver's silhouette from fifty feet away.

When I reflect upon Vicki's dad, I remember how confused he was. He tried his best to camouflage his confusion, but after a while, he'd just sit mutely and smile a lopsided grin. Her mom was inquisitive—she'd ask the same questions repeatedly, like a broken record. I don't know how caregivers endure days, weeks, months, and even years of hearing the same questions being asked over and over again! Talk about caregiver patience! And every time I'd assess Paul and Phyllis' health, I did a mental assessment of their caregiver as well, their daughter, because she was the one who was caregiving 24/7 and shouldering all the responsibility. In my practice, the caregiver is just as important in the physician-patient ratio as the patient I am treating. Without the caregiver being in sound mind, good physical health, and emotionally capable of handling the daily responsibility of caregiving, eventually, a problem will develop, and in all likelihood, caregiver burnout will occur.

After some reflection, I realized I want to address the impact caregiving has on the caregiver. In my opinion, the caregiver should receive the Nobel prize or the Man or Woman of the Year award. Most people do not realize the sacrifice caregivers make in order to care for their loved one with dementia. To be a caregiver is a true dedication of love!

Vicki was one of the millions of caregivers who have cared for, or are still caring for, a loved one. The following statements represent typical comments I've heard in my practice:

- "My dad forgot the stove was on; we almost had a fire."

- "$100,000 was missing from my mom's account. She bought stuff she never wanted."

- "My dad is getting isolated and avoids talking to us. He responds to us with a smile, but rarely talks."

- "My mom called the police last week. Though my dad isn't a stranger, she did not remember him."

- "My grandmother sees little creatures talking to her all the time."

- "My dad, who used to be a chemistry professor, has a hard time balancing his bank account."

Dementia usually starts when family members report a change. The patient is tested and based on the results, the patient will be informed if they have the dreaded D-word, dementia. The next question is ultimately, "Do I have Alzheimer's?" Once a diagnosis is made, eventually a caregiver volunteers, and it's only a matter of time before I can see the evidence of stress in the caregiver's face. Vicki was no exception to the *caregiver face*; however, I give her credit for making the best of a bad situation. She not only had one person with Alzheimer's to care for but two. One is bad enough to care for; two is even more stressful.

Caregivers are often sleep deprived, waking in the middle of the night to a loved one who turned the stove on at 2:00 a.m., or frantically searching every drawer or closet for a wedding dress at 3:00 a.m. Once awake, the caregiver has a difficult time trying to fall back asleep between the worry of what transpired and keeping an ear always tuned to any noise in the house. The lack of sleep eventually takes its toll on the caregiver. And some caregivers, like Vicki, actually quit their jobs in order to care for their dementia loved one. In this worst-case scenario, the caregiver is without an income at a time when expenses usually increase due to incontinence, wandering, respite help, and medical costs.

Then, there are those other Vicki's, scattered throughout the United States, who also are devoted caregivers to a loved one with dementia. Always keeping abreast of their loved ones needs, physically becoming tired and exhausted, emotionally anxious and yes, even scared. And don't forget, the caregiver's relationship with their immediate family and even friends is also impacted because the caregiver doesn't have enough hours in their day to provide the time that seems warranted for all the individual members of their family.

Each situation is unique, yet similar. A wife rushes her husband to the doctor stating, "My husband has dementia. I need insurance to help cover the costs at home." As you try to explain to the wife what health insurance doesn't cover, she laments to you, "My husband is a large man. I need help giving him a shower or to get him off the floor when he falls. I need *real* help!" The sad, horrible truth is health insurance does not cover respite help, which every caregiver needs. Respite help is strictly an out of pocket expense that many caregivers cannot afford. Health insurance will only cover medications, lab work, radiology, and physician visits. Depending on where they live will also depend on what services are available through their state or local governments. Available services are not treated equally throughout the United States, and getting off a waiting list for services can sometimes take months or even years.

Sometimes, Medicaid can help cover some of the expenses. And despite paying Medicare taxes throughout a person's working life, if someone makes $2,500 per month or more in retirement, they do not quality for Medicare assistance. A shocking truth, but one that families face every day.

Another situation I see routinely in my practice is the husband who comes to my office and tells me, "Doc, you started my wife on dementia medication, but there's been no improvement; we need to try something else." Here's another sad fact: unfortunately, prescribed medication for dementia is not expected to improve the memory or behavior conditions. As the patient's condition worsens, medication will only help in trying to calm the patient. The caregiver basically has to learn to adapt and live with the changing situation.

I've also been confronted by the husband who states his children, who live in other locations in the United States, accuse their father of not caring for their mother who has dementia. The children have based their concerns on rudimentary information they've gleaned from the internet and have no true reference to what caring for someone with dementia is all about. My answer in these situations is always the same, "You are doing a great job!

If you have questions, always ask me. I recommend you ask your children to schedule a vacation to help you with your wife, and when they come, *you* take a much-needed break or send their mother to them so they care for her for a few days. Trust me, they will learn very quickly how difficult caregiving is and realize what a great job you are doing."

I can't forget Dr. Google. The caregiver is confronted by other family members who have conducted a five-minute Google search and believe they know more about dementia and caregiving than the patient's physician. The poor caregiver is caught in the middle. On these occasions, my response is, "You cannot be a doctor by reading five minutes on Google; you need ten years of education to do that, and your loved one's caregiver is doing a great job. He or she is an amazing person, and you should be thankful for their dedicated service to your family."

And finally, there's the case of the caregiver who hired respite care for four hours every week, in order to have time to pay bills and accomplish other household chores that he or she is behind in doing. My advice to the caregiver, "Get out of the house for those four hours. Take a break, and don't even think of your loved one. Just go out and do something you like. Go to a movie, or meet friends for lunch; make time for yourself, or you will start to experience the effects of caregiver burnout."

I have lots of other similar stories I could share. Most importantly, I want to convey to you how great Vicki and all those other Vicki's all over the world are. They selflessly give of their time, emotions, and strength as caregivers for their loved ones with dementia. They sacrifice their jobs, future earnings, family, and much more in order to care for their loved one. Not many people will do that! I firmly believe that every caregiver deserves to be Man or Woman of the Year. At least recognize their hard work. Look them in the face and say thank you. Ask them how you can help, or ask them, "Can I give you a break for a few hours every week?" Don't be judgmental! Be supportive!

—Hany Abskhroun, MD

Introduction

I'm going to be perfectly honest with you. I have a long history of not knowing how to say no when someone asks me to do something or when I see something that needs to be done. My heart yells out, *Here, let me help!* Afterwards, my inner conscience groans and laments that once again, I jumped into a new project without thinking it through. In the back of my mind, I hear my inner demon laughing incredulously, *What the hell did you get yourself into?*

I wasn't always that way. As a child, I was a shy introvert who kept to herself. Other children probably saw me as an anomaly. I exhibited no interest or even curiosity in playing with other children, including my numerous cousins on my dad's side of the family. I attribute this to being an only child, raised by parents who'd been married eight years before I mysteriously came along. My world consisted of parents, grandparents, aunts, and uncles. I viewed my cousins as strange, little creatures, who I couldn't figure out. Trying to understand what joy they derived from running around, yelling, screaming at the tops of their lungs, hitting and fighting with each other, and getting into trouble was totally beyond anything I could fathom.

I was never encouraged to play with other children and spent a great deal of time with my parents and my maternal grandma, and they didn't seem to feel it was important. I admit I preferred it that way. As my maternal grandparents' only grandchild for ten years, my grandma treated me like I an adult. I can still see Grandma sitting in her green recliner, feet resting on the raised footrest in her golden-walled living room. The sunshine is sparkling through her glistening-clean windows. Her glasses are perched squarely on her nose, and her head of short, tightly curled hair is buried within the confines of the racing form she is studiously reviewing for the upcoming races. Every once in a while, she takes a sip from her Ark Lanes coffee cup and explains in voluminous detail the strengths and weaknesses of each horse, how they placed in previous races, and how well the horses did at other tracks. Grandma was a walking encyclopedia of the Hazel Park Race Track. My grandma could quote you the exact amount she'd won or lost on each horse, right down to the very penny!

My grandma was notorious for complaining mercilessly about my grandpa, a kind, quiet soul who worked hard his entire life. She also ridiculed any child I remotely showed interest in becoming friends with. The idea that I needed socialization with other children was as foreign to my parents and grandma as it was for me to go on a roller coaster ride or visit a toy store. In my mind, I was already an adult. I became an adult shortly after I graduated from diapers, bypassing childhood entirely. As a result, I grew up with an adult's perspective on life while imprisoned within a child's body. In reality, I was *never* a child.

So, it's not surprising that later in life, I found myself in the role of caregiver for my parents, both afflicted with Alzheimer's. It was never a question of *if* I'd care for them but rather *how* I'd care for them. How was I supposed to juggle a marriage, a full-time job, two pups, and maybe, if I was lucky, five minutes of *me time* once in a while. No one said life is easy. No one said life is fair. And no one said we have the right to a carefree existence. We all have one thing in common, no matter who we are. We are human. To be part of the sane human race is to experience emotions, compassion, and empathy for others. It also means when we are faced with challenges, we can either ignore the challenge or accept it. I was prepared for my role as caregiver because I didn't know the freedom associated with childhood. Because I was privy to an adult world at an extremely young age, it was easier for me to relinquish my role in the workforce and accept responsibility for my parent's health and wellbeing.

I've often heard people say God doesn't give you more than you can handle. Based on my life, God must have one hell of a sense of humor, or He has the mistaken assumption that I'm a much stronger person than I think I am. Or perhaps, to strengthen me, God is helping me to acquire a better understanding of the true meaning of life. Sadly, after my husband died, I learned more about love than I did when Matthew was alive. I made decisions that not only impacted my life but also the lives of my parents.

It isn't easy to take on the role of caregiver. It's an everyday challenge that will never get better. The only outcome will eventually be death. I took each day as it presented, with all its peaks and valleys. There were times when I wanted to scream out to a passive void, *When will this end? When will I regain some semblance of life as I knew it? When will I have the opportunity to have fun, live life to its fullest, and laugh with unadorned abandon?* Maybe never. Or, perhaps, what I experienced—the highs and lows of caregiving—would help me enjoy these truths with greater awareness and appreciation later in life.

At the end of the day, when I got ready for bed, I looked at my reflection in the mirror and reminded myself, that's me. Although I endured this experience alone—grieving for a spouse at the same time I was caregiving for my parents—I reminded myself each day I was doing the best I could. Depending on how the day had gone, I didn't always recognize or want to acknowledge the person who stared back at me. Perhaps that's another lesson from God as well. I didn't know what God's plan was for the future, but I knew I had to do the best with what I faced then.

At times, you may be offended by my frankness. That too was a challenge I faced when writing this exposé. Do I omit the reality so as not to offend the faint of heart or include all the harsh veracities to paint a clearer picture of this dreaded disease? Ultimately, I asked myself what my parents would prefer. Two things set my mom apart from anyone else I've ever known: her objectivity and her open mindedness. She influenced how I look at the world and how I treat people. Thanks to my mom, I believe I'm a better person. I am more accepting of others who are different from me, and I have a more tender, compassionate heart for those who are less fortunate.

My mom's heartfelt desire was to be a journalist, something that never transpired. Lost dreams are one of life's regrets common to all of us. Even though she couldn't speak for herself, I knew in my heart she would want to make a difference. She would want the honest, unsolicited truth about Alzheimer's and caregiving to be told. If she can't write about it herself, then I will do it for her. That's the least I can do for all that she's provided me throughout my life. As I mentioned earlier, being an only child allowed me to know my parents in a way that most children never have the chance to know their parents.

Being a full-time caregiver has been the most challenging role I've ever faced. Yet at the same time, it's the most rewarding experience I've ever encountered. If you are or have been a caregiver, there may be situations you can relate to. For others who haven't dealt with this challenge, I hope this narrative will better prepare you psychologically for what you may face if you are ever called upon to care for a loved one. As we all age, there will be a greater number of individuals who will find themselves caring for a loved one. No one should enter this world of caregiving blindsided without some idea of what to expect. Each Alzheimer's case is different. That's what makes this disease so difficult to deal with or find a cure for. This book is written for those who one day may face this challenge.

The Alzheimer's Association predicts there will be 15 million Americans with Alzheimer's by 2050. Currently, there are approximately 5 million cases in the United States, but in all reality, that's underestimated since there are many undocumented cases. I pray that someday a cure will be found for Alzheimer's. In the meantime, I sincerely hope that those who are called upon to care for a loved one will find some comfort in knowing that you are not alone in this battle. It's how you face the challenge, accept your role and all its responsibilities, and open your heart to God that will assist you in looking in your mirror each night and forgiving yourself for any transgressions you inadvertently struggled with during the day.

Caregiving for a loved one is not easy. I reminded myself it might be me one day who needs a caregiver. How would I want to be treated? Would my caregiver be understanding and accepting of what I'm going through? And would my caregiver still love me no matter what?

PART I

A Door Closes

Christmas Letter 2016

Merry Christmas!

'Tis the Season to count our blessings! We have a lot to be thankful for this year, no major health problems, car problems, or sinkholes. We are all healthy, together, and living in Florida. What more could we ask for?

Matthew and Vicki started the year with a mini vacation to Cedar Key, a small coastal town about two and a half hours north of Tampa on the western coast of Florida. Cedar Key is where they go to de-stress from daily life. They can even take the pups. It's a dog friendly place! The scenic beauty, tranquil surroundings, cheerful locals, and laidback atmosphere have made Cedar Key Matthew and Vicki's "special place."

The highlight of our year was celebrating Paul's 95th birthday on February 23rd. Paul shares a birthday with his brother-in-law Bob, and his nephew, Robert. All three celebrated together this year, just like they did five years ago. Family from Michigan, South Carolina, Minnesota, and Florida converged onto a rental house in Davenport, Florida, which we dubbed "Birthday Central," for a week-long celebration. Cousin Jim stopped by to join in the fun, Matthew and Uncle Bob played a round of golf at Providence's golf course, and we ate like it was going to be our last supper. Matthew treated us to his signature spaghetti dinner, and Cousin Dave made his world-famous ribs. To those who helped Paul celebrate his birthday, thank you very much. We love you!

Paul and Phyllis both have Alzheimer's. Paul still remembers family whereas Phyllis has lost recognition. In May, Mary Ann, a home health aide, was introduced into our lives. She comes Monday through Friday for three hours each day. Mary Ann makes their lunch, helps them exercise, takes Phyllis for walks around the block, and listens to their childhood stories. She's been a God-send for us.

Vicki continues to work with medical residents for an Internal Medicine Program at a local hospital. Matthew loves to golf, sing in the church choir, and communicate with family and friends via Facebook. The pups, Kipper and Katy, provide unconditional love and laughs!

May you have a Blessed Christmas Holiday and a
Happy & Healthy 2017!!!
Matthew, Vicki, Paul, Phyllis, Kipper & Katy

P.S. How about those Detroit Lions!!! No matter what happens post-season, they made us proud to be Lions fans!!!

CHAPTER 1

Christmas 2016, The Beginning of a Very Long Year

Week before Christmas

After a long, grueling day at work, followed by stops for Christmas shopping and groceries with heavy plastic bags and paper packages clutched precariously in my arms, I trudged from the garage into our home. My weary soul was shocked out of my exhaustion by a gut-wrenching, unearthly sound. I stopped. I listened. My first thought was it sounded like an elephant trying to get something dislodged from its trunk. Concerned, I quickened my pace as I passed through the laundry room into the kitchen. Standing in the middle of the kitchen, bent over at the waist, was my husband Matthew. The gut-wrenching sound was emanating from him. It sounded like he was desperately trying to barf up one of his lungs, without success.

"Matthew," I cried, "what happened?"

I couldn't believe how bad his cold had gotten in one day. He sounded fine the night before, and at church on Sunday, he sang his solo for the Christmas Cantata like a heavenly, melodic angel. Now, my dear husband sounded like he was on death's door. Matthew tried several times to straighten up and say something, but with each attempt, a new coughing fit would start, much worse than the one before. To get some relief, he bent over again, almost touching his toes trying to catch his breath and clear his throat. His face, what little of it I could see in this bent position, was bright red from his labors, as red as Santa's Christmas suit.

"Matthew, promise me you'll call your doctor tomorrow morning. With Christmas Eve on Saturday, his office will probably close early on Friday. Don't wait until the last minute. You don't want to be in the hospital for Christmas," I told him.

I remember saying those exact words to Matthew, a man who could be both ambivalent and kind-hearted, stubborn, and generous. On this occasion, he was being extremely stubborn trying to doctor himself with over-the-counter cough syrups and elixirs—magic potions that apparently were having no effect on curing a cold that only yesterday was an occasional sneeze and sniffle. As he tried to straighten up, his face was sweaty and reddish purple from all his exertions. He pulled his handkerchief from his trousers pocket and wiped the sweat from his face. He blew his nose, then shrugged me off with a dismissive flick of his hand as if I was one of Kipper's stray dog hairs stubbornly stuck to his pants. Turning his back to me, Matthew resumed preparations for our dinner. For a man who was rarely sick during the twenty-plus years I'd known him, I questioned his lack of response to my suggestion. It would have been obvious to even a child that he was a sick person.

As the week progressed, it was more obvious that Matthew's cold wasn't getting any better. Despite all my comments to the fact, he remained steadfast in his opinion that he didn't need to seek medical intervention. He believed he was doing a good job of trying to convince me he was feeling better, and he was counting on me being too distracted with the perpetual last-minute preparations for the Christmas holiday to notice how quickly his condition was deteriorating. Matthew was seventy-six years old, young enough to be more reasonable, yet too old to be treated like a child. One thing I learned during our marriage was just how far I could coax him, when to let up, and most importantly, when to compromise. If I coaxed him too much, he would firmly cement his opinion and obstinately refuse to hear reason. He didn't take instruction very well, especially from me. He may have won this round, but I was determined to knock some sense into his stubborn, thick-headed, Irish skull.

By the time I got home on Friday, December 23, I was looking forward to a three-day holiday weekend. Matthew finally admitted, which was hard for him to do, that he felt terrible. He reluctantly came clean that he'd been sweating profusely for several days, experiencing chills, high fever, and fatigue. Despite how he was feeling, I still couldn't get him to budge from his conviction that he didn't need to see a doctor. I went to bed that night with trepidation and concern. I punched my pillow mercilessly like I was going five rounds with a youthful Mohammed Ali while trying to figure out how to get Matthew's stubborn Irish butt to a doctor. After tossing and turning for several hours, I drifted off into a restless sleep. Matthew woke me an hour later. He was ready to go to the ER, a momentous decision. I was relieved, yet at the same time, *I was pissed off!* Why did he have to wait until early Christmas Eve morning to finally come to his senses? Based on how he looked and sounded, it was now inevitable he would be spending *his* Christmas in the hospital.

The hospital's Emergency Room was buzzing. Patients were everywhere. This was the second month of what was shaping up to be a very busy flu season. We sat in muted silence. Matthew felt like crap and kept coughing. I reflected on how to adjust our plans for Christmas Day. I was expecting my Aunt Lou and Uncle Ron to join us, like they normally do. They would understand

7

if we needed to postpone Christmas for a day or two. With my parents' Alzheimer's, I knew it wouldn't be a problem for them, either. In all probability, *I* was the only one concerned about postponing Christmas. I was the only one of us who still worked and had to plan vacation days carefully around my schedule. Being a GME Internal Medicine Coordinator at a neighboring hospital, the week leading up to the end of the month was always filled with a million tasks that needed to be done to close out the month and start the residents' next month. In addition to this being the end of the year and fiscal quarter, there were additional mandatory reports to be compiled, generated, and submitted. The world of Graduate Medical Education never stands still. It's in constant motion, for both the residents and the administrative staff. It was difficult to take vacation time for the rank and file in this very small department.

While Matthew waited patiently for test results, which was unnatural for him, he worked his Sudoku puzzle. After a while, he urged me to go home to check on my parents. Even though I was reluctant to leave, I knew he was right. My parents both had Alzheimer's. My mother's condition was more severe than my dad's. My mom, Phyllis, needed constant supervision. She used a walker, which she had named Tilly many years before. My dad, Paul, could be helpful in keeping an eye on Mom, doing simple tasks like pour a cup of coffee or take the dogs out to the pen. Dad loved his Detroit Tigers baseball and Michigan State basketball, coached by fellow Yooper, Tom Izzo. My parents could no longer be unsupervised for long periods of time, like overnight. Our dogs, Kipper and Katy, are both rescue dogs, adopted from the Florida Cocker Spaniel Rescue. While I was home, Matthew called to let me know he was being admitted. He was diagnosed with pneumonia.

At the time, we had no idea this was going to be the beginning of a life-changing year for us. In hindsight, we would have appreciated a hint of what was to come, like a message from God or a sign from an angel. Something, anything. I was too wrapped up in the inconsequential details that define life, especially all the particulars I've been known to focus on during Christmas. Incidentals in the long run really mean nothing, but they have a way of taking up time, clouding our thoughts, and driving us to distraction. In the long run, these things really aren't important, but at the time, we believe they have the utmost importance. Perhaps if we'd some inkling of what the next eight months would bring, we would have lived this time a little differently. But this Christmas, we were unexpectantly focused on Matthew's pneumonia diagnosis, assuming he would recover and be back to his robust, normal self within a reasonable length of time. Boy, were we wrong!

CHAPTER 2

The Countdown Begins

By the time I got back to the hospital, Matthew was still in the ER. He'd been given the option to either become an inpatient or be discharged home since it was Christmas Eve. He jumped at the chance to wake up Christmas morning in his own bed. And who could blame him? Matthew promised he would follow doctor's orders. Knowing my husband like I did, I knew it would only be a matter of days before he would resort back to his old habits of frequenting his beloved Publix, our local grocery store, or driving an hour to the Hardrock Casino in Seminole. And with me working, I'd have no idea what he was really up to.

We celebrated Christmas quietly at home with the pups and my parents. I called Lou and Ron the night before and explained the circumstances. They understood, of course. We agreed when Matthew was feeling better, we'd have our Christmas celebration. We got up lazily on Christmas morning, tore into our Christmas stockings, opened gifts, ate cinnamon rolls, and phoned relatives *up north* to wish them a Merry Christmas and to bring them up to date on Matthew's pneumonia diagnosis. Normally, I'm a voracious picture taker, but this Christmas I was more concerned with keeping Matthew comfortable and making sure he didn't overtax himself. A year later, I came to realize I had only a handful of photographs that captured our Christmas, and only a few of Matthew. I regret that grievously since it proved to be Matthew's last Christmas.

Within two days, I caught Matthew's cold, coughing and running a fever. And like with his cold, over-the-counter medications proved ineffective in alleviating my symptoms. Matthew was scheduled to see his primary care physician, Dr. Hany Abskhroun, on December 28 as a follow-up to his ER visit. As an ever efficient and cheerful Kelly, the doctor's nurse, checked Matthew's blood pressure and temperature, she made a comment, "Vicki, you sound terrible. You should see a doctor."

"I tried this morning to get an appointment with no luck. I'm waiting on a call back from his office manager."

"You don't want to wait too long; you really need to see a doctor. How about a quick care? Normally, you don't have to wait too long."

"I never thought of a quick care, could you recommend one?"

"There's a quick care on Mariner. Don't put it off, I'd hate to see you *both* with pneumonia."

After we left Dr. Abskhroun's office, I couldn't get Kelly's words out of my mind. I had a history of walking pneumonia and with Matthew sick, I couldn't afford to be sick myself. Between working full time, taking care of my parents, the pups, cleaning, and now doing all the cooking and laundry due to Matthew's illness, I had my hands full. Plus, I was trying to keep Matthew's activities in check as well. When I didn't hear back from my physician's office manager, I drove to the quick care Kelly recommended. Just as I was turning into the parking lot, my phone rang. It was my physician's office manager asking if I could be at their office within ten minutes. Since it would take us at least twenty minutes to get there from our current location, I passed.

When we entered the quick care, there were three people ahead of me. I registered and waited for my name to be called. Matthew sat next to me with his nose buried in his ever-present Sudoku puzzle. He was starting to feel better after a couple of days on antibiotics. Eventually, they called my name. A physician inquired about my symptoms, listened to my heart and lungs, and diagnosed me with bronchitis. I was emphatic in stating I was allergic to penicillin and Levaquin. He wrote a prescription and recommended I follow up with my primary care physician.

With two of us at home with bronchial problems, I prayed my parents would not catch what we had. It was bad enough we were sick; I didn't have it in me to play nursemaid to two additional patients, as well.

I felt sick as a dog with a low-grade fever accompanied by chills and coughing. This was the wrong time of the year to be away from work. Our staff was only me and my boss, so there wasn't anyone else to pick up the slack. I had no choice but to return to work to maintain some sense of status quo. I grudgingly got up at 3:00 a.m., went through the motions of getting ready for work, and taped a post-it note to the bathroom mirror for Matthew.

Good Morning I Love You!

Feeling like crap, freezing, can't warm up, coughing like crazy. I'll work just long enough to get some crucial things done then coming home.

Pups both pee'd @ 4:15, no poops.
Xoxo
Your Wicki Woo Who Loves You

As I pulled into the hospital's parking lot, the soundless, midnight blue sky looked like a bolt of satin serving as a somber backdrop for minuscule stars randomly scattered like a roll of dice in the predawn tapestry. I'd rather be home in bed huddled under blankets instead of at work with my teeth chattering—I was freezing! I clocked in at 5:00 a.m. and planned to work a few hours until the residents and attending physicians started to show up for Morning Report, which promptly started each morning at 8:00 a.m. Even with multiple sweaters and a scarf wrapped around my neck, I couldn't warm up. I ran reports, checked residents' compliance, and left notes for my boss and the residents of any issues. Before I left, I sprayed the air with Lysol to kill any germs I left in my wake and sneaked quietly back into the night like a thief who was desperately trying to avoid capture. I continued this routine for the rest of the week. Once I got home, I'd crawl into bed, bury myself under the blankets, shivering as I collapsed into an unfit slumber. Nurse Katy dutifully kept watch on Matthew's pillow. In the distance, I heard Matthew's intermittent coughing while I coughed in our bedroom. We were a pair of dueling coughing misfits, at times perfectly synced, performing a symphony as ear splitting as any rock concert held at Amalie Arena in Tampa.

Thursday, January 5, I saw my primary care physician. Although nearly finished with the antibiotics prescribed by the quick care, I didn't feel any better. I actually felt worse. My physician ordered a chest x-ray along with a new antibiotic. By Saturday night, the back of my neck was slightly itchy from what I assumed was the tag on the back of my shirt rubbing against my neck. When I found a pink rash on my abdomen two hours later, I was astounded. I thought about the itchiness on my neck earlier and despite my twisting and turning, I couldn't view my back in the mirror. I called Matthew, and he came into the bathroom. He looked at my back and confirmed what I couldn't see, a rash of small pink dots behind my neck and across my shoulder blades. I felt a little itchy, but nothing I couldn't ignore. I'd

13

had previous reactions like this to penicillin and Levaquin, so I wasn't concerned.

When I woke up the next morning, I was shocked to see the small dots were now larger. Some had transformed into large, bright red splotches over a larger segment of my body. As the day progressed, the rash continued to spread up my arms, under my armpits, under my breasts, and across my upper torso. The itching grew worse, and the intensity was now something I couldn't ignore. Anti-itch creams did nothing to mask the temptation to scratch my skin off. Lukewarm showers only soothed my raw skin for a limited time. Once I got clothes on, there was nothing I could do to ward against the material from rubbing against my highly charged and sensitive skin.

The splotches were larger on Monday, January 9, and the color of the rash had changed from bright red to a dull, reddish brown. The rash was now on my face and throughout my crotch and buttocks. Instead of calling my physician for an appointment, I went to his office as soon as it opened. Thankfully, they squeezed me in, and I saw my physician within the hour. By now, a sense of panic started to overwhelm me. I'd never had as severe a reaction to an antibiotic before. My physician was understanding and after a few minutes, he provided a tentative diagnosis—possibly Stephens Johnson Syndrome. He'd only seen one case like this before, so he called for a dermatologist referral.

I headed straight to Bay Dermatology, ready to plead for an appointment. When I entered the lobby around 10:00 a.m., it was packed with patients. Any hope of seeing a physician today seemed hopeless. The receptionist, though, took one look at me, listened to my story with compassion, and assured me they'd squeeze me into their schedule.

In less than thirty minutes, they called me into an exam room. A resident and physician came in, introduced themselves, asked questions, examined the rash, and said they wanted to biopsy it. The resident performed the biopsy, applied a bandage, and dismissed me with a prescription for prednisone. As I walked out of the exam room, the nurse stopped me with a concerned look in her eyes and said, "If there is any change, don't hesitate to contact us."

To say I was anxious about this turn of events would be an understatement. Our new year wasn't getting off to a good start. Upon reflection, I felt blessed and thankful we had Mary Ann, our ever-helpful home health aide to rely on.

Mary Ann joined our family in May 2016. At first, Matthew and my dad were both skeptical about a stranger in our home. For several years, prior to leaving for work, I'd prepare my parents' breakfast—cereal and a banana. I had to pick food that wouldn't spoil before my parents woke up several hours later. I'd pour the cereal into their bowls, place two bananas next to their cereal bowls, and I left water and grounds ready in the coffee pot. All my dad had to do was flip the switch on the coffee pot and pour the milk into the bowls. I'd also make their lunch—sandwiches, fruit, and a couple of Oreo cookies—my dad's favorite. I'd place these in a large, brown paper bag. On the outside, in big, bold black magic marker, I wrote **_PAUL—LUNCH_** and placed the bag conspicuously in the refrigerator. I'd also tape a large sign, also written in bold, black magic marker next to their TV in the family room. It said **_NOON—PAUL LUNCH, LOOK IN FRIDGE_**.

At first, this routine worked. When they'd get up in the morning by 7:30 a.m. or 8:00 a.m., Dad turned the coffee pot on, poured the milk into their cereal bowls, then poured their coffee, and brought everything to the breakfast table. Once they were done, Dad brought the dirty dishes to the sink, rinsed them, and left the dishes in the sink. Matthew later transferred the dishes into the dishwasher. That was our routine from 2012 until 2017. Once in a while beginning in the fall of 2015, when I arrived home from work, I noticed their lunch bag hadn't been touched. I'd ask my dad why they didn't have lunch that day. At first, it was obvious he was caught off guard, then he'd turn his head slightly and stare off into space for a minute or two like he was contemplating the most abstract math problem. Then, he'd shrug and say something like, "Guess we weren't hungry."

Matthew did what he could to monitor their behavior, but he was often out of the house running errands, playing golf, going to choir rehearsal, or trekking off to the Hardrock Casino hoping *Lady Luck* would be on his side. And when he was home, Matthew was often ensconced for hours at his computer, doing laundry, or watching Texas Hold 'Em on TV. He didn't interact much with my parents, day or night. When the episodes of the untouched lunch bag became more frequent, I reached the conclusion I needed help for Mom and Dad while I was at work. There was no denying this any longer. Mom's Alzheimer's had degenerated to the stage where she couldn't do anything to help. Dad's dementia had reached the point where he was getting more absent-minded and didn't pay attention to the signs I kept leaving him. I knew we needed help, but Matthew and my dad didn't see it that way. It took a while to convince them.

I called a family conference for Matthew, Dad, and myself during the winter of 2016. The time had come that we needed help while I was at work. Matthew reluctantly agreed. Dad was his normal, stubbornly mute self. Gray, angry steam spouted from his ears while his mouth was set in a stern, stubborn Finnish resolve. For two months, I contacted various home health agencies in Hernando and Pasco counties. Mom didn't need specialized care, just someone who could consistently come five days a week for a few hours to make their lunches, take Mom for walks, and monitor and entertain them. It would also be helpful if this person could tolerate Mom's repeated questions, incontinence, and tendencies to fall. The agency I selected was Amazing Angels, owned by Laurie Meyer. Laurie appeared to be compassionate and understanding of our needs and concerns.

Laurie matched us with Mary Ann, whose first day was May 27, 2016, the day prior to Memorial Day weekend. Lou and Ron stopped by, curious about the new person in our family. But in reality, they were more concerned this new person wouldn't abscond with our treasures.

It was difficult being at work that day. I kept wondering how everyone was doing. By the time I got home, I couldn't wait to hear about this new person who had entered our lives. As I rushed into the kitchen, I breathlessly asked Matthew as he was preparing dinner, "Well, how was it? What's she like? How did it go?"

Matthew stopped stirring a pot of spaghetti sauce. "I wasn't here when she arrived, but Lou and Ron were. She's real skinny, has long hair, and a loud voice. She's has ten kids, and her name is Mary Ann."

"Did she seem capable? How did Mom relate to her? How was Dad?" I was particularly concerned about my dad's behavior since he'd been so reluctant to have a stranger come into our home.

"Your Mom kept asking Mary Ann where she's from, and Mary Ann never lost her patience. She kept answering the same questions over and over. Dad was reserved, and he mentioned to Mary Ann she didn't have to stay. He tried his best to shove her out the door. She hung in there, and the pups loved her."

I was relieved my dad demonstrated some restraint and thankful Mary Ann had a fairly good first day. The only thing I was now concerned about was our lack of air conditioning. Days before our air conditioner gave up the ghost, the temperatures in the Nature Coast of Florida were hovering in the low 90s. I had opened the windows, which didn't help much due to the lack of breeze. Despite the sweltering temperatures, our life with a home health aide had begun. Mary Ann's competence, patience, and friendship has been demonstrated over and over. She was our personal amazing angel who we desperately needed. This became evident during the months to come.

Caregiving Tips from the Heart

Scattered throughout this book, I have provided tips to help caregivers. Many of these recommendations I've learned the hard way through the school of hard knocks, and some have been shared by other caregivers. Once you join the ranks of a caregiver, you will realize very quickly, tips of the trade are *shared*!

Caregiving Tip #1:

As soon as you learn that a loved one has dementia, do your research. Learn as much as you can about dementia and the type of dementia your loved one has. It's your best defense for dealing with this disease. The more you know, the better prepared you are, which ultimately makes facing those daily challenges a little easier.

Caregiving Tip #2:

Caregiving isn't for everyone, but *everyone* **can** be a caregiver. It's mind over matter. It's up to you and how much your loved one means to you. You might be surprised at the person within you who's waiting to be needed.

CHAPTER 3

An Unexpected Knockdown

Tuesday, January 10, 2017

As soon as I woke up, I stumbled out of bed into the bathroom to check the rash. Despite my prayers, the rash had continued to spread throughout my body like a colony of Florida fire ants bolting out of their disturbed ant hill. If I'd been scared yesterday, I was in full-blown panic attack now. I called my physician, who advised me to go the ER. I called Matthew, who was approaching the 14th tee at Seven Hills Golf Course. Matthew apologized to his golfing buddy, Wayne Raymond, and left immediately for the hospital.

My first antibiotic reaction occurred two years after we were married. After I had two wisdom teeth removed and had finished a round of antibiotics, I woke up in the middle of the night feeling like someone poured itching powder in my bed. I'd never experienced a reaction like that before, and I was perplexed. After consulting my physician, he diagnosed an allergic reaction to penicillin; his advice, never take penicillin again. Since that time, I've had similar reactions to other medications but nothing that lasted this long, of such severity, and such unbearable itching.

Less than two weeks prior, Matthew was admitted to the ER, and now it was me. As I sat anxiously in the waiting room, I sent Mary Ann a text message to update her on our current situation. She responded back that she'd come early to watch Mom and Dad. Mary Ann's presence in our lives was proving to be a blessing in more ways than one. After an hour's wait, they finally called me. The nurse took my vitals and after another long interval, a physician stopped by. His diagnosis: I was having an allergic drug reaction, something I already knew. He recommended, "Go home, take Benadryl, and by tomorrow, the rash should clear up, and you'll feel better."

"I took Benadryl Sunday night, and it did nothing to clear up the rash. You can see what it looks like now—Benadryl was like putting oil on a fire. I'm only here because my physician told me to come."

I walked out of the ER feeling like I'd wasted both my time and money. Turns out in the ensuing months to come, I'd feel the same way, scratching my head and wondering, "What the hell! They didn't do a damn thing to help!"

Thursday, January 12, 2017

Despite the low doses of prednisone, the rash was worse each morning. By Thursday, every inch on my body was affected, even the bottom of my feet and hands had erupted into ugly, red, pestilence corpuscles. As I fought back the tears, I looked at Mathew and cried, "What should I do?" I was feeling vulnerable, close to panic, totally out of control, and unable to understand why this was happening to me, and nothing Matthew said could console me. Instead, he wrapped his arms gently around me, mindful of the itching, and tenderly hugged me. Matthew was a super hugger, and his hug at that time was sorely needed and meant so much. Tears of frustration burned behind my eyes, fueled by fear and uncertainty.

I couldn't sit still, and I was anxious, so we stopped at the dermatologist hoping they had the biopsy results. The moment I saw my dermatologist, I burst out crying. This was so unlike me; I always prided myself on my self-control. I was known to face tough situations with a poker face, something which I attributed to my Finnish ancestry. The point had come where I needed answers, something positive to latch on to. It felt like I was swimming upstream, trying to stay afloat against strong, pounding waves, and as each wave washed over me, I was slowly sinking further and further below the surface. In a few weeks, I had gone from nursing my husband with pneumonia to becoming an itching, miserable, frightened person who had no idea what was happening.

My dermatologist evaluated the rash, and based on his recommendation, we headed on the 589 Toll Road to the ER at Tampa General Hospital for a suspected case of Stephens Johnson Syndrome. During this hour-long drive, I felt a range of emotions. I was frightened and unsure of what to expect. At the same time, a memory came to mind of a previous drive we'd made on this very same highway on the night of December 27, 2011. On that occasion, our eight-year-old pup Casey had been diagnosed with severe anemia by the emergency vet in Spring Hill. After his referral, we traveled in the dead of night to Blue Pearl Veterinary, frightened and concerned about our baby girl, Casey. Casey was the first pet Matthew ever had. They had a tumultuous beginning which, over time, evolved into a mutual love affair. It was a marvel to witness, even more so when you consider before Casey entered our lives that Matthew was known to ask friends, "Where does the animal fit in the food chain?" The outcome for Casey wasn't good, she reacted to a blood transfusion and based on the vet's recommendation, there was no hope for her. The next day, the vet put Casey down while lovingly cradled in her daddy's arms. Mommy cried unconsolably while whispering continually into Casey's ear until she took her last, peaceful breath, "Mommy and

Daddy love you. You are the best baby girl in the whole world. Always remember we love you."

Now, it was uncertainty mixed with fear that was squeezing my heart like a boa constrictor. I was concerned about my future but more concerned about how this might affect taking care of my parents. Yet at the same time, I also felt a sense of relief finally knowing, in all probability, we'd get some answers. Tampa General is where you go if the hospitals in Hernando County have no answers, or, if they have answers, they do not have experience in treating what you have.

Tampa General admitted me for observation, and I met with several dermatologists. After their evaluation, I was transferred to an area deep within the bowels of the hospital. Each dinky cubicle was cordoned off on both sides by curtains. The nurses' station was less than three feet from the foot of my bed, and there was no privacy curtain to shield me from the lights, conversations, or actions that took place at the nurses' station. I felt like I had a front row seat as the nurses performed on stage for my amusement. Around 2:30 a.m., I was transferred to a real hospital room with real walls, a bathroom, and privacy. Later that day, my physicians stopped by to inform me I didn't have Stephens Johnson Syndrome, and I'd be discharged later in the day. I immediately called Matthew and thanked God our prayers had been answered.

It was after 7:00 p.m. by the time I was discharged and picked up my prescriptions from Tampa General's Pharmacy. Matthew met me with the car, and our drive home was devoid of the tension and emotions we felt on the drive to Tampa just the day before. I had faith in my Tampa physicians and knew in my heart I was now on the road to recovery. I knew God had answered our prayers. Now, it was a matter of time for Matthew and I to recover and resume our normal, hectic lives. We were looking forward to leaving illness behind us, finally getting a positive start to this new year of 2017.

CHAPTER 4

A Match Made on a Diamond

When Matthew and I tied the knot on May 17, 1996, my parents lived in Spring Hill, Florida. It was a small burgh an hour north of Tampa in an area known as the Nature Coast of Florida. By this time, Dad, who retired in 1980 from General Motors Technical Center in Warren, Michigan, was enjoying retirement to its fullest. My parents spent their first year of retirement at their home in Washington, Michigan, outside Detroit. After a year, they moved to Aura in the Upper Peninsula, or, as most Michiganders call it, the UP of Michigan. Aura is located at the bottom of the Keweenaw Peninsula in Baraga County. My parents lived in Aura for eleven years before my dad contracted Lyme Disease. At the recommendation of Dad's physician, they moved to Florida's year-round warmer climate in 1992.

Dad was the sixth child of eleven—six boys and five girls. He was born on February 23, 1921, on the dining room table of the family farm in Aura. Paul was Finnish by birth and very proud of it. Finnish was the primary language spoken at home by his parents, siblings, and the majority of their neighbors in this closely-knit farming community. Paul also grew up with an undying love for the Finnish concept of SISU, a word that refers to guts, perseverance, and fortitude. Paul was quiet and soft-spoken and would rather have buried his head in the sand than confront an adversary. He lived for his family and his beloved Aura. Matthew, the man I married, couldn't have been any more different from my dad—they were polar-opposites in every way. When I married Matthew, this was one girl who didn't marry a carbon copy of her daddy.

Mom was born in Detroit, Michigan, on June 19, 1928, to Paul and Hilda Miller. Her ancestry is English and Dutch on her dad's side, Finnish on her mom's side. Hilda was born and raised in the small company town of Pequaming, known for its association with Henry Ford during the beginning of the twentieth century. It's located just outside of L'Anse, in the Upper Peninsula, a few short miles from Aura where my dad grew up. Phyllis was the oldest of three children, an only child for ten years before her parents adopted two-year-old Ronnie during the Depression. Peggy, the baby in the family, was born when Phyllis was sixteen years old. Phyllis was often called upon to babysit her younger siblings at their home in Hazel Park, a suburb just across the Detroit city limits. Phyllis enjoyed sports, especially swimming and basketball, and hoped to one day become a journalist.

Outgoing by nature, but shy on occasion, there was one event in Phyllis' life that defined her future and influenced her feelings about life, and ultimately my future as well. As a young adolescent, Phyllis was diagnosed with scoliosis. Throughout her adult life, despite having eleven spinal fusions when she was fifty, the pain and embarrassment of a deformed back always loomed in the forefront of Phyllis' mind. Clothes often didn't fit her well, and as she matured and styles changed, Phyllis became a master at camouflaging her misshapen spine. The pain, which often accompanied such simple chores like dusting, vacuuming, or typing, would plague her forever. I'm still haunted by images of my mom stretched out on the living room floor crying in pain. This was before pain management became a staple of medical science.

Phyllis and her best friend, Laura Mills, graduated from high school in June 1946. Since Laura had never been to the Upper Peninsula, Phyllis took great pride in showing her best friend the beauty and tranquility of the UP. The girls stayed at the farm of Phyllis' Uncle George and Aunt Elna. Aunt Elna asked her nephew, Jimmy Asorp, to chaperon the girls around the area and introduce them to people their age. One day, Aunt Elna mentioned to Jimmy there was a baseball game at the Aura Hall and she asked him, "Make sure you introduce the girls to that nice young man, Paul Heltunen."

The Heltunen family were neighbors of Elna and George. Paul had recently returned from serving honorably in the Coast Guard during World War II and was playing catcher for the local American Legion baseball team. After the game, Jimmy introduced the girls to Paul. Paul asked them, "Do you like ice cream?" And the rest is history. Paul and Phyllis were married three years later on May 21, 1949.

For most of their marriage, Phyllis took on the role of deciding force. She worked full time, took care of their home, cooked, cleaned, and did laundry. She managed their finances, planned vacations, bought the gifts for family events like birthdays and anniversaries, and scrimped and saved so Paul could enjoy the *toys* he yearned for. Her role meant she provided the discipline that was sometimes called upon later as a mother. When they were first married, Phyllis often accompanied Paul fishing and deer hunting. They were definitely middle class, hardworking, honest, and truthful people.

Shortly after Paul and Phyllis' wedding, Hilda had warned her son-in-law they shouldn't have children because of Phyllis' back. Coming from a large family such as Paul's, there were always babies born and nieces and nephews running around and getting into mischief. I can only imagine the mixed feelings Phyllis must have felt when she finally learned she was pregnant in 1956. I bet she was happy to finally become a mother, yet she must have had an inner fear and trepidation her baby may one day inherit the same painful back problem that plagued her. They were married eight years before their one and only child was born, me.

I was a Monday baby, born on March 11,1957. I was the first grandchild for my Miller grandparents and the twenty-first grandchild on my Heltunen side. When I was growing up, I spent a great deal of time with my Miller grandparents, especially after my mom went back to work when I was four years old. Family friends Jim Ferguson and his wife Mildred stopped by to visit one Sunday afternoon, which was the custom in those days. Jim and Paul had met at Coast Guard boot camp at the dawn of World War II and remained steadfast friends the rest of their lives. While sitting at the dining room table enjoying a cup of coffee, Jim mentioned he started a new company, Call-Ferguson Electric, and was looking for a bookkeeper. Paul piped up, "Phyllis is a bookkeeper," and before you could say, "Jack Frost," Phyllis had a new job.

Thus began a new routine. Mom dropped me off every Monday morning at her parents' home and picked me up every Friday afternoon after work. Wednesday nights, my parents stopped by to see me. As a result of this arrangement, which lasted 3 ½ years, I not only grew very close to my Grandma and Grandpa but also to my mom's sister Peggy, who was thirteen years older. Peggy felt more like an older sister to me than an aunt. It was Peggy who painstakingly helped me learn the alphabet in order to start kindergarten—this was before the days of Sesame Street. It was Peggy who introduced me to Detroit culture. I fondly remember our adventures to the Detroit Institute of Arts, Detroit Historical Museum, Detroit Zoo, and my favorite, Greenfield Village. If not for my Aunt Peggy, I imagine my life would have evolved in an entirely different direction.

My mom paid my grandma to take care of me, and grandma used that money to put Peggy through college at Wayne State University. My grandpa refused to put any daughter of his through college. He was the only son of five children. His parents were in real estate. Therefore, they were considered by many in Saint

Joseph's, Michigan, to be well off. One of my grandpa's sisters went to college, got married, and never used her education. My grandpa's parents died around the time he graduated from high school. The probate and attorney fees ate up the proceeds from the estate, which changed the direction of my grandpa's life—he could no longer afford to go to college. This must have been heart-wrenching for him. When my mom graduated from high school, she was offered a full, four-year scholarship to Michigan State University. However, after she heard her dad say for years he'd never send a daughter of his to college, coupled with Phyllis being the stubborn Finlander that she was, she turned down the scholarship. Phyllis was determined she didn't want to later hear her dad take credit for sending his daughter through college.

Despite his lack of higher education, my grandpa was always an inquisitive man. I remember seeing him sitting at the dining room table on Sunday evenings, intrigued by conversations with his sons-in-law, asking question after question, hanging on to every word he heard. As a result of his life events, daughters and college were always a taboo subject. In my heart, I believe if he'd had the opportunity, my grandpa would have jumped at the chance for a college education.

Although I was extremely close with my mom's side of the family, I did appreciate and love my dad's family, as well. Growing up, I was shy around children my age. I couldn't figure them out. I wasn't interested in doing the same things they excelled in, and my mom and grandma never encouraged me to play with other children. When we visited my dad's siblings, I hid behind my mom's skirts, clinging for dear life rather than play with my cousins. You couldn't have budged me with a stick of dynamite—I was glued to my mom's side. My cousins grew used to this and never asked me to play with them.

It was my Heltunen aunts and uncles who I most enjoyed being around, listening to, and watching. I was intrigued and fascinated to hear stories about life on the farm, especially those stories which related to their childhood. There was one story in particular that became family legend. Aunty Sippi—Sylvia was her given name—was a lively, animated soul. Sippi was the next child in birth order immediately after my dad. She always enjoyed telling this family tale with a twinkle in her eyes and a hearty chuckle in her voice. If I close my eyes, I can still hear her voice as she laughed with merriment, entertaining her spellbound audience—an audience as familiar with this tale as the storyteller was herself. She said, "In the middle of the night when everyone was sound asleep in their beds, I'd quietly crawl out of bed, tiptoe down the hall and around the corner, holding my breath, trying to be as quiet as a mouse. I'd sneak into the boys' bedroom, tip-toe between the beds, and feel around for their pants and cut off all the buttons. It was so funny the next morning. When they'd get up and pull on their pants and discover the buttons were all missing, you should have heard them hollering and scrambling around looking for something to help keep their pants up as they'd raced out the front door running to catch the school bus."

As an only child surrounded by adults all the time, I felt more like an adult than a child when I was growing up. My parents treated me as an equal rather than a child. My thoughts and opinions were often formulated from an adult's perspective rather than from a child's. I remember being in our basement in Centerline sitting in a rocking chair when I was around five or six years old, staring into space. I daydreamt about life with my doll hanging limp from my noncommittal hands, and thought, "I don't want to play with this doll. What if this was a real baby? I wouldn't want to take care of it. What kind of mother would I be? I can't have children; it wouldn't be fair to them to have a mother who wasn't interested in taking care of them. I'd rather travel and explore faraway places." I've always been a dreamer and thinker; I'm a true Piscean. My destiny was determined at a very young age.

My world also changed in an instant within days after I turned eleven. Just a few days before my birthday, my mom took me shopping for new clothes. This was a rarity since I normally was one of the last of a long line of female Heltunen cousins to receive hand-me-downs on a regular basis. When you look at some of the school pictures of my cousins through the years, you can often see the same dress on different cousins over consecutive years. Being able to buy brand new clothes—ones that hadn't graced the body of anyone else, ones that weren't faded or patched—I was so excited I felt like jumping out of my skin!

Less than a week later, after this memorable shopping excursion, I was upstairs at your colonial home in Lathrup Village, walking past the hall window. Tentative rays of a springtime sun shyly filtered through the partially opened window. A cool March breeze was softly lifting the curtain just enough to hint of a faint breeze outside. As I was about to start down the stairs, I heard my mom gasp behind me, "Stop!" She lifted my shirt and stared. When I turned to face her, the look in her eyes has forever been scorched into my consciousness—a look I will never forget. I didn't know how to interpret my mom's reaction but something within me hinted that life would never be the same again. Phyllis felt turmoil and anxiety she'd genetically passed down to her only child—a back problem she herself had suffered from most of her life. She was intimately familiar with what her child will now live with for the rest of *her* life. My world forever changed that day, along with my life's path.

Many decisions I've made since were inevitably based on this life-changing event. My mother felt like a failure since she couldn't shield me from a future of pain and misery, something she knew intimately. Knowing I had a great chance of passing this genetic defect to my children, I made the ultimate decision at an extremely young age to never have children.

My mom was the heart of our family. She was the person who nudged my dad, coaxed him into doing things his very shy nature was prone to balk at. Mom loved traveling, exploring new places, and had a great sense of adventure. She took pride in telling family and friends, "We've set foot in all fifty states!" Even though their visits sometimes consisted of driving through a state in transit to another location, in her mind, simply stepping foot into a state meant she visited that state. And no matter where she went, my mom always saw beauty in everything she saw.

When we toured Scandinavia, a young man in Norway offered to take us up in his seaplane to see the fjords and glaciers. While my dad cringed at the thought of going up in a small six-seater plane, he adamantly put his foot down. My mom and I saw this as a once in a lifetime opportunity to see nature up close and personal. It was majestic seeing reindeer in their natural habitat walking through knee deep snow. That captures my mom's sense of adventure and love of life.

At times, I felt like an appendage of my mom. We had the same body type, shaped like a pear. We both had high cholesterol. It was always difficult for phlebotomists to get a blood draw from us. Our backs were deformed since we both had scoliosis. And in our middle years, we both tended to gain weight easily. Our opinions and ideas about world events often mirrored each other. Although she had been raised by parents who were narrow minded, my mother didn't let her parents' thoughts and opinions influence her own. She was ahead of her time in her beliefs regarding justice, honesty, and compassion for those unjustly wronged by society. She truly missed her calling when she didn't become a journalist. I have so many wonderful memories of my mom, memories which now make the current years that much harder to grasp and accept.

Caregiving Tips from the Heart

Caregiving Tip #3:

> If you are fortunate to have family or friends willing to help, ***LET THEM HELP YOU!*** Don't be shy, don't think you can do it all yourself. If you try to take on all the responsibilities, all by yourself, at some point you will become resentful, angry, and burned out. When someone asks to help, write down their name and phone number. Let them know you'll contact them as soon as you have dates and times for them to choose from. If you don't schedule them when they offer, they may not ask a second time. It's a daunting responsibility to care for someone and any assistance you can get will help you, maybe not as much at the beginning, but as your loved one transgresses into the next phase, that's when you will *desperately* need their help. **DON'T WAIT**—get your help trained *now* so they are used to caregiving for your loved one. Then, when you *really* need them, they will know what to do and can probably anticipate what's needed before you will.

Caregiving Tip #4:

> Always remember, someday you may be in need of a caregiver yourself. How would you want your caregiver to treat you? On many challenging occasions, this thought instantly sobered me when I wanted to throw the towel in and walk away.

CHAPTER 5

Mom's Different, Can't Quite Put My Finger on It

I can't pinpoint a definitive date when I first noticed my mom's dementia. I guess it was sometime around 2006 or 2007. Like with so many victims of Alzheimer's, she was a master at masking the symptoms. Perhaps I hadn't noticed at first because I was always busy at work and easily distracted when I visited them. Maybe it was because I was married to a man who felt a sense of jealously regarding my relationship with my parents, friends, and family. Or maybe I simply didn't want to admit there were subtle, noticeable changes with my mom.

Although her mother had been diagnosed with Alzheimer's in the late 1980s, I didn't know enough about the disease to realize there could be a genetic link. My dad's health was okay. He'd suffered an abdominal aortic aneurysm in 1998. He was one of the lucky 2% who made it to the hospital alive, survived the surgery, and survived the crucial 24-hour window immediately after. Other than two additional aneurysms, he was doing as well as could be expected for a ninety-plus-year-old. My mom, on the other hand, was slowly digressing into a world of confusion, uncertainty, and forgetfulness. Our world was changing and not for the better. I was in denial and figured she was simply getting older. Older people tend to forget things once in a while, what's the big deal? I thought, *Alzheimer's? No way. Others get that but not my family.*

In 2008, my husband Matthew and I sold our home and moved in with my parents. Matthew was concerned about my mom's repeated questions and forgetfulness. He had prior experience with these symptoms. His first wife was diagnosed with schizophrenia when she was in her early thirties. The scars he still bore from those days permanently seared Matthew's heart. He had vivid memories of being a young patrolman advancing through the police ranks while he dealt with a wife who was exhibiting odd behaviors.

Once we moved in with my parents, it became apparent, even to me, my mom was having problems. Being around someone 24/7, it became impossible not to recognize there was something wrong. My dad, though, continued to act like nothing was the matter. Whenever I approached him about her, he changed the subject, found excuses, or took the pups out to the pen.

During those years, Mom gradually relinquished household chores to my dad. He washed their clothes, cleaned their half of the house, made their lunch, drove them wherever they needed to go, and took care of their cat, Musti. Mom sat in her lazy-boy chair, cuddling Musti. She watched TV, did word search puzzles, and read an occasional book. She also sat at the breakfast table for hours and played solitaire or put together jigsaw puzzles. For a woman who used to enjoy reading books and doing 1,000-piece puzzles, her world drastically changed. She went through *the motion of reading* a book and worked on only twenty-four-piece puzzles, sometimes with difficulty.

While I was at work, Mom's world consisted of my dad, their cat Musti, Matthew, and our dog, Casey. My dad had never been a great conversationalist, and Matthew avoided any interaction with my parents, whether I was home or not. They spent their days in solitude side-by-side in identical blue recliners, watched television, took an occasional nap, and once in a while got up to use the bathroom. That was their days—Monday through Friday. Once I came home, Mom chattered non-stop, trying to engage me in her conversation while Matthew hovered in the background. He got angrier by the minute because he couldn't have a few private minutes with his wife.

Each night, we all sat together in the breakfast room for dinner. Matthew cooked dinner, I'd set the table, and he and I cleaned up afterward. That was our routine from the time we moved in with my parents in January 2008. In the beginning, our dinners were fairly routine. We ate while making general conversation, like any average family. By 2010, subtle changes were noticeable. Mom would ask a question, "Where are you from originally?" followed a couple of minutes later with the same question. Then, a few minutes later, her signature question again. It was easy to lose your patience and make a rude comment you later regretted when you heard the same question repeatedly. It's hard to explain how challenging it was to hear the same question in the same tone of voice by the same person over and over again, day after day. It wasn't really conversation since the person asking the questions wasn't listening to your response. It's like they were rehearsing for a stage play, repeating the same dialogue over and over, hoping to get their lines right.

Mom was craving human conversation. She'd be intrigued by the people she met in doctor's offices, waiting in lines at restaurants, or at church. Mom tried her best to strike up a conversation with anyone sitting within four feet of her. I always knew how her conversations would start with her signature question, "Where are you from originally?" The questionee didn't always recognize there was something a little unusual about Mom, and they'd tell her where they were from and sometimes have an actual conversation with her. After Mom repeated her signature question a couple more times, her unwitting listener either continued to play along by answering her questions over and over again, or they'd turn away. Sometimes, they immersed themselves in a conversation with someone else or buried their head in a magazine or their cell phone. I witnessed people get up and move to a chair as far away from Mom as they could get. I watched and listened, oftentimes wanting to crawl under my seat or pretend I didn't even know her. I grew frustrated by the minute, helpless this intercourse was taking place, yet at the same time, I'd marvel at how these complete strangers could sometimes be so accommodating in her yearning for conversation.

The following is a typical Mom dialogue, consistent with the years 2010-2016:

Mom: "Where are you from?"
Chance Individual: "Michigan."
Mom: "Michigan? So am I—where in Michigan?"
Chance Individual: "Outside Detroit."
Mom: "Have you been to Hazel Park? My parents live in Hazel Park."
Chance Individual: "No."
Mom: "Have you been to the racetrack there?"
Chance Individual: "No."
Mom: "Have you been to the U.P.?"
Chance Individual: "No."

Sudden silence, about fifteen seconds later...

Mom: "Where are you from originally?"
Chance Individual: "Michigan."
Mom: "Where in Michigan?"
Chance Individual: "Detroit."
Mom: "Have you been to Hazel Park? My parents live there."
Chance Individual: "No."

Mom: "My husband is from the U.P."
Mom: "We used to live there until we moved to Florida."

Ten seconds would go by with the chance individual desperately trying to immerse themselves in a magazine or their cell phone, avoiding all eye contact with Mom.

Mom: "Where are you from? I'm from Michigan."
Chance Individual, by now squirming in their seat: "Never been there, I'm from Timbuktu."
Mom: "Have you been to Hazel Park? That's where my parents live."
Mom: "Have you been to the racetrack there?"
Chance Individual, looking for a way to escape, shouts angrily: "No!"
Mom: "That's where my parents live. I saw them today. They stopped by."

Mom loved these interchanges with her new, temporary friends, and her conversations are typical of Alzheimer's patients. And as her Alzheimer's advanced, she got adept at not accepting the *I can't hear you* body language some adopted, and she'd sometimes get right in their face demanding a conversation.

One of the sad things about Alzheimer's is the end of meaningful conversation as it's no longer possible. People who were once vibrant and full of life with hopes and dreams are now drastically reduced to a robot-state, repeating themselves and frequently frustrating those close by or a target for conversation. Patience becomes next to impossible when you are asked over and over again the same questions. A couple of months of this is bad enough. How about five years of this never-ending barrage of questions? Even saints reach their limit. It grates on the nerves, taxes your patience, and drives you insane! There were times when I'd hear the start of her signature question, *Where are you from?* and I'd wish she'd just stuff a sock in it and shut up! I got to the point I treasured going to work despite the stress of the workday. At least I could escape. Matthew, on the other hand, was subject to her performance every day.

I felt stuck in a quagmire of loathing, hating to be saddled with a mother who no longer knew how to act like a normal, civilized person. Was it my unwillingness to accept the truth that my mom had Alzheimer's? Or was it my ineptitude at understanding the situation and my unwillingness to work within it? Plus, I felt a sense of shame at the same time. In those days, just hearing the word *Alzheimer's* sent shivers up my spine. Alzheimer's was the disease where people went berserk, wore their clothes inside out, talked gibberish, and acted uncontrollable. I believed Mom would get better. It'd take a little time, but she'd be back to her old self. Call it stupidity, call it ignorance. I was doing everything in my power to ignore our situation. I was just as bad as my dad. At least at work I could have real conversations with real people about real, meaningful things. I sometimes dreaded going home and used the excuse of running errands to postpone the inevitable. I became an expert at knowing how to delay walking into the house. In the back of my mind, I can still hear Matthew telling me, "You're not home enough. You have to be home more; your parents need you!" I didn't want to listen. Work was my escape, yet I wouldn't admit it.

Just prior to 2014, I started taking my parents to their primary care physician. The first time I met their physician, Dr. L., the first thing he said to me in a rudely, condescending manner was "it's about time!" I was taken aback by his opening statement, unsure how to respond to it. Did he assume my parents had informed me of my mom's diagnosis? No, they hadn't. I connected the dots and deduced my own conclusion. Did he sit down and discuss possible treatment options with me? No, he didn't. And after I did my homework and asked him about medications to slow down the onset of Mom's Alzheimer's—a question I asked him several times—his response was always the same, "The side effects..." He never elaborated on his opinion and never provided any information or resources to assist me in taking care of Mom at home. At the time, I was working full time driving over two hours to get home at night. If your loved one's physician isn't providing you the answers to your questions or assisting you in regard to community and county resources, I highly recommend you look for another physician who will work *with you* rather than against you. Both you and the physician should be working *together* for the betterment of your Alzheimer's loved one. A physician who doesn't listen and won't meet you half way is like butting your head against a brick wall. It won't affect the physician, but you'll have one hell of a headache as a result of your frustrations.

I felt fortunate when I finally found a primary care physician for my parents, Dr. Hany Abskhroun, who specializes in elder care. He was also Matthew's physician when we needed him most. He listened and worked with me. A good, caring physician who listens and responds to your urgent needs is like having a million bucks in the bank. You can rest at night knowing you have a physician who looks out for you and your loved one. Let's face it, when you are an Alzheimer's caregiver, both you and your loved one are a package deal. Whether your loved one or the caregiver are having health or other problems, caregiving will be affected and vice versa.

By 2014, Mom started to say over dinner that she saw her parents that day. Mom's voice became animated, sometimes concerned. If you didn't know any better, you'd believe she actually saw her parents. The first time I heard this, I was shocked. My grandpa had passed away in November of 1982, and my grandma passed in March of 1999. I listened to Mom, who dominated the conversation. When she finally paused to catch her breath, I jumped right in and informed her, "Your parents are dead." At the end of the table, I saw my dad frantically waving his hands trying to tell me to disregard what she's saying, ignore it. Sometimes, Mom reacted, sometimes she didn't. I later learned it was the wrong thing to do. At the time, I didn't know any better.

The majority of Mom's conversations at the time focused on visits or phone calls she claimed she had with her parents. This was especially true at dinner time if she was sundowning.

Since we still had a landline phone in the house, Mom made every effort to grab the phone whenever it rang. One day, when I walked into the family room, she was on the phone having an animated conversation with a total stranger. Since she still had some recollection of her surroundings, Matthew and I were concerned she'd provide too much personal information to these complete strangers. We wanted to thwart any chance of having her identity stolen or worse, someone coming to the house with the intent to cause bodily harm or to take advantage of them. Matthew and I both had cell phones, and we decided the only way to circumvent any future problems was to discontinue the landline phone. At first, this created a problem since my parent's still had family and friends who called them. Someone would call and hear a disconnected message and wonder what had happened. My parents lost track of some friends as a result, while others wrote a note asking what was going on.

It was difficult for my dad to admit to friends, and even some family members that Mom didn't remember them. Fortunately, at that time, Mom still remembered her best friend from high school, Laura Mills Stach—the same Laura who was with Mom when she met Paul back in 1946. However, as with her sister, memories faded quickly.

The following is a typical Mom conversation between 2014–2016:

Mom: "My parents stopped by today."
Vicki: "They did? I'm surprised."
Mom: "We had a nice visit. I'm concerned because they aren't feeling well."
Vicki: "I'm sure they will be feeling better soon."
Mom: "Where are you from?"
Vicki: "Michigan."
Mom: "So am I. Do you know Hazel Park?
Mom: "I need to see my parents. Paul, we need to see my mom and dad. Let's go!"
Vicki: "I'll take you this weekend. Paul doesn't drive anymore, and I have to work tomorrow."

Mom: "We have to go now. Come on, Paul, let's go. We
     have to go see my mom and dad."
Vicki: "Your parents are on vacation. They aren't home."
Mom: "Paul, we have to see Mom and Dad. Mom isn't
     feeling well. Let's go!"

It took me a while, but I finally smartened up and accepted the fact my mom had Alzheimer's. I began reading everything I could about the disease. Hallucinations, I learned, is a common characteristic of Alzheimer's when patients are in the middle stage of the disease.

The Alzheimer's Association classifies Alzheimer's into three basic stages—mild or early stage, moderate or middle stage, and severe or late stage. During the mild stage, the patient can still live by themselves, take care of their finances, drive, and enjoy some semblance of life as basic forgetfulness and confusion starts to invade their everyday existence. The moderate stage, which tends to last the longest, is where I determined my mom to be at this time. Hallucinations, sundowning, confusion, repeated questions, incontinence, and the inability to take care of themselves are just a few of the characteristics that differentiate this stage. The severe stage is when the patient loses control of communication, is totally bed bound, experiences problems with swallowing, loses their appetite, and is totally dependent on others to take care of them. This severe stage of Alzheimer's signals impending death.

Sundowning is a characteristic of the moderate stage of Alzheimer's. The loved one will experience greater confusion and is easily agitated and more prone to hallucinations and mood swings. Sundowning usually occurs later in the afternoon or evening. Mom's sundowning usually started mid-to-late afternoon, just before dinner. I learned to turn all the lights on in the house just before I anticipated the start of her sundowning. Researchers have discovered a correlation between the waning of sunlight at the end of the day with the onset of sundowning in the late afternoon. Dad's restlessness and anxiety when he couldn't sleep at night was also an example of sundowning. He'd ask for a sleeping pill, which never alleviated his sundowning symptoms and never helped him sleep.

There were times when Mom's sundowning got so bad in the late afternoon, she'd insistently state over and over again, "Paul, we have to go see my parents. They aren't feeling well!" No matter what I said to her, Mom kept repeating the same thing over and over again, like an old vinyl broken record. Through trial and error, I learned a trick that worked every time. On those occasions when distracting Mom at home during her worst sundowning was not working, I bundled her off to the car and drove her around the neighborhood for about ten minutes. I pointed out beautiful trees or houses. She loved looking at trees and always enjoyed viewing houses. After a few minutes, she was distracted enough that I could bring her back home. Mom could spend hours sitting in the back yard or on the front porch admiring the beautiful and majestic trees, listening to the birds sing, admiring the colorful flowers, or pointing to the billowy, cottony clouds in the sky, stating "See that dog up there. Look at the man over there; he's got a big nose!" Mom loved looking at clouds, nature, and beautiful houses. Her Alzheimer's clouded imagination could always see people and objects in every cloud she saw.

Etiquette at the dinner table started to take a turn for the worse around 2015. Mom dominated the dinner conversation with repeated questions and talked about seeing her dead parents. Around this same time, she started sneezing a lot. With her Alzheimer's, Mom no longer had any idea what proper table etiquette was. All of a sudden, when Mom would start to sneeze, she didn't know when to stop. By the third sneeze, Matthew yelled, "Mom, blow your nose!" She disregarded what Matthew said and kept sneezing, sometimes six or seven times, until she naturally stopped. The more times she'd sneeze without blowing her nose, Matthew grew angrier. By the time she finally stopped sneezing, she had snot dripping out of her nose and running down her chin. Eventually, she'd reach behind her where we kept a box of tissues on the window ledge. If Mom couldn't find the tissues, then she grabbed her napkin, even if it was encrusted with food, and started to blow her nose. What especially blew Matthew's gasket was when Mom wouldn't turn away from the table to blow her nose. What made it even worse was when she'd shove her finger up her nose, twisting it like she was digging for gold. At times, I expected to see her finger poke out her ear and wiggle at us. When this occurred, Matthew got up from the table in utter disgust and outrage. He'd angrily pick up his plate and silverware and stomp into the kitchen, his face redder than a fire engine. Steam coursed from his ears like a pot of boiling water burling away on the stove. He'd noisily dump everything into the kitchen sink and park himself either in front of his TV or hid in the computer room, anywhere so he'd be as far away from Phyllis as he could get. Throughout this uproar, Dad continued to eat as though nothing had happened, totally unfazed by what had just taken place. I, on the other hand, was stuck in the middle, sympathizing with Matthew on how disgusting this was, yet I understood what Mom was doing came naturally to her in her altered state. We experienced this type of sneezing/snot behavior several times a week for about a year before the symptoms started to manifest itself with my dad. Then, we had dueling snot blowers at the dinner table, which grossed out both of us. That was when Matthew and I started eating dinner off of TV trays in front of our TV.

My parents were served their dinner at the breakfast room table while Matthew and I ate our dinner in the living room. This satisfied Matthew because he no longer had to witness such uncouth behavior, and he could eat in relative peace and quiet. It also provided us with some quality time. Unfortunately, my dad did not understand why we were no longer eating dinner together anymore. Anything that kept the peace with Matthew helped. Otherwise, he could be difficult to live with and kept reminding me how unhappy he was with this living arrangement. He seemed to forget it was his idea for us to move in with my parents, yet he was only unhappy living with them when it suited him. Otherwise, Matthew enjoyed the benefits of living in their house without the responsibilities of home ownership. That responsibility was left to my dad, since it was his house. But as Dad's condition gradually worsened, I was left holding the bag.

Because Matthew was home more frequently than I was, he often cloistered himself in the computer room for hours with the door firmly closed. A closed door, though, was often seen by Mom as an open invitation. She was always curious about what was on the other side. Whenever she opened the computer room door and start to wheel herself inside, all hell broke loose. This always grated on Matthew's nerves and he exploded, yelling, "Phyllis, get out of here, and close the door!" Mom sometimes replied back, "It's my house," as Matthew flung his arms around pointing to the door. Matthew was never shy in informing me of Mom's indiscretions when these forays took place.

It wasn't until Matthew became sick in 2017 that I stopped using errands as an excuse for coming home. When I wasn't at work, I was home taking care of Matthew and my parents. Having lunch with friends or dinner out with my husband were things of the past. Instead, our home gradually took on the feel of a prison as we adjusted to the uncertainty we were facing.

CHAPTER 6

The Six Weeks I Now Treasure

My physicians at Tampa General prescribed high doses of prednisone. I soon discovered prednisone worked wonders for opening the tear ducks and lubricating my dry eyes. However, prednisone also worked as a stimulant on me. It left me wired and unable to sleep. After three days of an average of twenty minutes of sleep a day—not all at the same time—I jumped around the house like a bopping rave dancer. Eventually, I grew totally exhausted and fell into the closest chair or sofa and crashed. Despite being so tired, you'd think I'd sleep like the dead, but after a few short minutes, I'd wake up bug-eyed, bouncing off the walls again. I grew confused, unable to focus and unable to comprehend simple conversations or phone calls. And despite my eccentric behavior, it took forever to get anything done. It was obvious I was going to have to take some time off from work.

My sleeping habits changed since marriage—now I woke up at the drop of a hat. Before, I slept like a log. Many times, the culprit was Matthew's loud, erratic snoring. He could have woken the dead. He sounded like a cross between a lighthouse foghorn and a bull in mating season. His snoring never had a constant rhythm; it was irregular syncopation to the nth degree. Then, when you least expected it, there was total silence. I held my breath, waiting for his snoring to resume. When it didn't after a few seconds, I nudged him in the ribs, which triggered an upstart of his offbeat, spasmodic symphony. He resented those occasions when I dragged my butt out of bed and crashed on the family room couch, putting as much space between myself and his booming, jarring snoring. In his mind, a wife's place at night was beside her husband in bed, no matter how bad his snoring got. When you added in the side effects of the prednisone, sleep became an evasive antidote for insanity.

Due to my lack of sleep, I doubted my judgment, my sense of reasoning, and even my memory. It must have been similar to what my mom had been facing when Alzheimer's first began raising its ugly head and claiming her as its latest victim. In the beginning, there's enough of your common sense and awareness to know something isn't right, but you can't necessarily put your finger on it. You exist in a partial fog, which only gets foggier as time goes on. The difference was I knew I'd eventually wean off the prednisone and be back to my normal, functioning self. For Mom, she would never again regain her normal self. Instead, she was robbed each day of her precious memories, ability to converse, and the knowledge to live independently. Nothing triggered a fragment of her past when she saw family photographs. It was like she was looking at someone else's life, not her own. Many times, she didn't even recognize herself.

At this point, Mom didn't know who I was fifty percent of the time. I was prepared for this, but nothing could ease the gut-wrenching, heart-stopping pain of that first time my mother no longer recognized me. It took my breath away and stopped my heart. I read about this, so I was intellectually prepared for this to eventually happen. But it still hurt like hell, like someone stabbed me in the heart and twisted the knife down into my stomach. I couldn't help but reflect upon the memories we shared. Decades were now lost to her: my childhood, my high school graduation, our dogs—Penny, Lady, and Boo, our many vacations and travels, my wedding and marriage to Matthew, and our other family who we were always so close to. Memories we once shared are now mine alone to treasure and hold dear as the lone custodian. This reminds me of the pregnant woman who says, "I'm eating for two." Now, I have to remember for two. It's amazing what the human brain can remember and just as easily erase.

Mom continued to remember who her husband, Paul, was. For years, I often told friends, "Paul will be the last person she forgets." Mom didn't know Matthew. Sometimes, she knew her brother Ron and his girlfriend Lou, but she had no memory of having a sister. Other family members and dear friends gradually evaporated from her consciousness, as well.

After dinner on January 17, 2017, I called EMS. I determined by Mom's body language and her use of incoherent words that she was having stomach pain. It's difficult to obtain a true analysis of what someone with Alzheimer's is feeling. Since we all ate the same dinner that night, General Tao chicken and tater tots, and she was the only one in pain, I knew it wasn't food poisoning.

This was the third time within weeks a member of our family was a patient in the ER. First Matthew, then myself, and now Mom. The ER was extremely busy. Mom was delegated to a gurney outside an exam room. Privacy was non-existent. You could hear, with little effort, the conversations in the curtained exam rooms, nurses conversing with other patients on gurneys in the hallway, and the conversations taking place between nurses, PAs, and physicians at the nurses' station located in the middle of the ER. A radiology tech came to transport Mom for tests. I hunted for a chair and camped out alone in the spot where her gurney had been. About an hour later, Mom was wheeled back to her obscure little patch of floor, and we resumed our wait. Mom spent the time staring off into space, counting the ceiling tiles, and fingering the blanket that kept her warm. Eventually, she was admitted to an observation status. Due to overcrowding in the hospital, it took a while before she was comfortably settled in a room. Before I left, I explained to the night nurse, "Phyllis needs to be supervised 24/7, or she'll try to get out of bed, wander the hospital, and look for someone to talk to."

The next day, I met with Mom's nurse. The test results showed Mom had an impacted bowel. In other words, she was constipated, and it appeared she'd been constipated for a while. I was surprised because she had frequent, messy accidents even with a diaper. Whenever I heard a distinctive, gaseous, gurgling sound rippling from the depths of her stomach, like a blast of trumpets played under water announcing the opening of Parliament, I knew I had nanoseconds to get Mom to the bathroom. If I didn't, a liquidly, brown explosion would erupt from the lower extremity of her body ejecting rivers of stinky, globby diarrhea cascading down her legs, leaving a poop trail in her wake on the cream-colored carpeting. Once in the bathroom, the real fun began—getting her pants down, stripping off her diaper, and sitting her on the toilet. Her shoes and socks were removed *before* the actual clean up started. Often, her diaper would have a large pool of liquid, mushy feces within the bowl of the diaper. I'd try to contain as much of this mess within the diaper so it wouldn't add to the mess already on her legs, in her crotch, and around her anus. She also pointed out the spots she thought I had missed during the cleanup. She didn't realize, in her befuddled mind, that I was still trying to clean her up and what she was doing was actually delaying the process. She'd touch those areas with her hands and then reach out to me to clean her hands by wiping them on me.

These types of accidents occurred frequently for at least the last couple of years, so I was perplexed on how she could be constipated. I never saw a physician, only very helpful nurses and the case manager. As the nurse explained, the accidents Mom was experiencing was feces from around the blockage. As with older people, their bowel movements become erratic with age due to medications, often compounded by a more sedentary lifestyle, and the tendency of the elderly to refrain from drinking water. They become dehydrated, and it effects their bowel habits and intestinal blockages may occur. The plan of care was to give Mom an enema. However, with Mom's past history of twisted intestines, the nurse was unable to successfully give Mom an enema. With each unsuccessful attempt, Mom howled in pain. Mom was discharged home in basically the same condition she was in as when she was admitted to the hospital. She had prescriptions to take Colace and MiraLAX several times a day until she eliminated the buildup of feces in her bowel and intestines, something which could takes days or even a week. All I could think was we'd be paying a hospital bill for something I was now stuck having to correct. Maybe I should send them a bill.

Mom was full of energy and happy after her car ride home January 19. In her world, she didn't know where she'd been, didn't remember what had gotten her there, and had no recollection she'd even been out of the house. Smiling, efficient Mary Ann was waiting for us when we drove into the driveway. The two of them resumed their normal routine of walks around the block, lunch, putting puzzles together, listening to music, and talking. Life was at least back to normal for some of us.

As Mom and Dad's normal routine resumed under the watchful eyes of Mary Ann, I tried to accomplish small tasks, which normally would have taken a few minutes, but these days consumed hours for my efforts. At night, when everyone else was gradually falling asleep, I was wide awake. I was never one to watch a lot of TV but TV became my best friend. I found myself watching movies I normally wouldn't watch, movies geared more to an adolescent rather than a person almost sixty years old. My sleeplessness altered my sense of humor. I hate to admit I found those adolescent movies very entertaining with their thin plots, juvenile high-jinxes, and sub-rate acting. I had the attention span of a teenager. Or, as I liked to believe, I was finally hitting my pubescent teen years later rather than sooner, which I had never experienced psychologically when I was a teenager. I guess I was rounding the circle of life in a backward motion. I've never been normal, so why should *now* be any different!

The previous year, Matthew and I both agreed Mom and Dad could no longer stay by themselves over night. As a result, we were no longer able to take a vacation together. This meant no more long weekends to Cedar Key, no more extended weekend trips to Philadelphia to see Matthew's family, and no more opportunities to attend family events out of state. Several family members had passed away recently, and I wasn't able to attend their funerals. I give our families a lot of credit. They understood my parents' condition and fully supported Matthew and I taking care of my parents to the best of our abilities.

Matthew had been chastising me for the last couple of years that I needed to be home more. He wanted me to be around my parents like he was—he had a front row seat to how quickly my mom's condition was deteriorating. However, I was in a catch 22. If anything happened to Matthew, his pension would die with him. He had retired several years before we met. Also, he was seventeen years my senior. The odds were in my favor I would outlive him. Matthew didn't believe in life insurance, so I wouldn't have a safety net to fall back on if I quit my job and something happened to him. Plus, I was too young to draw Social Security. My earnings working in Florida for the past twenty years were much lower compared to most areas in the country. On many occasions, when we were first married, I plead that I'd love to move back up north so we could be closer to our families, and I could make a more competitive wage. Each time I brought up the subject, Matthew dug his heals in and refused to budge. He wasn't even open to the idea of moving to Tampa so I'd be closer to where the higher paying jobs were. I was stuck where I was, which meant neither of us were happy. Matthew was mad because I was still working. I was pissed because I had no hope for promotion at my job. At the same time, I was mad at Matthew for his selfishness.

However, being home for a short time opened my eyes. Matthew was right, working closer to home was no longer an option. I needed to be home 24/7. Just last summer on a bright, lazy Saturday morning, my phone rang shortly after I arrived at church for a line dancing class. I almost didn't answer it, assuming it was a crank call. But that little voice in my head urged me to answer it. It was Matthew on the other end, letting me know they didn't know where Mom was. I heard a hint of desperation in his voice, which said a lot because he was a former cop who had been trained to stay calm and cool under the most trying and difficult situations. Both Matthew and Dad had been home at the time, but neither noticed when Mom walked out. They'd been cruising the neighborhood in Matthew's Equinox looking for Mom without success.

I don't know how I got home—I was on autopilot. I prayed Mom would be found safe and sound. As I approached our home, Matthew's SUV wasn't in the driveway but a strange car was. I parked my car and ran up to the woman who was standing near her vehicle. It turned out she was a neighbor who lived on the next street and with her was Tina, our neighbor who lived directly behind us. As they were driving on Deltona Boulevard, a very busy street with two lanes of normally heavy traffic two blocks from our house, they noticed Mom on the other side of Deltona. They questioned why she was there and why no one was with her. They knew Mom had dementia and were used to seeing Mary Ann walking Mom around the block. They stopped their car, coaxed Mom into the car, stowed her walker in the trunk, and drove her home. Thank goodness these two neighbors were traveling Deltona at that particular time and knew Mom and where she lived. They were definitely two precious guardian angels at the right place at the right time. I'd hate to think of what could have happened if a stranger had stopped instead, picked Mom up, and possibly harmed her. It's amazing she got across Deltona without being hit by a car.

Wandering is a common occurrence of Alzheimer's patients. If they get out of the house once, there is a good chance they will try to wander again. As a result of Mom's treacherous adventure, I designed a sign for her walker. My friends at Joni Industries constructed the sign out of thick, dark blue plastic with white lettering. I attached the sign to her walker with plastic ties. The sign stated her name, our address, and our cell phone numbers. If she got out of the house again, her rescuer would know who she was, how to contact us, and where she lived. It was like putting a band-aid on a severed artery; at least it provided us with some peace of mind. Mom was intrigued by the sign. As she became more kinetic, she sat in her chair, reached down, and pulled the sign up towards her so she could read it. Mom still recognized her name and was mesmerized to see her name in print so prominently displayed on her walker. She was also captivated when she saw her name listed in the Prayer List in the church bulletin. On those occasions, Mom spent the entire church service staring at her name, nudging Paul once in a while as she happily pointed to her name in the bulletin.

I accepted the fact I needed to be home full-time, but I couldn't just quit my job without an income in case anything happened to Matthew. I searched online for work from home jobs and found some dubious opportunities. They'd promise you high weekly incomes for only a few hours of your time. Even with my heightened sense of anxiety and sleeplessness, my inner consciousness was still strong enough to warn me away from those opportunities that sounded too good to be true.

I broadened my internet search to caregiving. I was curious if there was a way I could get paid for taking care of my parents. I learned of a government program in Michigan and Pennsylvania that would pay a family member a minimal amount for caregiving a loved one. At that time, though, Florida wasn't listed. There was a link buried within the online article about caregiving contracts. The article explained how an attorney could draw up a caregiver contract and spell out terms and conditions including an hourly rate. Employee taxes would be paid by the employer, in this case, the loved one in need of care, while the caregiver kept track of caregiving hours. Based on what I read, a caregiver contract sounded like a possible solution to my dilemma. I showed the article to Matthew, who thought it sounded promising. But because he was cautious, he reserved judgment until we learned more about it.

GMI ♡ U!

Hi Sweetie Pie,

Taking pups for a brief walk before the
sun comes up.

Didn't sound like you got much sleep
last night, heard lots of coughing. How
r u feeling?

Be Back Soon!

V, K, & K xox woof, woof!

By the first of February, I'd been on prednisone for over a
month. I couldn't sleep, sometimes up for thirty-six hours. The
rash looked better with no further eruptions, but there were still
large, reddish-brown splotches all over my body. The itching
continued to drive me nuts. My back, abdomen, arms, and legs
looked like a couple of cats had been using me as a scratching
post. I yearned for my old life of running errands, seeing friends,
and enjoying a glass of wine occasionally. You never realize how
good you have it until something happens to disrupt your world.

During that time, Matthew and I didn't leave the house
except to go grocery shopping or to a doctor's appointment.
We were both getting a little cabin fever from the isolation. The
variety of medications Matthew was on improved his symptoms
but didn't entirely knock out the pneumonia. When our friend
Molly Lutz called to invite us to a party, we hesitated for a few
minutes and then jumped at the chance to get out of the house.
Our mutual friends, John and Lillian Falcone, were visiting
from Boise, Idaho. Matthew became friends with the Falcones
back when he first moved to Spring Hill, in 1993. They met at
church, St. Frances X. Cabrini Roman Catholic Church, and
Lillian was also instrumental in Matthew's joining Stage West

Community Playhouse. Since they were dear friends, we knew they'd understand we couldn't stay long. We hadn't seen John and Lillian since they moved to Boise a couple of years earlier.

Good Morning I Love You!
February 3, 2017

Dear Matthew J.,

Happy Birthday to You! Happy Birthday to You!

Despite everything, I'm so happy I'm able to spend the whole day with you. Next year we'll celebrate to make up for this year! Hated hearing you coughing so much last night.

We Love You! xoxoxoxoxoxo

Wicki Woo Who Loves You, Kipper & Katy, too!
xoxoxoxoxoxoxoxoxoxoxoxoxoxoxoxoxoxoxoxoxoxox

The party was scheduled for February 3 at Timber Pines' restaurant, an upscale, gated retirement community skirting Highway 19 in the heart of Spring Hill. Matthew was in his environment holding court amongst our friends, Molly, John and Lillian, Betsy and Don Glasson, Saul and Roz Leibner, and Libby and Linda Campo. We all shared a common bond with Stage West as the unifier to our friendship. I met Lillian and Molly when we worked on *The Essence of Molly*, back in 1995. *Molly* was the first show I worked on at Stage West, and it proved the stage-set for Matthew and my courtship. Betsy played Victoria to Matthew's Toddy in *Victor/Victoria*, a musical which won them both HAMIs, the equivalent at Stage West to the Tony award on Broadway. Matthew strutted on stage each night in a sexy, black sequined dress, black nylons, high heels, and fluttering a fan, which was a real show stopper. Saul directed Matthew and Betsy in *Rumors* at Richey Suncoast Theater, and the always smiling Libby worked her make-up magic for most of the shows these friends appeared in. As treasured friends, we reveled in being together that night, sharing stories, taking selfies, laughing with shared love, and reminiscing about departed friends. Later, we treasured our memories of this night with a mournful heart.

After the dinner party with our Stage West friends, Matthew and I continued home to celebrate his 77th birthday with cake and ice cream. Each year, I baked Matthew his favorite cake, chocolate with chocolate frosting. And every year, I tried to decorate his cake with very little success. My printing, in green icing in honor of the good Irishman he was, always looked more like a four-year old had scripted it rather than an adult. The letters were usually lop-sided, tapering from large to small, and just barely fit on the cake. Matthew, bless him, always took my lack of cake decorating skills in stride. He never laughed or ridiculed. Instead, he'd extol how tasty and moist the cake was.

Unbeknownst to us at the time, this was Matthew's last earthly birthday. I'm thankful his last birthday was fun-filled, enjoyable, and surrounded by friends who meant so much to him. It was truly a gift from God that still brings tears to my eyes when I think about it. I also feel blessed we had the chance to spend six weeks together at this time. Despite being sick, this proved to be the last vacation we shared together. Maybe it wasn't much of a vacation, being sick as we both were, but we were together without the distraction of my job. I now treasure those six weeks as a gift from God. In hindsight, if only we had known at the time what was to come within the next few months…I would have done everything in my power for Matthew's sons, Matty and Michael, to have joined us as we celebrated Matthew's last earthly birthday.

Caregiving Tips from the Heart

Caregiving Tip #5:

People with Alzheimer's and dementia are prone to wander. Contact an Alzheimer's support group, local police or sheriff's department, or senior services for a scent kit. A scent kit includes a box, a glass jar with lid, and directions on how to obtain the scent of your loved one. If your loved one wanders away, consult your local police or sheriff's office. Inform them you have a scent kit for tracking purposes. *NEVER* assume your loved one will not wander.

Caregiving Tip #6:

You can't predict when someone will suddenly meander away from you. Be prepared, and have a game plan to circumvent this from happening. Nothing is scarier than when you realize your loved one is missing. **YOU** are in charge. They are dependent on you for their safety. Don't let them down.

Caregiving Tip #7:

Use a nightlight in your loved one's bedroom. The light will provide a sense of security for your loved one, and it will make it easier for you when you check on them during the night.

CHAPTER 7

A Glimmer of Hope

Between the beginning of the year and mid-February 2017, Matthew and I either visited a doctor, were patients in a hospital, or had tests done a total of fifteen times. I, at least, was finally improving whereas Matthew couldn't shake his pneumonia. As each day progressed, a new set of symptoms developed. Days after his birthday, Matthew again experienced fevers, body aches, and night sweats, often changing his t-shirt three or four times during the night. As he noted in his diary on February 7, he had "crushing chest pain at bedtime." The following day, the chest pain had subsided, but he was now having upper abdominal pain throughout the day and into the night. By 4:00 a.m. on February 9, after a fitful sleep, Matthew was again in the ER with excruciating abdominal pain. When the PA asked him to rate his pain level on a scale of one to ten, with ten being the worst, Matthew said, "Eleven." After an array of tests, x-rays, CT scan, ultrasound, and endoscopy, plus another round of Levaquin and Flagyl, he was diagnosed with an inflamed pancreas. Upon review of the chest x-ray, his pulmonologist, Dr. X, was consulted. The spot on Matthew's left lung had increased in size since his last chest x-ray taken during his Christmas Eve ER visit.

Matthew's first experience with Dr. X, a pulmonologist in Hernando County, was in the summer of 2015. His primary care physician at the time referred Matthew to Dr. X when he identified a spot on his left lung during a routine chest x-ray. Since Dr. X showed little concern about the spot, Matthew saw no reason to worry either. He didn't even tell me at the time. Every couple of months, Dr. X ordered blood work and performed breathing tests in his office. It wasn't until the following year, when a bronchoscopy biopsy was scheduled, Matthew finally told me about the spot. We were thankful in 2016 when the results came back negative for cancer.

Matthew's second bronchoscopy biopsy was scheduled for February 13, 2017. Matthew wrote in his diary on the 15th, "half the night coughing fluid." This time, just like the previous July, we were praying nonstop. Waiting on biopsy results is one of the most debilitating things a person can go through. Your mind can't think about anything else as you pretend to go through the motions of daily life, trying to convince yourself everything will be fine. Meanwhile, in the back of your mind, you can't shake the fear of a dreaded outcome. Waiting days is hard, but waiting a week is agonizing. Prayer was our common companion. Matthew wrote the following entry upon learning of the results, "Researched lung anomaly online, waited all day for call from Dr. X, 4:40 pm [received call from Dr. X] tumor benign, prayers answered." For a second time, we were spared a cancer diagnosis. It was cause to celebrate! Psychologically, this good news did wonders to help Matthew get a restful night's sleep as his diary on February 18 attests, "Rose at 7:30, decent night's sleep, each day a little stronger, mind frame better ☺."

I returned to work on February 15. It signaled our lives finally getting back to a semblance of normalcy. My work day started at 6:00 a.m., so I'd be home by 3:00 p.m., a half-hour after Mary Ann left at 2:30 p.m. to pick up her children from school. Most of the time during this 30-minute interval, Matthew was home to supervise Mom and Dad, but on those rare occasions when they were by themselves, my heart would erratically pound as I raced home to take care of my charges. By now, Dad wasn't keeping a good eye on Mom. He fell asleep, walked outside, or took the pups to the pen. Any unsupervised time gave Mom free rein to get into unintentional trouble. She didn't do things on purpose; she simply didn't know any better. I had to hide things from her view. If something was within her grasp and she noticed it, she picked it up, and if she picked something up, it usually didn't find its way back to where she originally found it. Mom had a talent for hiding things in places that could take hours or even days to find, if you were lucky enough to find it. Later that year when I was cleaning the garage, I found an invoice tucked into the back of one of Dad's workshop drawers with a past due date. Only one person would have put it there—Mom. If you asked her where something was, she made up a story about "that girl, she had it," or, she looked at you with a blank stare, not comprehending what you were asking and wouldn't reply. I always knew it wasn't Dad who was hiding things. If he picked something up, he asked you about it and then put it right back down where he found it. I felt fortunate Mom and Dad were at different stages of this disease.

Once I got home from work, I was a full-time caregiver entertaining Mom, sitting outside with her on the front porch, or playing music, which she loved. Despite her lack of memory, if you played a song from her youth, she not only recognized it, but she still knew the lyrics and sang in a loud, boisterous voice. Mom especially loved patriotic songs like the "Star-Spangled Banner" and "America the Beautiful." Even with the computer room door closed, Matthew could still hear Mom merrily singing from the family room, off-key and out of sync with the music. And every time, he yelled out to her to no avail, "Phyllis, at least sing in tune!"

Mom didn't know what singing in tune meant, and she didn't care. She heard music that triggered a deeply buried memory. Mom reacted to something, and I was thankful. During these musical flashbacks, Mom was happy. You saw it in her body language, in her sparkly eyes, and in the happy smile radiating from her face. Music recognition and remembering song lyrics from their past are characteristics common for many who suffer from dementia and Alzheimer's.

The sad thing about Alzheimer's, there is no cure, only death. It is a slow death that robs the victim of their memories, disrupts their ability to walk, and gradually decreases their appetite and ability to swallow. Medications, so far, can sometimes slow down the progress of the disease. Sometimes, if the victim is lucky, they will die of other physical ailments before the disease advances to the final stage.

As the disease progresses, caregivers witness the deterioration of their loved one's life, cherished memories, and the ability to love. From a caregiver's perspective, it's a shitty way to die. The victim's body is usually healthy and strong. However, the victim has no idea what's going on. They are trapped in a world of confusion occasionally riddled with brief moments of semi-lucidity. Some victims become violent toward their caregivers, while others become shy, withdrawn, and want to hibernate within their little world. Another characteristic of Alzheimer's is there is no cookie-cutter pattern of behavior. In every moment, each victim has their own unpredictable behavior.

I've been fortunate; Mom is usually in a good mood. She's normally pleasant, smiles a lot, wants to engage you in conversation, but her words are often gibberish and don't always make sense. She can no longer identify common items like clothing or the foods she eats. Thank goodness she *normally* isn't violent, although there have been random times in the past, like when she started to balk at taking a shower, she became difficult to handle.

I have friends and family who take care of loved ones with Alzheimer's, and they've told me horror stories of what they've had to endure. These caregivers have talked freely about their parents, spouse, or friend who rants and raves, has temper tantrums like a five-year-old child, slaps, hits, bites, and locks their caregiver out of the house. They wear their underwear over their clothes, and make random phone calls. They turn the stove on and light matches. They overdose on medication because they don't remember if they took it. They curse profanity, have paranoid symptoms, hallucinate, and pick up their own feces and smear it on themselves or the walls. So far, I've been one very lucky caregiver!

When you look at someone with Alzheimer's, you can recognize the disease in their blank, staring faces. Their eyes no longer sparkle with life; it's like looking into the lifeless face of a child's baby doll. You see their eyes, but there's no soul shining through, only blank, vacant stares. No longer do their eyes hint at the person they used to be.

The best way to describe a person's gait with Alzheimer's is to compare them to a walking zombie. Their walk takes on a stiff-legged, unbalanced, unsteady gait like the zombies we see in the movies. As the disease progresses, these characteristics worsen. The patient eventually becomes bed bound if they live long enough. Death becomes the savior that returns the lost memories to their soul.

Caregiving Tips from the Heart

Caregiving Tip #8:

NEVER assume your loved one will remember which vehicle is yours in a parking lot. **ALWAYS** walk with them to your car, and secure them in their seat with the seat belt.

Caregiving Tip #9:

Having a diaper bag in your car for emergencies is helpful. Incontinent loved ones can have accidents any time and being prepared saves you time, embarrassment, and frustration. The following are recommendations for the well-stocked diaper bag: 3-4 clean diapers, plastic bags (for the dirty diaper and clean up materials), baby wipes, plastic or latex exam gloves, clean pants, and clean socks. Accidents can happen. Be prepared!

Caregiving Tip #10:

When you travel in your vehicle with your loved one, have them sit in the back seat on the right side rather in the front passenger seat next to you. This will keep your loved one from touching knobs, opening and digging in your purse, or distracting you as you're driving. You can still see them using your visor mirror. Have the following items in the back seat to help distract your loved one after they lose interest in the scenery flying by their window: magazines, colorful children's books, stuffed animal, or a doll.

CHAPTER 8

Getting Back to Normal, or so We Thought

Thursday, February 16, 2017

Good Morning I Love You or GMI ♡ U!

Sounded like you got back to sleep earlier this A.M. Kipper was sounding like you, snoring. You two sounded like a stereo!!

Hope you can get some rest today.

I should be home around 3:30, one stop.

XOXOXOXO

Your Wifey ☺

Despite how he was feeling, Matthew tried to make the best of each day. When we were first married, Matthew, who was born and raised Catholic, sang in the choir at St. Frances X. Cabrini Roman Catholic Church, Spring Hill, Florida. He'd been very active in their music ministry: choir, lector, and fundraisers. However, Matthew being Matthew, after a couple of years, he eventually grew disgruntled with their new choir director and quit all the activities he was involved in.

Matthew not singing in a choir was like a fish out of water. He shared his frustrations one day with his golfing buddy, Wayne Raymond. Wayne responded, "I'm always looking for strong voices in the choir at the UCC. Why don't you sing with us?" The choir in question is the Spring Hill United Church of Christ, or, as we've come to affectionately call it, the UCC. The UCC also happens to be the same church my parents and I attend. Wayne had been the music director there for many years, and it didn't take long for Matthew and the choir to develop a mutual admiration society for each other. Matthew found a new choir family, and they were thrilled to have him!

Matthew's love of music first manifested itself as a child growing up in his hometown of Philadelphia, Pennsylvania, also the birthplace of Dick Clark's American Bandstand. As teenagers, Matthew and his friends congregated on the narrow streets of South Philadelphia, crooning to the moon, singing all the latest top ten hits so popular during the mid-1950's, "Don't Be Cruel," "Why Do Fools Fall in Love," and "You Send Me." After he married, Matthew was too busy as a police officer advancing through the ranks of the Philadelphia Police Department and raising a young family to have time singing to the rooftops. Once he moved to Spring Hill, Florida, in 1993, Matthew jumped at the chance to join the choir at his local parish, St. Frances Cabrini. It's through his Cabrini choir friends that Matthew became a member of Stage West Community Playhouse.

Matthew had a passion for learning; he made the most of his retirement years. He took singing lessons to develop and strengthen his voice from a variety of competent music teachers in Hernando County, the last being his friend, Robbi. Whether it was learning the fundamentals on how to develop the range and depth of his voice or understanding how to straighten his golf drive or learning the finer points of stage direction, Matthew had a zest for life that made him a hard person to forget. One of his favorite Stage West stories he loved retelling related to his first assignment as a member of Stage West, "I stopped by when the theater was in the final stages of construction. Bob Child and a few others were busy, so I asked them if they needed any help. The next thing I knew, I was down on my hands and knees helping to bolt the cushioned seats into the cement floor."

Matthew's unexpected love of theatre led him to accepting a variety of theatre roles at Stage West, gracing their stage in over thirty theatre productions during our marriage. He sang, danced, acted, directed, stage managed, created playbills, and worked construction. Matthew appeared onstage not only at Stage West Community Playhouse in Spring Hill, but also at Ritchey Suncoast Theatre in New Port Richey, The Show Palace in Hudson, Tin Pan Alley Productions in Port Richey with John Timpanelli, the former Mellinia Studio in Brooksville, and lastly, under the direction of his friends at the Live Oak Theater, also in Brooksville. Each theatrical production was a learning experience for him. Matthew made new friends. He felt alive. He tingled with the excitement that only another performer can relate to. For the younger cast members, Matthew was lovingly known as "Uncle Matt," always willing to take pictures, help with lines, or give encouragement. For the more seasoned thespians, he was simply referred to as "Matt." The first year we were married, Matthew was involved in seven different Stage West productions. There were a couple of years, starting in 1998, when Matthew and I together produced the playbills for Stage West's shows. Matthew's love of theatre and music allowed him to give back to his community with a song in his heart and an entertaining vision.

It helped Matthew tremendously during the winter of 2017 when he resumed choir rehearsals at the UCC, especially in preparation for the Easter Cantata. Even though his voice wasn't the caliber he was used to, it was sustenance for his soul. It was what he needed to give him the drive to keep going. It wasn't only the distraction of attending choir rehearsals and practicing at home. It was also the friendships he developed with each choir member along with his love of God that helped Matthew get through each day, even those days when he was at his lowest. Matthew still attended the 4:00 p.m. Saturday Vigil Mass at Cabrini, but Sunday mornings, he was faithfully at the UCC bright and early at 9:00 a.m., ready for the last choir practice before the church service started at 10:00 a.m.

> *Good Morning I Love You!*
>
> *My Darling Vicki,*
>
> *You thought I didn't know how to write, well I hope this proves you wrong. I'll be looking for you at church this morning, in your usual place in the back row. Save me a place after the anthem.*
>
> *Love, Hugs, and Kisses,*
> *Butchie*

Sunday mornings, I sat with my parents in our usual pew, the last one on the left side of the church. In this spot, I had a clear view of Matthew in the last row of the choir on the right side. When the choir sang their anthem, I always recognized Matthew's strong voice over the rest of the choir. Whenever I mentioned this to him, Matthew got mad and said, "The voices in the choir are supposed to blend. You shouldn't be hearing my voice above the others." No matter, I could always recognize his strong, clear, tenor voice when he sang with the choir.

65

At the UCC, Matthew was synonymous with a song many of us, myself included, still think of as Matthew's signature song, a version of Leonard Cohen's, "Hallelujah." Matthew spent hours hypnotically engaged with his computer, day or night, glued to iTunes. It was during one of these forays he discovered the Kelley Mooney version of *Hallelujah*, lyrics which tell the haunting story of the crucifixion and resurrection of Jesus Christ. I distinctly remember when Matthew first showed me a video of Kelley herself singing, backed by an all-female choir. As I listened, I was captivated by the lyrics sung by Kelley's beautiful voice. Goose bumps suddenly appeared on my arms, and tears rained uncontrollably from my eyes. I was spellbound, spiritually moved. And so was Matthew.

Matthew started singing the Kelly Mooney version of "Hallelujah" at church, and within a short period of time, he was asked to sing it at funerals. Ladies in our congregation came up to me and said, "I've asked Matthew to sing that song at my funeral." His voice had the right timber for these spiritual, emotional lyrics. I was always amazed as Matthew sang these gripping words, words he sung from the very depth of his soul. When his voice broke, like it always did in the middle of the song, you would have sworn Matthew was reacting to Christ's death as only a direct eye witness could. The emotion in Matthew's voice as he sang these moving lyrics always brought tears to my eyes. Today, whenever I hear the opening notes to "Hallelujah," I immediately think of Matthew, and cry.

When I returned to work on February 15, my mornings resumed starting at 4:00 a.m. Before leaving the house around 5:30 a.m., the last thing I did was write Matthew a note and tape it to the bathroom mirror. He wasn't shy in letting me know if I left home without leaving him a note. On those rare occasions when I did forget, I knew I'd receive a terse text message later in the morning asking, "Did you forget something? Where's my note?" The following note, and he kept them all, is from Friday, February 24, 2017:

GMI ♡ U!

Hope you got some restful sleep last night. Both pups peep'd and poo'd at 4:50 am. Keep an eye on Kipper, he had me take him out several times last night. I'm dragging my butt as a result. No stops on way home, be home by 3. Pizza tonight, it's Friday?

Love you,
oxo Your Wicki xox

Matthew was a creature of habit, and his day always started with the same routine. He got up between 8:00 a.m. and 9:00 a.m., checked his blood counts, shaved, exercised, showered, dressed, spent two long hours reading the newspaper, ate breakfast, and completed the newspaper's puzzles. Matthew had a daily routine and nothing or no one had better disrupt it! When he read the paper, he didn't gloss over headlines. On the contrary, he read every single word, including all the editorials. There were times when I noticed something in the newspaper, perhaps the obituary of a friend or an article or cartoon I thought he'd enjoy. I circled it and wrote a brief note to capture his attention. It's things like this I now miss so much, the simple things only Matthew and I shared. At the time, they seemed so mundane, ordinary, so every day, so unimportant. They were things I took for granted at the time, but now I've come to realize these simple things mean so much. I wish I could get this time back, push a replay button, play it back in slow motion as I treasure the memory like I've never treasured anything else before.

Matthew kept a diary, and a day didn't go by when he didn't make a notation. These accounts of his life, written in black ink in his distinct penmanship, recorded the everyday occurrences. Things like when he woke up, what he did that day, what we had for dinner, golf dates, etc. Reading his diaries now bring tears to my eyes. I wish I had been more prudent. I relied on Matthew to know what was in *his* best interest. I should have been more forceful regarding his health. It wasn't always easy to help him to see reason, and, as a result, I feel a great sense of guilt and remorse to this day.

MATTHEW'S DIARY   *Friday, February 24, 2017*
Rise 8 am. Folks fed breakfast at 10 am, Mary Ann unable to come-hospital with son, babysat Mom until 2 pm-outside-up & down street to mailbox-pizza early 3 pm
SW (Stage West) at 7:30—meds at 9:00

Just the summer before when Matthew was feeling fine, he even considered firing his pulmonologist, Dr. X. Matthew believed he didn't need Dr. X, a physician who never developed a clear, concise diagnosis during the two-year period Matthew was his patient. Now, it was February, and the pneumonia-like symptoms he was suffering from were not abating. I was again trying to convince Matthew he needed a second opinion. My concerns, as far as Matthew was concerned, continued to fall on deaf ears.

As winter gave way to early spring, Matthew became involved in a project at the UCC. He volunteered to take the congregations' photographs for an updated version of their church directory. Mary Lou worked with him. Mary Lou was a steadfast, dedicated member of our church. She was a quiet woman with a wickedly great sense of humor. Mary Lou, though, had never worked with Matthew before. It was only a matter of time before they butted heads.

I remember a specific Sunday morning after church when Matthew was setting up to take Sandy and Barb's photograph. He was taking a little longer trying to adjust the overhead light from glaring off Barb's glasses. A line formed in the hall. Others waited patiently to get their picture taken. As Matthew asked Barb to turn her head this way and that, never satisfied, Mary Lou started getting impatient. Matthew picked up on her disgruntled body language and said something in his sometimes-brisk manner that got Mary Lou's dander up. When I looked at Mary Lou, I could tell she was trying very hard to keep quiet. She rolled her eyes heaven ward, like she was asking for patience. I looked at her, trying not to laugh and said, "And I live with him!" The look she gave me was priceless, like "I don't know how you do it!" There have been times in the past when I thought this same thing. Those close to Matthew knew he could be cantankerous, selfish, and opinionated. At that moment, I was seeing something in Matthew I hadn't seen since before last Christmas. I was thankful to finally see a hint of his old feistiness. In my heart, I was thinking, *If he's being a fussbudget, he's starting to feel better. Thank you, Lord!*

March 2017

We were both looking forward to having a date night in celebration of my birthday, something we'd missed since before Christmas due to our health. What better place to celebrate than our favorite restaurant in Spring Hill, Nouvelle Cuisine. Matthew never wanted to go to Nouvelle Cuisine unless he could drink wine. A couple years before, at the advice of his physician, he had ceased drinking beer and wine, and switched, instead, to O'Doul's, a non-alcoholic beverage. It was only on special occasions, like our birthdays or anniversary, when he drank wine. With my sixtieth birthday, and both of us currently off meds, we had a double reason to celebrate. Matthew also invited our friends Wayne and Sherrie Raymond to join us. Wayne and Matthew were golfing, choir, and Stage West buddies of long standing. It promised to be a great evening!

When we walked into the restaurant, we were warmly welcomed by Isabelle, a Belgian transplant who speaks English with a faint Belgian accent. She was the consummate hostess, like she always is. I was never sure which Matthew looked forward to more: his engaging conversations with Isabelle or the mouthwatering, delicious food. We were creatures of habit, always ordered the same meal at Nouvelle Cuisine, garlic shrimp as an appetizer, followed by the most mouthwatering, tender, and delicious chateaubriand. You could cut it with a fork! Even though I've often been tempted to order something else, it was the tradition we shared of this meal that counted most. This was something we enjoyed and looked forward to, just like we enjoyed our annual trips to Cedar Key. I'm not sure which of us enjoyed the 2011 Chateau Fourcas-Borie Leistrac-Mecoc more that night, me or Matthew. It was a great night at our favorite restaurant with dear friends, hosted by our favorite restaurateur. Who could have asked for more? And again, like at Christmas, I only took a few photographs—not of Matthew, not of our friends, and not of myself. I took photographs of the wine we drank. My thought was we were enjoying the wine so much I wanted to make sure we'd know what to order the next time we came, never dreaming there'd never be a next time.

Since my birthday was on a Saturday, I scheduled a couple of days off from work, a treat to myself since we felt our lives were finally getting back to some semblance of normalcy. On Monday, Matthew and I took the pups to Hernando Beach to have a picnic. Due to the rainy, overcast, and slightly cooler temperatures, we parked and had a tailgate picnic instead. We had a great time despite dodging the raindrops. We were together, us and the pups. That's all that mattered! The day also reminded me of another day twenty-one years before, March 11, 1996.

My birthday that year fell on a Monday. I scheduled the day off. Matthew and I planned to spend it together. That day was also gray, rainy, blustery, and cool. Matthew picked me up at 11:00 a.m., dressed in a raincoat. I had no idea what he had planned. He was keeping it a secret. As he was driving, I noticed he was heading toward Hernando Beach, in the direction of Pine Island. Matthew parked at Pine Island, told me to get out of the car, and walk to the end of the pier. As I was walking, I was buffeted by gusty winds, my hair was blowing all over, and I was thinking to myself at the time, "Thank goodness it wasn't raining!" Occasionally, I felt a raindrop but nothing that required an umbrella. When I got to the end, I waited a minute and turned around to face the direction I just came from. Matthew was walking toward me. He had stripped off his raincoat and was dressed in a tuxedo, caring a large bouquet of beautiful, red velvety long-stem roses with the biggest smile I've ever seen on anyone's face. When he reached me, he handed me the roses and reached in his pocket for a freshly laundered handkerchief which he then placed on the ground at my feet. He bent down on one knee, extended his hand, and reached up for mine and asked, "Vicki Lynn, will you do me the honor of becoming my wife?" I was both ecstatic and surprised. I immediately said, "Yes!" Matthew had a romantic soul, which mirrored my own. Perhaps that's why we became soulmates!

Good Morning I Love You!

Hard to go back to work after the great birthday I had. Thank you Sweetie Pie for a memorable couple of days!!!!

Pups both pee'd at 4:40, no poops. I'll be working a little late tonight, try to get some rest. Let's eat lite tonight??

XOXOXOXO

Your Wicki Woo Who Loves YOU!!!

Matthew was lured to Spring Hill in 1993 by his friends, Tommy and Diane Lyons. Each year, Tommy and Diane welcomed

Matthew and their fellow Philadelphia cop friends, Jack Lyons (no relation to Tommy), Jimmy Hunt, and John Ford to their home for a week of warm Florida weather, golf, and friendship only true friends can enjoy.

It was Tommy who called one day after Matthew retired, knowing full well Philadelphia was in the grip of a fierce winter snowstorm, "What are you doing still living in Philadelphia? You should be in Florida. You could be golfing right now!" To the chagrin of his family, Matthew fell for it "hook, line, and sinker," or, in golf language, "par, birdie, and eagle." His daughter-in-law Diana couldn't understand why Matthew would move, especially now since she and Michael had recently adopted a beautiful, blond-haired baby girl. It didn't make sense to her that Matthew would move so far away when he loved his family so much, especially since Matthew had gotten in the habit of stopping by their home in the mornings, taking turns reading the newspaper with his son Michael as they drank their coffee, ate a donut, and caught up on shop talk. When Matthew announced he was moving to Florida, this family dynamic changed.

After Matthew and I were married, I started to refer to Matthew's friends, Tommy, Jack, Jimmy, and John, as the Philly Five. All five had worked together as police officers with the Philadelphia Police Department, all were associated with the Philadelphia Emerald Society, all loved golf with a passion, and all five loved getting together having a great time hanging out. Tommy was the first to die in 2007, John passed away in 2013, followed by Jimmy a few years later. By 2017, only two were left, Jack and Matthew.

Matthew wrote in his diary on March 18, "JACK LYONS passed away ☹." Jack died unexpectedly while recuperating from surgery. We were still in shock when we attended his memorial service at the American Legion on March 22. Jack was one of those people everyone loved. Matthew spoke at the service, mentioning his fifty-plus years of friendship with Jack plus their pride of being Marines, the times they worked together as police officers, and their shared Irish heritage. Fighting back tears, I remembered the times we got together, tall, lanky Jack with a headful of hair, well over 6' 2", towering over short, paunchy, slightly bald Matthew at 5'7". Seeing the two of them together was like seeing Mutt and Jeff. After the twenty-one-gun salute, Matthew and I tearfully walked back to our car. As we were slowly driving out of the parking lot, one of the soldiers who took part in the ceremony motioned for Matthew to stop. He rolled down his window, and the soldier handed Matthew one of the shell casings, stating, "Since you and Jack were friends for over fifty years..." Matthew, honored by this simple gesture and having a hard time choking back his tears, responded in the only way a Marine could. "Semper Fi." No two words could have conveyed more. In my heart, I couldn't help but feel a sense of foreboding, *Now, there's only one left from the Philly Five, Matthew.*

CHAPTER 9

One Very Good Week in April

April 2017

We were buoyed by the fact Matthew was having more good days than bad and started to believe the worst may be behind us. I was back to work, and Matthew was scheduled to play golf on Monday. Easter, a time for rejuvenation and rebirth, was just weeks away.

Monday, April 3, 2017

GMI ♡ U!

Hope you enjoy your day golfing, Mr. Veas, say Hi to Wayne for me. Hope it's as beautiful today as it was yesterday (but not as hot). Don't forget your sunscreen!

Xoxoxoxoxo
Your Wicki Girl

PS
Dad was still up at 4:30 am, gave him a sleeping pill since he was up all night, I'll text Mary Ann to come earlier. Keep garage door down when you leave and unlock front door

Matthew had a passion for golf. He was a purist of the game; he took golf *very* seriously. Matthew played by the rules and expected those who played with him to play by the same golden golf rules, as well. There were times when he got mad. It was either because he knew the person he played with had cheated, or he was discouraged by how he was hitting the ball.

As much as Matthew enjoyed playing golf with his friends, the person he most loved playing golf with was his son, Michael. Whereas Matthew's prowess as a golfer came from copious practice, Michael's golfing talents came naturally, at least that's how Matthew explained it. I remember many times when Matthew came home from his trips to Philadelphia, spellbound in admiration as he related to me the latest round of golf he played with Michael. As Matthew used to say, "I wish I could hit a ball like him!"

Through the years, Matthew played golf at a variety of challenging golf courses, both in the United States and in Ireland.

75

He dreamed of playing golf at Augusta National Golf Club, in Augusta, Georgia, the home of the Masters Tournament. It was a dream, however, that never materialized. The closest he got was when we visited family in Aiken, South Carolina, and took a drive to Augusta to drive by the course. We parked across from the entrance of this bastion of golf greatness. Matthew humbly walked across the street and stood on its hollowed driveway—more like his feet floated—and I took his picture. Next, Matthew knelt down and kissed the driveway. That's how much his dream meant to him. Sadly, that was the closest Matthew ever got to playing the one golf course in the world he cherished most, Augusta National, the home of his favorite PGA tournament, the Masters.

April 6, 2017 marked the first day of the Masters Golf Tournament. Second to his love of playing golf, Matthew loved watching golf on TV. He watched every single PGA sanctioned tournament, but he especially loved watching the Masters! Matthew programmed the DVD to record every available televised minute of play. Then, about twenty minutes into the recording, he clicked the button and started watching the recording from the beginning. That way, he could skip through the commercials, yet not wait long before watching the play-by-play action.

Matthew had his favorite PGA golfers too. I can still see him glued to the TV enthusiastically, cheering on Tiger and Phil. Sitting on the edge of his recliner, sweating those difficult putts right along with the pros, putts Tiger always mastered. We watched the Masters and the Ryder Cup together, spellbound by the mastery of these amazing golfers. We celebrated when Payne Stewart won the U.S. Open in 1999 and cried when he tragically died just months later in a freak plane accident.

Matthew embraced the next generation of professional golfers as well with as much enthusiasm as he cheered on his revered Tiger. I can still hear him shouting, calling out names in an animated voice, names now seeped in golf glory…"atta boy Jordan!" and "Bubba, you can make it!" and "Rickie, my boy Rickie!" and "Dustin, wow, look at that ball fly!" and "Rory, Rory, Mc-A-Rory!" and "Kooch, Kooch!" He shouted out words of encouragement, trying to direct these men to where their lost balls had landed in the rough. Or, even worse, he moaned in disappointment when a golfer's ball fell just short of clearing a water hazard. Matthew was fond of sharing his golf knowledge with me, and he always clarified his statements with, "...and he's a really good guy, a nice person..." like he really knew them personally. I had a hard time keeping a straight face on these occasions, but that was Matthew. I believe if he'd been born under different circumstances, in a place more conducive to playing golf than the cement jungle of South Philadelphia and if he'd been born with the natural talent like his son Michael, Matthew would have preferred to have been a professional golfer rather than a police officer.

Despite how much I wanted to play golf with him, I was a driving disaster with a golf club. I have no hand-eye coordination, so most of the balls I hit either dribbled a few feet or I missed the ball entirely or sliced it or yipped it. On those rare occasions when the ball actually sailed through the air, I stood there totally mesmerized, thinking, "So, that's what it feels like to hit a golf ball!" Meanwhile, Matthew stood behind me silently applauding with a big smile radiating on his face. I did get proficient at *wanting* to toss those darn clubs as far as I could in frustration. No matter what I did or how often I practiced, I couldn't master the art of golf. Matthew even provided me with golf lessons. Those golden lessons didn't improve my golf game much. They only proved how inconsistent and atrocious I played.

Matthew started the first week of April playing golf with his buddy, Wayne, at Seven Hills Golf Course and ended the week watching Sergio Garcia win his first Masters. He was feeling good, despite tiring easily, especially after singing on Sunday with the choir at the UCC. We even had a Friday date night at Carrabba's followed by a concert performed by the Timbertones. This week in April was probably one of the best weeks Matthew had all year. It also turned out to be the second to last time Matthew played golf, the last time he watched his beloved Masters Golf Tournament, and the last happy weekend we enjoyed as a married couple. Matthew was feeling better. We enjoyed the moment never realizing within a few, short days, our world would again change, and not for the better.

CHAPTER 10

If Only I Had Stood My Ground

Matthew started having urinary pain on April 10. Sometime early in the morning of the 11th, he believed he passed a kidney stone. He golfed with Wayne on the 12th, attended church services on the 13th, attended Stations of the Cross at Cabrini on the 14th, and by Saturday the 15th he noted in his diary, "feeling poorly, pancreas acting up." Easter Sunday the 16th, he sang a solo with the choir. But in all honesty, his voice didn't sound strong, which bothered him. Later that night he wrote, "upper abdominal pain all weekend, no dinner, passed kidney stone during night." Monday, April 17, Matthew stopped by his physician's office. He was referred to a gastroenterologist, who prescribed a liquid diet and Tramazol, a synthetic opioid for pain relief. "Slept 8 hours—need to be aware of this addictive med…pancreatic pain continued thru the day into night," he wrote on Tuesday. By 1:00 a.m. Wednesday the 19th, Matthew's pain tolerance had reached his limit. We found ourselves once again in the ER.

After tests, Matthew was diagnosed with a nonfunctioning gallbladder in addition to the proverbial pneumonia. The doctors hinted his gallbladder may be causing his abdominal pain. Matthew was scheduled for surgery the next day. The day of his surgery I left work by 1:00 p.m., checked with Mary Ann regarding the folks, and then hightailed it to the hospital. Matthew was still in his room on the 3rd floor. Within minutes, he was transported to preop.

While we were waiting in preop, a woman walked in and introduced herself as the assistant anesthesiologist. As she was reviewing his chart, I mentioned, "Are you aware Matthew has had pneumonia since Christmas Eve? That's one of the symptoms he was admitted with. Do you believe it's prudent to do surgery now? Why can't this wait until the pneumonia clears up?"

Her response was, "I wasn't aware of that," as she continued flipping through his chart. She asked a few more questions then left. I didn't feel good about this surgery. A patient having pneumonia symptoms for almost four months, in all logic, doesn't sound like a good candidate for surgery. Matthew didn't raise a concern, though. All he wanted was relief from his pain. Within minutes, he was wheeled out of preop and into surgery.

I waited anxiously in the surgical waiting room on the first floor. Tucked in a corner is the surgical tracking board. Listed on the board are codes corresponding to patient names, their surgeon's name, and where the patient is currently located during the surgical process: preop, surgery, or postop. After about an hour and a half, I received a phone call from his surgeon. The surgery went well, and I should be able to see Matthew shortly. He was in postop. Despite my uneasiness, my prayers were answered. I guess I worried for nothing.

I waited, and waited, and waited. No one came to escort me to postop. Every time I checked the surgical tracking board, Matthew's code kept showing him in postop. After an hour, my sense of thankfulness started to change to one of panic. That little voice in my head, which originally felt surgery wasn't warranted at this time, started to gnaw at my gut. My stomach felt like it was being gnarled from the inside by a giant piranha. A headache was brewing at the top of my skull, radiating down my neck and down between my shoulder blades. I couldn't understand why no one came to get me. As each minute passed, my panic escalated into a life all its own. I knew something was wrong. I could feel it in my bones. I needed to find out what had happened, and I needed to know *NOW*!

I first called the 3rd floor nurses' station and asked to speak to his nurse. I explained my concern, and she put me on hold for a few minutes and came back on the line assuring me Matthew was in still in postop. That didn't help much, I already knew that based on the surgical tracker. I was in a daze. It had been a tough year so far, and it was only April. I didn't need another crisis in my life. I walked out of the surgical waiting room and out to my car. I needed to get out of that place. I needed to see the night sky, get a breath of fresh air, and evaluate the situation. I must have sat in my car for about a minute when my phone rang. The caller was female, and she didn't identify herself, but she did inform me when they went to remove the intubation tube after surgery, they couldn't get Matthew to breath. They worked on him for over an hour before the decision was made to reintubate him. He was in the ICU. I thanked her for the information. My worse fear had been confirmed. I was numb. I was also close to tears. I'm not sure how I kept it together. I wanted to hit someone, hit them hard, wring their neck with my bare hands, anything to take back the last couple of hours and firmly forbid this surgery. I was beside myself with anger and frustration. I tried to compose myself. I needed to be strong for Matthew's sake.

I took the elevator to the ICU. The first person I saw was the unit secretary seated at the nurses' station. I explained why I was there. She asked his name, and I provided it. She checked her list and told me he wasn't there. After all the anxiety and trepidation I'd been feeling, her news just set me off. At this point, I'd reached my limit. My voice must have gone up a couple of octaves as I voiced my frustration. No matter what I said to this person, she kept repeating he wasn't there, and I kept stating what I had been told. We were obviously at a stalemate. I resigned myself this was a hopeless situation. I wasn't getting anywhere, so I left. I took the elevator back down to the first-floor surgical waiting room and sat down. I needed to regroup and think things through. Why did everything have to be so damn complicated?

Shortly after I sat down, a woman about my age walked out of the elevator and walked straight toward me. She introduced herself as the charge nurse for the ICU and stated she overheard my conversation with the unit secretary. I restated what I knew at this point. She was understanding of my feelings and asked me to follow her back upstairs. I waited outside the ICU. After a few minutes, she returned and provided me with the information I so desperately needed. "Matthew's surgery went well," she informed me. "When he was in post-op, they attempted to remove the vent, but he wasn't breathing. They worked on him for over an hour and had to reintubate him. He's still in postop, and he will be transferred once he stabilizes to the ICU." I remember listening to her and thinking at the time, "If only someone had listened to me and why hadn't anyone notified me when this drastic turn of events happened?" I was hungry, exhausted, and lethargic. I thanked her for the information. It was basically, again, the same information I heard earlier. I went back down to the waiting room and sat down in the same chair I'd been sitting in prior to the charge nurse locating me. I sent a text message to Matthew's sons, letting them know their dad's surgery was over but there was a complication, and he'd be in ICU for a while. I wanted to go home, but something kept my butt glued to that chair. As I was sitting there staring off into space, lost in thought, several staff members filtered by, obviously having just finished their shift. One of these people was the assistant anesthesiologist who introduced herself in pre-op. When she saw me, she walked up to me and asked if I had a few minutes. She told me the same story I'd already heard before, which by this time, I could have recited word for word.

I asked the question that kept nagging me, "Why didn't anyone come to let me know what was going on? I was worried. I was frightened."

"I apologize that no one came out to talk to you. We were all working on your husband, trying to get him to breathe. We were very busy, and everyone was involved. I worked on your husband for an hour and a half. We did everything we could to avoid having to reintubate him, but we had no choice." Her tone was sympathetic, caring.

I'm not sure how I got home that night. It had been a long day, and the last five hours were excruciatingly painful. It wasn't a physical pain, but a gut-wrenching pain from within my soul that slowly crept into my heart, mind, and consciousness. I wish I had been more adamant with his physicians, demanding the postponement of Matthew's surgery. I wish I could have convinced Matthew this surgery should have been delayed by days or even weeks until he was stronger. And I wish I could turn back the hands of time to a year ago when Matthew wasn't sick.

I could understand after two months of random, abdominal pain that Matthew wanted relief. He was tired of being sick, had a low pain threshold, and he saw the surgery as a possible way of feeling better. Instead, it ended up accelerating his pneumonia-like symptoms. From this point on…Matthew's health never improved.

CHAPTER 11

A Major Setback, a Need for Prayer

I contacted my boss to let her know I'd only be at work for a short time in the early morning because I needed answers. The only way to get those answers was to camp out in Matthew's room while waiting for his physicians to round on him. Friday morning, I met Matthew's nurse. She was professional and informative, preparing me in advance for what I'd be seeing when I walked into Matthew's room. Patients on a vent are normally medicated so they won't fight having an intubation tube down their throat. Only when medical staff anticipate removing the vent do they awaken the patient. Matthew had awakened several times during the night. Each time, he was confused, angry, frustrated, and looking for answers.

Despite his nurse's warning, I was shocked. What I saw was worse than I imagined. Matthew's bed was slightly elevated, and he appeared comatose. There was a clear glass container attached to the wall behind his bed with a suction tube attached to the vent. Secretions from Matthew's lungs were being suctioned into the container by the tube that ran from his mouth into the container. The container was about half full of a cloudy, whitish, gray foamy matter. It was a gooey mass that looked like a combination of lung slime, nose snot, and throat secretions you'd cough up if you are pneumatic. It was disgusting to look at and difficult to ignore since the container was less than two feet behind his head. A few sheets of paper and a pen were on the bedside table next to his bed. Matthew looked so vulnerable. I'd never seen him like this, and it was difficult to witness. As I looked at him, I said a silent prayer. And I was compelled to do something I've never done before. I called my church.

I always believed my relationship with God was between Him and me. What I prayed for, I prayed to God. I didn't see the point in getting a third person involved. In this case, I was overcome by a spiritual need that was stronger and more compelling than anything I'd ever felt. For the first time in my life, I needed to reach out to my church. Seeing Matthew in this shape, I knew he needed all the prayers he could get. When Marty, the Administrative Assistant at the UCC answered the phone, I explained the situation. She informed me Pastor Robin was out of town and Donna Ives, a retired minister and a member of our congregation, was on call. She'd contact Donna immediately. I also reached out to Wayne. I knew Wayne would want to be informed of his golfing buddy's unexpected change in condition.

Matthew awakened about ten minutes before Donna arrived. With the intubation tube in place, he wasn't able to talk. He was agitated and angry. I could relate to what he was feeling. As he tried to write his questions in pidgin English, which was often difficult to decipher because his normal legible script looked more like chicken scratches. He even resorted to drawing pictures. With his mind fuzzy from medications geared to keep him sedated, Matthew was having an extremely difficult time trying to communicate. Donna was a trooper. She talked non-stop, said a prayer, and played right along with Matthew's frustration and anxiety. After about thirty minutes, she left. I was now alone with my husband and didn't have a clue what to do next. This was not what we expected. When he was awake, Matthew's temper was brutally directed at his poor nurse and myself. He was scared, angry, and frustrated due to lack of answers, and the answers he was receiving didn't jive with what he wanted to hear. And I couldn't blame him.

When Matthew finally fell back asleep, I sat on the couch and took a photograph. As they say, a photo speaks a thousand words, and I knew I needed to communicate to his sons and bring them up-to-date on his condition. Michael, Matthew's younger son, and his wife Diana were on vacation with friends in Marco Island, Florida. I didn't want to disturb their vacation, but this turn of events I believed they would want to know about. I sent the following text to all four, Michael, Diana, Matty, and his wife Deb:

"Just took this photo of your dad, he had to be reintubated after the surgery yesterday. He needs your prayers. I haven't seen any doctors yet. Will update you once I know more."

Within minutes, I received messages from Matty, Deb, and Diana. I noticed Michael deleted his phone number from the link. I was surprised at first. I didn't know how to take this, but with time, I realized seeing his dad in this condition, so helpless and frail, was something Michael just couldn't handle at this time. They were extremely close, like two peas in a pod. Then again, I didn't want to deal with this either, but I had no choice. Nothing was working out as we'd hoped. Matthew wasn't the only disgruntled, angry person in that hospital room.

Throughout the day, a parade of physicians popped in and out. I didn't get much information from them. His pulmonologist, Dr. X, was one of the last physicians I saw that day; he came late in the afternoon. I cornered him, hoping to get an answer to a question that had been bothering me all afternoon. "Dr. X, I learned earlier today the spot on Matthew's lung has increased in size. What are you going to do about that?"

Dr X didn't turn to face me. Instead, he mumbled into the computer screen in front of him, "We'll deal with that later."

And he left it at that. I had a difficult time restraining myself when I heard such a lame ass response. I believe Dr. X had been lackadaisical in treating Matthew's condition. Matthew had been seeing him since the summer of 2015, and with each visit, Matthew was slowly losing confidence in him. And with each visit, Dr. X would throw out possible diagnoses like, "It could be BOOP," or "it might be MACK," or "possibly it's interstitial lung disease." Each time, it felt like he was casting out a fishing line hoping we'd take the bait, and he could finally reel one in.

Dr. X had performed a bronchoscope biopsy the summer before when we waited on pins and needles for the results. We humbly and profusely thanked God on that occasion when Matthew learned he didn't have cancer. A bronchoscope biopsy was again performed in February, just two months before, with the same diagnosis: no cancer. By this time, seeing Matthew in bed with an intubation tube taped to his mouth, I was in no mood to keep taking crap from this physician. Whether Matthew agreed or not, I was determined to fire Dr. X. In my opinion, a jackass would have better luck trying to figure out what was wrong with Matthew than this doctor could. If Dr. X was stymied, he should have admitted it and referred Matthew to another pulmonologist or a specialist. Instead, he strung him along for two long years as Matthew's condition silently and unknowingly kept getting worse. I hate ineptitude, especially in the medical field when a person's life is at stake. Matthew hated doctors and didn't find many he trusted or respected. This physician did nothing to gain Matthew's trust or mine. Not putting my foot down sooner is something I will have to live with for the rest of my life. I kept thinking to myself, *I should have been more forceful, more tenacious.*

CHAPTER 12

Happy Anniversary

Matthew's diary entry on Friday, April 21, 2017, "Notable: nurses attention to my needs was sorely lacking on this day—this continued thru 7 PM x AM shift and into Saturday 7 AM shift." This was Matthew's impression of his ICU nurses. It doesn't necessarily mean it was true. Matthew was pissed off being intubated. He fought the vent; it was painful for him, and he took his anger out on anyone who was within firing range, especially his nurses. He was like a grizzly bear caught in a trap fighting with all its might to get free. You'd think once the intubation tube was finally removed, he'd be calmer and relieved. That wasn't the case. Matthew was discharged from the ICU at 4:00 p.m. on Saturday, April 22. I had a funny feeling once he was discharged, the hospital doors were immediately bolted to ward against his reentry. I've also wondered if a message went out hospital wide, "Elvis has left the building!" A hospital joke, which often refers to when AHCA, the Florida healthcare governing agency, has left a hospital after an unannounced visit. In this case, Matthew was in the guise of AHCA. His poor nurses—they should have received combat pay—they earned it!

Matthew wasn't home long—less than 24 hours—when he experienced the same abdominal pain that landed him in the hospital just days before and resulted in surgery. As his diary attests on Sunday, April 23, 2017, "Recovery not going well. Continued stomach discomfort, loss of appetite, insomnia-spending day and night on recliner." He continued to cough up sputum. Matthew placed Styrofoam cups strategically around the house, which became his spitting cups. When a cup was full, he tossed it in the trash and replaced it with another. Personally, I hated seeing those cups around the house. The contents turned my stomach, and I had a hard time restraining myself from heaving. He also had cups in his car so he could spit when he was driving. He'd been spitting up sputum since February. Each month, the amount of sputum gradually increased in volume. Prior to the surgery, he didn't need Styrofoam cups to spit into, the amount could be contained using a tissue. It was only *after* his gallbladder surgery the volume and frequency became overwhelming.

Four months of illness and uncertainty were not only affecting Matthew physically, but psychologically and emotionally as well. He wrote in his diary Monday, April 24, "Turning Point. Overwhelmed by depression, early row with Vicki—feelings of isolation. Prayers for some understanding. Called Vicki at work to explain my feelings—told her I needed her help to get through this illness." I don't remember what we talked about during that phone call; he wasn't communicating his inner thoughts or feelings. As was his nature, Matthew often kept true feelings and emotions buried deep within his soul. Did he have a premonition there wasn't going to be a magic pill to cure him? Had God given him a message? Did Matthew have a sixth sense that gave him a preview of what was to come? His sleeping was restless between the coughing, spitting up sputum, and his intermittent stomach pain. He didn't have much to be thankful for these days. I regret he felt compelled to shoulder this alone.

Besides the reoccurrence of abdominal pain following his surgery, his surgery also affected his oxygen levels. Less than a week after surgery, Matthew's primary care physician ordered him back to the ER. Dr. Abskhroun believed Matthew had reached the point where he needed oxygen 24/7. If he wrote an order for oxygen, home delivery would take days. If the hospital ordered oxygen, it would be delivered the same day. We immediately went to the ER. The ER physician Matthew was instructed to ask for was busy on another case, so Matthew was assigned to someone else. This physician assured Matthew, "I was told about the phone call from your primary care." Matthew's oxygen levels were low. He was told to walk up and down the hallway several times. After three hours, he was discharged home with the promise from case management that oxygen would be delivered to our home the same day.

Matthew's diary testifies to his frustration at this time, and it's not surprising as a result, depression was setting in, "returned to ER 1 PM—3 hrs.-oxygen level tests released at 4 PM with promise of oxygen delivered to home-later learned that documents promised by hospital showed I did not qualify—When will it end?" His primary care physician believed Matthew needed oxygen 24/7. The hospital where the surgery took place didn't see anything wrong with his oxygen levels and disregarded Dr. Abskhroun's concern for Matthew's oxygen intake. During this time Matthew was steadily losing weight. He was now down to 150 lbs., normally he'd weigh between 175-180 lbs. The seat of his pants were drooping, his pantlegs were dragging on the floor when he walked, and no matter how much he tightened the belt on his pants, he was swimming in his clothes. He was reluctant to get new clothes assuming, again, he'd recover and later regain the lost weight. He was sleeping more often, propped up in his recliner, which provided some relief from his coughing.

Matthew was devoted to his cell phone. He carried it everywhere. He complained for months it was getting difficult to charge. The male end of his charging cord wasn't sitting into the female receptacle very well. When inserted, he'd assume it was charging, but when he checked it later, he discovered the cord was dislodged. It wasn't until Matthew was in the hospital in April that I tried to charge his phone and realized what a pain-in-the-ass this was. So far, 2017 had been a shitty year for him. I thought Matthew needed something positive, so I bought him a new cellphone on April 29. One of the first people Matthew called using his new Apple 7 cellphone was his sister Bobbi, in New Jersey.

Matthew normally drove to Philadelphia once or twice a year to get his "hugs and kisses" as he used to say. Back in February, when he assumed he'd be feeling better by summer, Matthew made reservations to fly to Philadelphia and rent a car for two weeks to help celebrate his son Michael's birthday on June 14. After his gallbladder surgery, Matthew realized he probably wouldn't be well enough to travel any time soon, let alone fly to Philadelphia in June. He successfully canceled the car reservation through Enterprise. However, Spirit Airlines wasn't very accommodating. The airline required him to submit a document from his physician stating he wasn't well enough to travel. Matthew obtained the letter and forwarded it to the airlines. Spirit Airlines accepted the letter and cancelled his reservation, but instead of reimbursing Matthew the cost of his ticket, they informed him he had three months to book another flight. The way Matthew's health was deteriorating, it was obvious he wouldn't be flying anywhere within the next three months.

May 2017

Matthew was showing signs of sleeping a little better, and as a result, he'd have a few days when he felt pretty good. Tuesday, May 2, "Again able to sleep in bed after V leaves for work at 4:30 x 9:30 ☺ Shave—weight 148-haven't been that low since 1960." He went to Publix to grocery shop, mopped the kitchen floor, cleaned the bathroom, and did laundry. Each day, he felt a little stronger, his appetite was getting better, and he was starting to believe he was finally making a breakthrough. Then again, he'd felt that way before.

Matthew saw his pulmonologist, Dr. X, on Friday, May 12. As he wrote later in his diary, "CT scan from Wednesday shows a shadowy left lung-fluid, which I've been coughing up the past

3 weeks. Begin steroid/prednisone tomorrow. Lunch w/Vicki at Ruby Tuesday and shopping." A definitive diagnosis was still elusive.

Good Morning I Love You! May 17, 2017

Matthew, Happy 21st Anniversary!
It's hard to believe 21 years have gone by so quickly. I'm looking forward to sharing the next 21 years with my loving husband. You were right, it only gets better!!!

Love, Hugs, & Smooches,
oxo Vicki xox

PS I can't wait until our date tonight!!!!

May 17th was our 21st wedding anniversary. For many years, we planned a mini vacation to celebrate. The last couple of years we'd been going to Cedar Key with the pups. We stumbled upon the Old Fenimore Inn in 2012. Our good friends, Gene and Peggy Grady, had recently moved to Ft Myers from Ohio. We were looking forward to seeing them. Gene had been the best man at our wedding, and Matthew and I had been witnesses to theirs. Our anniversaries were only a few days apart. Since we'd only had Kipper and Katy a couple of months, Matthew was reluctant to leave them at a kennel. Finding a dog-friendly hotel on or very near the beach in Ft Myers proved to be a problem. The only places I could find were booked. I asked Matthew, "What do you want to do? Neither of us want to stay on the interstate, but that's all I can find that are dog friendly or will accept two dogs."

"We don't have to go to Ft Myers. We can visit Gene and Peg another time. See what you can find somewhere else."

I didn't want to go far, even though my parents could stay by themselves at that time. This was 2012, but I wanted to be close to home just in case. After I had surgery in 1996, Matthew and I had a relaxing couple of days in Cedar Key, a small coastal town reminiscent of Florida at the turn of the century. Cedar Key had the advantage of being less than two hours from home. It was easy to get around, and they had accommodations that were dog-friendly. I made a reservation at the Old Fenimore Inn, a place that became our de-stressor place to go. Matthew and I loved it and so did the pups. It was the pups first vacation with Mom and Dad, and they loved having our undivided attention. In the years to come, if we didn't get to Cedar Key for our anniversary, then we'd visit for another occasion. Cedar Key represented our time together. No parents, no job, no extraneous obligations or commitments—it was just us—Matthew, Vicki, Kipper, and Katy Veasey!

This year, however, a trip to Cedar Key was out of the question. Matthew wasn't strong enough, and his condition was too unstable. Walking into the kitchen after work, I was greeted by two dozen pink roses, a beautiful card, and the promise of dinner out. Before Matthew got sick, going out to dinner was something we enjoyed, but it didn't seem special. Now, the thought of going out to dinner filled me with overwhelming excitement and happiness, just the two of us out of the house together. Wow! I felt like I'd won the lottery!

Normally, for special occasions such as this, we went to our favorite restaurant, Nouvelle Cuisine. Since Matthew was now on prednisone, going to Nouvelle was out of the question since he couldn't have a glass of wine. As Matthew used to say, "It just wouldn't be the same going to Nouvelle Cuisine without having a good glass of wine to wash down such a great meal." In our hearts, we were still assuming we'd have next year to celebrate our 22nd anniversary at our favorite restaurant. Instead, we went to Red Lobster, praying our friend Isabelle would forgive us. We gorged ourselves on cheese biscuits, shrimp cocktail, and coconut shrimp! The waitress took our picture. When I look at this photograph,

I saw I was overweight. My face and cheeks were still puffy from the prednisone I'd been on earlier, and Matthew looked incredibly emaciated. His skull prominently stood out like a skeleton. It looked like the skin on his face had been shrink-wrapped, his cheeks were sunken, and there was hardly any life shining from the depths of his eyes. Matthew's eyes looked sad, like he had a secret he regrettably couldn't divulge. It was obvious he was not well despite his half-hearted attempt to smile for the camera.

While the performance on the main stage at this time focused on the perils of Matthew, the show on the auxiliary stage didn't change much from day to day. Since I clocked into work at 6:00 a.m. Monday through Friday, I didn't see Mom and Dad until I got home in the afternoon at 3:00 p.m. By then, they'd had breakfast and lunch. Mary Ann had worked her magic on them for three hours, and I kept watch over my flock from 3:00 p.m. until they went to bed. Life with Mom and Dad was coasting along, thank goodness! I had enough on my mind being worried about Matthew except for one little thing that started to make me wonder.

Most nights, Dad was sundowning. Between intermittent sleep and his restless legs, Dad didn't get much sleep at night, and sleeping pills didn't help much. Mom, on the other hand, slept peacefully tucked into her bed like a swaddled, little infant. A couple of times when I checked on Mom during the night, I noticed she wasn't wearing her diaper. I found her diaper in the strangest locations. It was flung over her headboard, on her dresser, under her bed, mixed within clothes laying on the chair, or laying on the floor next to her bed. Sometimes I never even found it. My only solution was to wake her up to put a diaper back on her. Otherwise, her bed would be dirty in the morning. I tried talking to her but no response. *Nudge her, are you kidding!* I resorted to shaking her, talking loudly, moving her foot, and pinching her arm. Nothing worked. When Mom slept, she was out cold. After going through this assortment of tricks a couple of times, she finally woke up groggy, not comprehending. I needed her to stand up so I could put her diaper back on. While I was putting her diaper on, I asked her why she took it off, which was stupid of me. Dah! This is a woman who doesn't always remember her name, has no idea where she is, who I am, or what day it is. Is she really going to remember taking her diaper off? And I never caught her in the act! I mentioned this to Dad several times, and he always feigned ignorance. I gave him the lecture about how important it was for Mom keep her diaper on *all* the time, even in bed. He kept telling me, "She must be taking it off herself." A part of me didn't believe him. It wasn't in her nature to do that. Yet Alzheimer's patients have a tendency to do strange things. When you think you have them figured out, wouldn't you know, they do something totally off the wall which catches you off guard and leaves you scratching your head and thinking, *How'd she come up with that?*

June 16 was Matthew's last appointment with Dr. X. This same day Matthew's primary care physician ordered a second opinion with a pulmonologist. I was trying to get Matthew to switch pulmonologists for the past year with no success. After what Matthew had been going through this year, I finally convinced him he needed a new doctor. I knew the pulmonologist for him to see—Dr. O. Dr. O was a pulmonologist affiliated with Regional Medical Center Bayonet Point, who worked with my residents. Dr. O regularly attended Morning Report at 8:00 a.m., and my residents not only respected him, they loved him as well. I made an appointment for Matthew to see Dr. O on August 21, the first available. Dr. O was going on vacation in July, and if a cancellation occurred in the meantime, his office manager would let me know. August seemed so far away.

As Matthew prepared information for his August appointment with Dr. O, I was busy at work with orientation for our new internal medicine residents. Dad's appetite was decreasing, he even tossed out his breakfast cereal on several occasions, which was very unusual for him. Mom fell in the hobby room, and Matthew had a difficult time getting her up.

When I came home from work one day, the corner of the wall in the breakfast room had a large gouge in it, and there was drywall debris scattered all over the floor. I was shocked and perplexed. Mom was the first person I saw when I looked around the house. She was sitting alone in the family room. When I asked her what happened, I couldn't get a straight answer. I soon found Dad coming out of the bathroom. I asked him what happened to the wall. He looked at me with a blank stare and shrugged his shoulders. He had no idea and never even noticed it. I scouted for Matthew, who was sequestered in the computer room, intent on listening to a song on iTunes. Asking Matthew about the wall produced another blank stare, but at least this time I got a response, "What wall?" I went back to the gouge, looked closely, and thought a while. I compared the height of the gouge to the height of Mom's walker. I had a gut feeling I knew what happened. Mom was probably rushing for the bathroom, misjudged the corner, banged into the wall, and kept right on a-goin'. Despite his lack of strength these days, Matthew insisted on repairing the corner. I believe doing chores like this was his way of trying to feel normal. His love of golf had been shelved since he last played on April 12. Coughing as much as he was and spitting up sputum, he couldn't sing with the choir, two hobbies Matthew loved! He needed to feel needed, and this provided the perfect venue.

I must commend Dr. Abskhroun and his staff. Many times during the summer, Matthew called stating he couldn't breathe or the coughing was wearing him down. Mary always told him, "Matthew, we'll squeeze you in. Come when it's convenient for you." He took her at her word. One such visit was on June 21. His pancreatic pain was acting up again. Dr. Abskhroun referred Matthew to the ER where he was admitted again, as he had been numerous times in the past. Matthew's white cell counts were elevated. He was given Dilaudid and prescribed another dose of antibiotics. Chest scans and MRIs were performed, but he didn't have stones, so no surgery was warranted. There was still no diagnosis for this random pancreatic pain. He was discharged on June 23. This hospital stay did accomplish one thing. He was finally approved for home oxygen. The first delivery arrived at 4:00 p.m.

It was a new experience for Matthew and I to have oxygen tanks in the house. The deliveryman from Rotech was very helpful. He went over the guidelines and showed us how to monitor and change the tanks. Matthew used a cannula, a plastic device inserted into each nostril. The oxygen flows from the tank into the cannula and into Matthew's lungs. There is an elastic cord that stretches from ear to ear to help keep the cannula in place. Matthew was either tethered to an oxygen tank or the concentrator by a long, clear, plastic tubing which allowed him to walk from room to room.

The oxygen concentrator, a box about the size of a small suitcase, replaces having to be constantly attached to a heavy oxygen tank. The concentrator makes oxygen and produces three distinct sounds—loud enough where you can't help but hear it—especially the third sound, which is louder than the first and second sounds. It always reminded me of an air conditioner when it abruptly shuts off.

You can't use open flames in the house when oxygen is in use. I was constantly worried I'd accidentally light a candle, and we'd all be blown to smithereens. We were concerned about the dogs. Would they step on the tubing or be tempted to play with it? We were also worried we'd trip over it ourselves, but our worries were unfounded.

The first night Matthew put the oxygen concentrator in our bedroom next to our bed, what a mistake that was! Neither of us got any sleep that night. However, at least the sound of the concentrator had a regular rhythm as opposed to Matthew's loud, erratic snoring. The next night, he moved the oxygen concentrator to a corner of the living room and made sure the tubing was long enough so he could get in and out of bed during the night. That worked much better. Also, as our good friends Wayne and Sherrie mentioned to us, after a while, you don't even hear it, and they were right.

Matthew's diary June 26, "Mom slipped in kitchen, no walker, tough standing her up." I'm not sure how Matthew got her up. It must have taken every ounce of will power, strength, and stamina that his severely weakened body had. This was a man who, just the year before, had no problem picking Mom up and getting her back on her feet. Now, he used every ounce of strength to help her up. This was the second time she fell within the last couple of weeks. And when she went down, it was like trying to lug dead weight. Mom no longer had any muscle tone, so whenever you'd try to lift her, she cried out in pain. She wasn't hurt physically, but with her Alzheimer's, Mom had a very low pain threshold.

Matthew's health insurance assigned a representative, Cathy, to monitor his case. Cathy provided Matthew a sounding board, someone he could talk to who listened objectively and provided him with feedback and recommendations. The recommendations helped prepare him for what, in all likelihood was coming in the very near future. Two years later, Mary Ann confided in me it was Cathy who first approached the idea of hospice or an assisted living facility to Matthew.

In the midst of all this turmoil in our lives, there was one, amazing miracle. Our granddaughter Meghan gave birth to a beautiful baby boy, Michael Francis Gavaghan, on June 29. Matthew was so happy, another boy in the family! He stared at photos of baby Michael with a look of such sadness, you could tell he yearned to cradle that little bundle of joy lovingly in his arms. It was like he was looking at a future he knew didn't include him. While our family in Philadelphia was celebrating this miraculous, joyous birth, in Florida, we were preparing for the worst and hoping for a miracle ourselves. We were praying God would hear our prayers, be merciful, and deliver us back to the life we led just a year before. That life at the time seemed mundane and boring. Now, boring never seemed so precious!

Matthew seldom attended church at this time. At first, he attempted to go to the 4:00 p.m. Vigil Mass on Saturdays, but when he started coughing, he couldn't stop. Once he started spitting up sputum, he was reluctant to sit next to someone when he had to frequently spit into a cup. Matthew wasn't attending the UCC on Sundays either. During summer, the choir was on hiatus until September. Easter Sunday, quite fitting as it turned out, was the last time Matthew sang with the choir.

July 2017

We made the best of each day. I was still in denial, going through the motions of everyday life, trying to keep one step ahead of reality. At night, I prepared dinner and cleaned up, did laundry (which he still attempted to do each week despite my protests), and ran more of the errands he used to run. When I was at work, I constantly thought of Matthew. We attempted to do the simple things that helped us pretend our lives were normal.

> *Monday, July 3, 2017*
>
> *GMI ♡ U!*
>
> *Hi Sweetie Pie! How r u feeling?*
>
> *Looking forward to being home tomorrow, July 4th, Yipee!!!*
>
> *Try to rest, don't overdo today.*
>
> *How about hoagies tonight? If you feel up to it, would love to curl up and watch a movie tonight. Maybe u can find a good one for us to watch tonight.*
>
> *Love, hugs, & smooches,*
> *Your Wicki Girl XOXOXOXOXO*

We had an uneventful July 4. Matthew recorded in his diary, "Vicki ordered a rest day for me—did minimal-folded clothes, cleaned dishes-shortness of breath comes quickly, even walking to the bathroom." The following day, he noted, "bank, Walmart, Publix-wore me out…" We continued to enjoy the simple things in life like cuddling in bed, Friday night pizza, or watching a movie. Never knowing, if perhaps, this might be the last time Matthew might be doing this.

Matthew wrote the following on Saturday, July 8, "V & me & pups snuggled for 1 hr ☺." Turns out, this was the last time we snuggled together. Katy buried herself between us, wiggling her tail, and inserted her snout into Matthew's cupped hand as submission. At the end of the bed, Kipper rolled back and forth with a goofy smile on his happy face, exposing his tummy, hoping for some belly rubs. Such simple things, such precious times. I now wish I'd known that was going to be the last time we'd cuddle together in bed because I never would have gotten out of bed. I would have pressed the pause button to let time stand still. Maybe that way, the inevitable future would never have caught up with us. As long as we were cocooned in our bed, with the door closed, it felt like we were safe. Nothing could intrude, interrupt, or harm us. However, life isn't like that. Eventually, you have to get out of bed, face the day, and see what happens. It would have been so much easier, though, to just pull the covers up over our heads and pretend this was all a bad nightmare and we'd wake up the next morning, refreshed, bushy-tailed, and life was back to normal like it had been just the year before.

CHAPTER 13

A Downhill Spiral Quickly Going Out of Control

By July 13, Matthew was using smaller, portable oxygen tanks which eliminated the long tubing and made traveling much easier for him. We were impatiently waiting for August 21, his appointment with Dr. O. This same day, Matthew wasn't feeling well and stopped by Dr Abskhroun's office, which resulted in an oxygen level increase and a new round of medications. The next day, July 14, we had our usual Friday night pizza. Afterward, Matthew wasn't feeling well, his diary entry attributes this to, "ate too much ☹."

Early the next morning, Matthew awoke in excruciating pain. By 1:40 p.m., he was in the ER. He was in the hospital for a few days, discouraged he didn't see a physician until he threatened to leave. This was the last time we enjoyed our traditional Friday night pizza. Despite the pain, I believe Matthew felt it was worth it. It was too bad he didn't get to enjoy a nice glass of Pisano with his pizza.

Wednesday, July 19, Matthew had an 11:00 a.m. appointment with Dr. Abskhroun, as a follow-up to his hospital visit. He had no pain, and his vitals were good. The day before, he'd gone to Cabrini and requested a prayer for the sick. Later in the week, he composed a note for the church bulletin at the UCC, thanking everyone for their well wishes. He received so many get well cards from his friends at the UCC. Also, on July 20, Matthew visited our friend Sig Stock at Evergreen Woods, an assisted living facility in Brooksville. Sig was a friend from our Stage West days. We shared so many theatre memories of Sig and his wife, Evelyn. Sig was always willing to help with set construction and worked effortlessly to make every theatre set a masterpiece. After visiting Sig, Matthew told me, "If I ever get that way, just shoot me."

> *Good Morning I ♡ U!*
>
> *You must be exhausted! I heard you coughing most of the night. Try to rest today, don't do anything, I'll do laundry tonight. K & K went potty, both p & p @ 4:50*
>
> *XOXOXOXO Your Wifey XOXOXOXO*

Friday, July 21, Matthew experienced night sweats and a fever over 101. The next day, Saturday, he attended the Vigil Mass at Cabrini. Sunday, he was having trouble breathing. Despite his breathing struggles, Matthew made this note in his diary, "Spieth wins OPEN!!"

When Dr. O returned from his vacation, I updated him on the drastic changes in Matthew's condition, asking if he could see Matthew sooner. In the back of mind, I couldn't help but think, *he might not be alive on August 21*. Dr. O listened to my concerns and graciously accommodated my request. Matthew's appointment was moved up to August 4th.

Shortly after 12:30 p.m., July 25, Matthew called me at work. He was in the ER, the second time this month. He was having a hard time breathing for several days. It had gotten so bad by 11:35 a.m. that he called 911. He was in respiratory distress. He spent two nights in a partitioned cubicle across the hall from the ER. A physician talked to him regarding post-op hospital care, the options were rehab, assisted living, or hospice. None of these recommendations seemed feasible to him at the time. Matthew was having problems breathing but we, or at least I, didn't believe he was dying. By the third day, Matthew was in a regular room. His roommate was a friendly gentleman who talked nonstop and was a widower. He mentioned to Matthew his wife used to work for a local funeral home. If we ever needed a funeral home to contact them, mention his wife's name. It was like listening to a TV commercial. Matthew was intrigued. I felt uneasy.

Matthew was discharged on July 28. In my opinion, he now appeared in worse shape physically than he had been prior to his admittance to the hospital. He recorded in his diary, "home health care, nebulizer trmt & antibiotics, My poor darling Vicki is being overwhelmed by this H.H.C. needs of her folks and now her husband. Humana Nurse 4 pm." Overwhelmed was an understatement! Matthew's oxygen levels kept getting increased. His sleep was sporadic, his appetite was minimal, but at the same time, his coughing and spitting up sputum was almost nonstop.

Matthew had a follow-up appointment with his primary care physician scheduled for Monday, July 31, which was rescheduled for the next day, Tuesday, August 1. I picked Matthew up. He wasn't strong enough to drive any more. Kelly took Matthew's vitals, left the room, and returned soon with Dr. Abskhroun. He reviewed Matthew's vitals, retook his vitals, rechecked Matthew's oxygen levels, and retook his vitals a third time. Dr. Abskhroun spent over an hour and a half with Matthew during this time. No matter how often he rechecked Matthew's vitals, the numbers never improved.

Finally, Dr. Abskhroun told me, "Take Matthew straight to the ER, but don't take him here in town where you've been taking him. They haven't been able to help him. Take him directly to Bayonet Point."

The tone of his voice sent shivers up my spine. This was the first time I started to get scared. Prior to this, I believed if Matthew received a correct diagnosis and the right medications, he would recover. Now, after what I witnessed and heard, it was finally sinking in. A diagnosis and some pills probably weren't going to provide a cure.

Even though Dr. Abskhroun had given me strict orders to drive Matthew directly to the ER, I had to stop home to pick up his insurance card and driver's license. I hadn't expected I'd be taking Matthew back to a hospital so soon, and I didn't have those documents with me. After I pulled into our driveway, I mentioned to Matthew, "I'll only be a minute. Wait right here." Matthew insisted on getting out of the car and walking into the house.

Matthew indignantly stated when he walked into the kitchen, "I'm hungry. By the time we get to the hospital and they admit me, it will be too late for dinner, and they won't feed me."

"Matthew, Dr. Abskhroun was emphatic. He said drive straight to the hospital."

"I don't care. I'm eating before we go!"

I could tell it was a lost cause. He was already scrounging in the refrigerator, pulling out a couple of eggs and butter, banging the cabinet doors looking for a frying pan.

With Matthew in the kitchen, I ran into our bedroom to locate his insurance card and driver's license. I switched purses just the day before, so I went to that purse expecting to find his cards, but they weren't there. I rechecked every zippered compartment, the outer pockets, nothing! Dammit! I ran back into the living room, dumped my current purse, and looked through it with the same result, no cards. By this time, Matthew was sitting at the breakfast table eating a fried egg sandwich and drinking a glass of milk. I can still see the pissed look on his face, angry for being told to go again to a hospital, mad that I couldn't find his cards, and fearful of what this next step of his journey had in store for him. As I angrily muttered to myself trying to block out the vision of a very enraged Matthew, I could see my parents in the background sitting in their recliners in the family room watching TV, totally oblivious to what was going on.

As Matthew finished eating, I continued hunting for his cards. I checked my dresser, nothing. I checked the bathroom counter, no cards. In a last-ditch effort, I checked the top of Matthew's armoire, bingo! I found his driver's license and insurance card held together by a binder clip. With everything that had been going on, I'd forgotten I'd placed his cards on his armoire. The case of the missing identification documents had been solved. Matthew was fed and an angry argument had ensued, but we never had a chance to kiss and make up.

We eventually got back in my car and proceeded twenty-two minutes south to Bayonet Point Hospital, where I worked. As we walked into the ER, I asked if Dr. B was working that night. The nurse responded, "He should be here any minute."

"Would you please let him know Vicki, who works with the residents, is here. I'd appreciate it."

Within minutes, Dr. B walked in. He took one look at me and asked, "What are you doing here?"

"It's my husband. His primary care told me to bring him here. He's been in and out of our local hospital since Christmas Eve with pneumonia symptoms. He was discharged a couple of days ago and was worse when he came out then when he went in."

I made the introductions and brought Dr. B up to date on Matthew's condition. I also informed him Matthew had an upcoming appointment scheduled with Dr. O, who had agreed to become his new pulmonologist. I can't explain it, but having Matthew at Bayonet Point provided me with a sense of peace and hope.

Matthew was admitted, and knowing from past experience it could take a while to settle him in a room, I left Matthew in the competent hands of his nurse and went home. I still had to feed my parents a belated dinner, take the dogs out, and eat something myself before dragging myself to bed. As Matthew's text to his family later that night testifies, he anticipated that he'd be discharged the next day,

> "Bayonet Regional, this is the hospital that Vicki is associated with…I'm admitted overnight for observation. Vital numbers are stable and care is good. Hope to be home tomorrow after the tests are reviewed by MD."

The next morning, August 2, just before the residents' Morning Report, I talked with Dr. O. He informed me Matthew was now under his care and he'd already started a plan of care. Later in the morning, I walked across the parking lot to the hospital to check the mailroom and to take a short break to see Matthew. I saw one of my residents, Dr. Fred Smith, and asked him if he knew anything about my husband's case. Dr. Smith is a quiet person, with a serious demeanor. He was evasive about my questions, deferring instead until they had more information. Upon entering his ICU cubicle, Matthew was cheerful, and I saw a look of hope in his eyes, something that had been missing in a very long time. He was happy he'd finally met the all impressive Dr. O, and Matthew admitted I was right—Dr. O was so much more knowledgeable than Dr. X. Matthew, for the first time since this illness manifested itself finally had confidence in his medical team as his text to his family on August 3 states,

> "I AM IMPRESSED. In the past five hours I have been attended by 4 Doctors, 1 Physician Assistant, three Interns and a gaggle of very professional Nurses. Tuesday early morning some of these people will perform a medical procedure (biopsy) that will reveal a different condition."

Matthew conveyed to me he had total faith and trust in his Bayonet Point team. His life was in their hands and he had no qualms about their skill, knowledge, or aptitude in getting the job done. Matthew also had faith in God. His plan of care consisted of an increase in steroids, 125 mg twice daily for the next four days in preparation for a surgical biopsy scheduled for Monday, August 7. X-rays taken in the ER showed less fluid buildup in his left lobe as compared to the chest x-ray taken a week earlier at our local hospital. During these four days, Matthew was feeling good, and his voice was raspy. He was alert, communicative, and enjoying his meals. Matthew was also visited by teams of physicians, including residents. George, a parishioner from a local Catholic Church, visited Matthew to give him communion. Rev. Robin DeAngelis, our minister from the UCC, visited Matthew and gave him anointing of the sick.

Of all the physicians Matthew met during this time, one stood out from the rest: Dr. Beverly Latimer, a new resident who joined our GME team just a month earlier. During new resident onboarding, I discovered Dr. Latimer and I shared the same birthday, March 11. I made a comment to her about this, and we quickly became friends. When Matthew was admitted to the pulmonary ICU, Dr. Latimer sought him out and introduced herself. Beverly has a compassionate heart; she's young, spirited, and a cancer survivor. Despite the differences in their ages, I believe their lives intertwined at this time for a reason. Although I visited Matthew several times each day, my visits didn't have the same impact on him as Beverly's did. It could have been her willingness to visit him, talk with him, or, most importantly, having someone to talk to, listen to, and understand the unspoken fears he was facing. Beverly had been in Matthew's shoes recently herself. She could relate and empathize with what Matthew was going through. Matthew needed someone who could be impartial yet compassionate, understanding yet strong. My emotions, which I thought I was keeping in check, were too emotionally charged to provide him what he needed. A shortfall of mine, I didn't recognize what he needed until it was too late. Beverly's friendship was the medicine Matthew was craving, although destined to be short-lived. God brought these two together to remind Beverly the importance of being a compassionate physician who listens with her heart, and He brought Beverly into Matthew's life to ease his fears. Beverly's life is in front of her, like a dawning sunrise, whereas Matthew's life was behind him, like a sunset that's slowing fading into the horizon. Matthew's brief friendship with Beverly was what he needed at this time, and I am eternally grateful.

For me, that first week with Matthew at Bayonet Point was a blur. I left the house around 5:00 a.m.; the sky was as dark as the bottom of an unlit coal mine, and the only signs of humanity were vehicle lights racing up and down Highway 19 in transit to obligations, jobs, and other mysterious destinations. Sirius XM blared from the speakers the minute I backed out of the driveway, tuned to channel eighteen, the Beatles Channel. The Beatles Channel had debuted just a couple of months earlier on May 18, 2017, the day after our 21st wedding anniversary.

For some unexplainable reason, the Beatles, whether collectively or separately, was the music I felt compelled to listen to at this time rather than my customary Hits 106 with DJ Marvelous Marvin. Hearing old favorites, friends from times past, songs in their familiarity helped to sooth and comfort my crying soul. I felt so alone at this time, trying desperately to be the glue that held everything and everyone together. Hearing my old friends, songs I'd listened to throughout my life, "Yesterday," "In My Life," "Photograph," "Help," "Imagine," "While My Guitar Gently Weeps," "Maybe I'm Amazed," "I'm Looking Through You," "Blackbird," and "Junior's Farm," strengthened and bolstered me emotionally. It helped me get through the days, which consistently introduced new challenges and setbacks. It was comforting to know *my friends* would be there for me tomorrow and the next day, as I coasted blindly by tears on this journey that was terrifying my lonely, weeping heart.

Hearing *my friends* also reminded me of fond memories from my childhood, bringing me back to a safe and protected time in my life. It was a time without illness, when my parents were strong and vibrant. It was the time when I was a pensive third grader at Annie Lathrup Elementary School in Lathrup Village, Michigan. It was there that I met Lynette, Kris, and Becky. We formed a friendship in Mrs. Hawkins' third-grade class. Lynette was tall for her age with curly, shoulder-length brown hair and a mischievous, impish twinkle in her eye. Her Texas twang always gave her away as a recent transplant from Dallas. Lynette was our leader. It was her idea to form a Beatles fan club; she adopted the character of Paul McCartney. Kris was average height, slim, with short, straight blond hair. Kris was the total opposite of Lynette. Whereas Lynette was spunky, Kris was reserved and quiet. People were drawn to Kris' soft-spoken demeanor. Kris' Beatles persona was John Lennon. Becky, like Lynette, was tall for her age. She had brown, uncontrollable, long curly brown hair that bordered on frizziness. Becky, like myself, was a follower. Becky's character was Ringo Starr and mine was George Harrison.

Every day during third-grade recess, we pretended we were the Beatles, playing our imaginary instruments before a throng of screaming, hair-clutching, fainting fans. Our voices didn't come close to the harmonies sung by the Fab Four, but you couldn't find more loyal fans than us. These three girls were the first real friends I ever had in life other than the neighborhood kids I'd met just two months earlier. Our friendship, though, was short lived. Mrs. Hawkins felt we had developed too close a friendship, and upon graduation into the fourth grade, we found ourselves divided between the three fourth grade classes. Our friendship never regained the same closeness we shared in third grade. Till this day, third grade is my favorite. Whenever I hear a Beatles tune, my heart warms, my eyes light up, and my mouth inches skyward into a soft smile as I'm nostalgically transported back in time to when my Beatles friends-in-arms were young and care-free—Lynette/Paul, Kris/John, Becky/Ringo, and myself/George.

On these mornings, before clocking in for work, I quietly slipped into Matthew's room, tiptoeing up to his bed. He was usually asleep. I stood there and looked at him. I guess I was trying to absorb him, taking in every nuance of his being, watching as his chest softly rose and fell with each breath. Sometimes, I gently wiped the perspiration from his brow, straightened and tucked his blanket gently under his chin, and checked his cannula to make sure it was in place within his nostrils. I now treasure those quiet interludes. It would have been the perfect time to utter those loving words that so easily slip off the lips of lovers. His breathing was quiet, quiet like a tomb, almost as if it was hinting at something soon to come.

Matthew's surgery was scheduled for 2:00 p.m. Monday, August 7. The night before, he sent me the following text,

> "I just took a shower using their special pre-surgery soap on the body then shampoo body soap. The hot water felt so good. I shaved after that so I won't need one tomorrow. Sleep peaceful my sweetheart Wicki Woo."

August 7, 7:25 am, the morning of his scheduled biopsy, Matthew texted me the following,

> "Good Morning I love you. Stop calling my doctor at home LOL. Beverly came by before her meeting. I cleaned up my act after P & P scrubbed my bum put on cream brushed teeth combed hair. No eating so I'll rest a bit then pack stuff in case I'm moved, love you."

Because his surgeon was called to an emergency at another facility, Matthew's surgery was rescheduled for 5:00 p.m. At 7:27 p.m., I sent the following text to Matthew's family,

> "MATTHEW UPDATE: I just spoke with his surgeon, despite the weak condition of his lungs he did well with the surgery. He thought it looked like pulmonary fibrosis, Path Report will take a couple of days. When I asked for a gut impression, he hedged his bet, possibly cancer won't know until Path Report. So, keep praying. They

are trying to take him off vent, he might go to ICU on a vent and leave it up to Dr. O to wean him off tomorrow, three months ago he swore he'd never let anyone vent him again (which means when he wakes up he will be a bear!). At least an hour more before I'll get to see him."

Matthew was in PACU for an additional two hours before they transported him to SCU. I was relieved the surgery was over. It had been an extremely long day I couldn't have gotten through it if not for the services and friendship of our home health aide, Mary Ann. When needed, Mary Ann stayed late and came back, depending on what was going on with Matthew. Mary Ann made dinner, took the pups out, and put Mom to bed on those nights when I needed to be with Matthew at the hospital. Also, being a devote Catholic, Mary Ann often sent text messages to Matthew letting him know she was praying for him and saying the rosary on his behalf. There were many people praying for Matthew—family as far away as Philadelphia and friends as close as across the street. Even Mary Ann's youngest son, eight-year-old Dominic, asked his class one day, "Please pray for my mom's friend Matthew. He's sick in the hospital." With so many people praying for Matthew, what could go wrong?

Matthew was sleeping well and two days after his surgery, he wrote the following in his diary, "out cold the rest of the day and night once I hit the OR." Two biopsies were performed. I did everything I could to keep myself busy. I prayed like I'd never prayed before. I didn't like making bargains with God for favorable results. God is too smart to accept bargains made in haste. I knew, though, in my heart what we'd be facing was God's plan whether I liked it or not.

Between the text updates I was sending Matthew's family each day, my visits to Matthew when I took a break from work, and the text messages we were sending to each other throughout the day, Matthew was never out of my thoughts. I texted Diana, our daughter-in-law, on August 8 at 3:42 p.m.,

"MATTHEW UPDATE: When I saw Matthew this morning, they had already removed the vent. He doesn't like the oxygen mask, but his oxygen levels today have been in the mid-70s-high 80s when the optimum levels should be in the mid-high 90s. I spoke with the nutritionist who asked about his likes and dislikes, they are trying to determine a meal plan to help him gain weight. He's been a bit of a grouch today, bossing his poor nurse around and complaining about her. She's just doing her job keeping her eyes on his stats. Once I speak with a physician, I'll send update."

I sent an inner department email to Jane, the new Director of Food Services at Bayonet Point, and a friend of ours from Stage West, to apprise her of Matthew's condition. Jane visited Matthew, and they reminisced about the various shows they'd been in, their mutual friends, and how Stage West had been a pivotal part of their lives. Following their visit, every day Jane would concoct nutritious shakes to help increase Matthew's appetite, hoping they would do their magic.

In the past, whenever Matthew mentioned anything relating to his hypothetical death, I got weepy and cried. Now, this was a possibility, Matthew didn't approach the subject with me, yet it was the third element in our marriage at this time—it was hovering amongst us like a ten-ton gorilla wanting to play. So, instead, we tiptoed around the subject, avoiding anything meaningful. We kept our conversations light, inconsequential, and feckless. Was this deliberate, or were we too scared to face something we didn't want to admit? Or, were we that sure the Path report would prove negative and Matthew would be discharged from the hospital within a few days? Waiting can be the hardest, cruelest, most excruciatingly painful thing to endure when a loved one's life is in the balance. Patience was not a virtue of Matthew's, nor mine, at this time. We had each other. All that mattered was being together for as long as we could, despite an unsettling feeling our time together was ephemeral.

CHAPTER 14

The Last Judgment

Wednesday, August 9 dawned like any other day in Florida. The sun rose in the east, and the temperatures blasted the earth. The humidity was steamy, and birds sang in the trees. And on such a fine day, we received the verdict. It was a verdict we weren't expecting, one that broke my heart. It was a verdict that divulged the million-dollar answer to the million-dollar question we'd been asking all year, *What's wrong with Matthew?*

I received word earlier in the morning regarding the Path report. However, I didn't know when his physicians planned on telling him. I had a scheduled appointment for Dad's eye treatment in the afternoon—he had macular degeneration in both eyes, the left eye wet. I considered cancelling it so I could be with Matthew when he received the results. However, I felt in my gut Matthew would prefer to be alone when he received the news.

After taking Dad for his eye treatment, making dinner for my parents, and getting Mom tucked safely into bed for the night, I drove slowly back to the hospital. I didn't want to go, but I couldn't put it off any longer. Before walking into Matthew's room, I paused to take a breath, to regroup and fortify myself. I let it out slowly, steeled myself for this conversation, and walked into his room with a loving smile in my eyes and crying in my heart. Matthew was sitting up in bed, stoic, matter of fact, and handed me a piece of paper with two words written on it, mucinous adenocarcinoma. Matthew had cancer.

Matthew was already doing his homework trying to learn as much as he could about this rare form of lung cancer. A type of lung cancer characterized by mucus, fever, and cough, all symptoms he'd been gradually experiencing since Christmas 2016. The mucus he'd been expectorating for months was in effect "mucus secreted by cancer cells...commonly discharged as sputum."[1] As Matthew's cancer kept going undetected and untreated, the production of mucus he was experiencing was proportional to the rate of cancer cells being produced uncontrollably by his tumor.[2] That night I sent two texts, within three hours apart, to Matthew's family,

"MATTHEW UPDATE #1: I just called Dr O because Matthew communicated earlier he had been in to see him, I was tied up with my dad's eye appointment so I couldn't be there. It is lung cancer...possibly what they saw in right lung is cancer invading that area as well...Dr O has already spoken with oncologist, Dr M, who I would say is the best oncologist in Hernando/Pasco counties. He conducts Morning Report with my residents every morning. He's tough as nails and won't mince words. They could butt heads, two extremely opinionated people. In all likelihood when I asked if Matthew would be hospitalized by the weekend, probably not. I'll let you know tomorrow."

"MATTHEW UPDATE #2: The type of cancer is mucinous adenocarcinoma, it's an extremely rare form of lung cancer, just dozens of cases diagnosed, mortality rate is low. Typical forms of treatment: surgery, chemo, radiation. Often affects both lungs. Chief symptoms:

shortness of breath, coughing up sputum, night sweats, fever, unexplained weight loss, wheezing, which your dad has been experiencing all year since Christmas. His attitude is good, he's started to conduct his own Google research, he swears he will put himself into the hands of Dr M, no self-doctoring which we know he tends to do. He finally has an answer and that in itself has provided a sense of relief."

We had an answer. Neither of us liked it, but it was the cards we'd been dealt. Matthew was upbeat, hopeful, and determined to be a survivor. No matter what happened from this date onward, it was a relief to finally have a diagnosis, something Dr. X failed to do. If we hadn't changed pulmonologists, I suspect we may never have had an answer to our million-dollar question.

I received a text from Diana on August 8. Matthew's sons wanted to surprise their dad. Michael and Matty were flying to Tampa Friday night, and they'd surprise their dad Saturday morning, August 12. It was difficult to keep this surprise to myself, many times during the ensuing days I was tempted to blurt out, "Guess who's coming to see you? Aren't you excited?" I kept my mouth shut. Boy, was it difficult!

Saturday morning, I took my time driving to the hospital, I wanted to give Matthew and his sons some personal time together. Matthew had been moved into room 2767 on August 9, a private room with monitoring devices. As I walked into Matthew's room, around 11:00 a.m., I was greeted by the three of them in animated conversation. You could tell in a second these three were obviously happy to be together. It had been a year since Matthew's last visit to Philadelphia. As I hovered in the background, I was mesmerized by their carefree banter resorting to their usual exchange of quoting lines from their favorite films, catching up on cop gossip, and just enjoying being together. I left them after an hour, giving Matty and Michael their last, cherished hours with their dad.

I returned at 6:00 p.m. Matty and Michael were in rapt attention as Matthew was sitting up on the side of his bed talking nonstop, in a raspy voice. You could tell he was talking too much. He had to stop periodically to catch his breath. Suddenly, a nurse rushed in checking his monitors, trying to get Matthew to stop talking and get back into bed. Another nurse ran in followed by a third. They were all agitated, concerned, yet highly professional. Matthew couldn't figure out why they were all in his room. His monitoring devices were going off the chart. He was heading into respiratory distress, and he didn't even know it. Matty, Michael, and I stood on the sidelines dumbfounded, shocked, worried, and frightened of what this sudden, unexpected turn of events could mean. Within a few short minutes, Matthew was transported back to the surgical ICU where he had been transported from just three days earlier. What started out as a promising day with an amazing surprise turned drastically into a deleterious, downward spiral that stopped our hearts. How could his condition change so drastically? Did he talk too much and drain his energy, and thus his oxygen levels crapped out? Why couldn't this have happened *after* Michael and Matty flew back to Philadelphia so they could enjoy what little time they had left with their dad? Or did God believe they needed to witness this for themselves in order to better understand the dire condition their father was in and to prepare themselves and their families for what was to come? It felt like I was back on that dreaded roller coaster with everything spinning out of control, and I had no power to slow it down or get it back on track. Why couldn't we catch a break finally?

Monday, August 14, 2017—a day I will never forget. I was standing within the doorframe of my office at the conclusion of the residents' Morning Report when Dr. M stopped briefly in passing to give me the results of his analysis of Matthew's condition. Dr. M was the oncologist assigned to Matthew's case. The residents respected him, just like they did Dr. O. I knew with these two physicians on Matthew's case, Matthew had the best medical team possible.

Dr. M was his usual brisk, slightly cocky self, like he was conducting a business transaction. He informed me the cancer was now invading Matthew's right lung, and he wasn't strong enough to withstand another surgery, chemo, or radiation. The prognosis was Matthew had 24 to 48 hours. I was shell shocked! I was numb. It was hard to breath; my throat was dry, constricted. I had a hard time catching my breath. I couldn't talk; I was paralyzed with fear. I so desperately needed a shoulder to cry on, and despite there being a crowd near me, no one offered to provide the comfort I so desperately needed. No "I'm sorry." No "do you have any questions?" No "I wish I had better news for you." Anything would have been appreciated to cushion this devasting blow. I remember standing there wishing and hoping this was all a bad dream, and I would wake up with Matthew snoring loudly next to me in bed. Instead, the residents were streaming past me, talking, jostling one another, noisily heading out the door as they made their way back to the hospital. I was left there, trying to control the kaleidoscope of thoughts and emotions that were racing through my mind, trying to figure out what my next step was. At this point, I was going to have to start thinking for both of us, the responsibility was now firmly, squarely on my shoulders. I wanted, in reality, to run in the opposite direction and never look back. My love for Matthew stopped me in my tracks and helped me to realize we had one final step in our journey together, namely, to help Matthew die peacefully and with dignity surrounded by those he loved and who loved him.

My thoughts were a jumble as my feet carried me to the hospital, rushing as quick as I could to Matthew's side. He was now on maximum oxygen. His comprehension was affected as was his sense of alertness and focus. He was barely eating or drinking anything. It was so hard to see such a drastic change within less than 24 hours in this man who had been everything to me, a man who now looked like a brief hovel of himself.

As I stood quietly, lost in thought at his bedside, I noticed his opened diary on the table next to his bed. I picked it up. His last entry was written on August 10. It consisted of notes listing the physicians who visited him that day, and Dr. M was ordering a brain scan. His writing looked so unrecognizable compared to his normal script. I absently flipped back through the pages and noticed the legibility of his writing had been changing drastically since August 1, reflective as his oxygen levels kept increasing in volume as his days left on this earth kept dwindling in number. Also, within the last couple of days, his fingers had started to atrophy, first on his right hand and then his left. It had been suggested that perhaps he fell asleep on his right hand. In reality, subtle indications I learned afterward of impending death.

I moved the lone chair from the corner and sat down next to his bed. As I stared into his slightly comatose eyes, fleeting thoughts floated through my mind—random, crazy remembrances like our Friday pizza nights, Matthew's loving embraces, trips to Cedar Key, our wedding, Matthew's first cruise, his son Matty's college graduation, playing ball with Casey in the pool, great-granddaughter Elysia's birth, Christmas in Philadelphia, the times we took the pups to the dog park, our trips to Atlantic City, his performances in shows like *1776*, *Joseph and The Technicolor Dream Coat*, and *Nuncrackers*, and his last performances in *Around the World in Eighty Days*. I thought of Matthew nudging me awake after falling asleep watching TV. I thought of shows he directed, putting his heart and soul into each production—*The Sound of Music, One Flew Over the Cuckoo's Nest, Blithe Spirit, The Day They Kidnapped the Pope, Damn Yankees*. I remembered our sorrow when we lost Casey and how beautifully Matthew sang his *signature* song. So many treasured memories, chapters of our lives, fragments suddenly appearing as dreamlike visions of my soul, flooding every corner of my consciousness. They weren't in any order, just cascaded and randomly exploded like colorful fireworks on the Fourth of July. I was reliving brief snippets of our twenty-one years together, a life I didn't want to relinquish.

"Matthew," I whispered, "you promised me 97 and out, you're cheating me of 20 years. I was looking forward to those next 20 years together." That was a joke between us. He'd tell me and his physicians he planned to live until he was 97 and then, out the door. I used to ask him, "why not shoot for 100?" He'd just look at me and smile.

There was so much left unsaid between us. It seemed we had lost our last chance to express those intimate thoughts, those expressions of love, words spoken from the heart that asked for forgiveness of past transgressions or wounded pride. I felt cheated not just of those twenty years he'd promised me, but cheated of those last, cherished sentiments spoken tenderly of love between a husband and a wife.

I eventually returned to work, not sure what I actually accomplished that day. When I later returned to Matthew's side, it appeared there was no real change in his condition. It was obvious he was sinking fast. I was notified he might be discharged on Wednesday. That gave me twenty-four hours to make up my mind. I not only needed to come to grips with this sudden death sentence that was hovering over our heads like a thundercloud threatening to erupt any minute, but I also had to come to terms with my living situation. I had my parents and pups to think about. In addition, my aunt and uncle were both in poor health themselves. Everyone was sick around me. The only healthy ones were the pups and I.

Tuesday morning, August 15, I met with my boss and told her I needed to take FMLA. Matthew's condition was terminal. He had just days left, yet in my heart, I still hoped and prayed once he came home, I could nurse him back to a semblance of health so we could have one last Christmas together. I arrived at work extra early that morning, cleaned out my desk of all personal items and was ready to start FMLA as soon as I spoke to my boss. At 9:00 a.m., I walked out of the GME department with thoughts only of Matthew and how to get through the next couple of days. I never looked back.

I spent the day with Matthew, asking questions of his nurse, the residents, and anyone who could provide clues on how to take care of him at home. He was basically bed bound at this point. Once in a while, they repositioned him either in a recliner or bed, where he drifted off into a deep, peaceful slumber and woke periodically. I tried to coax him to take a few sips of water or juice, maybe a spoon of pudding or Jello, with little success. Jane continued to send her nutritious shakes for him, a few sips was basically the only nourishment Matthew was receiving.

It wasn't in my vocabulary to ask about dying. I guess I figured if I didn't ask about it or think about it, it wasn't going to happen. His nurse mentioned something about hospice. I spoke to a pleasant woman about it later in the afternoon. I signed papers, and that's all I remember.

Once I spoke to hospice, all of a sudden, the "D" word became a reality. How did this happen? Why is this happening? Is there a way to negotiate with God, postpone this by a couple of years? Can we playback the last three years and relive them? *This can't be happening! I Don't Want It To Happen! I WON'T LET IT HAPPEN! I CAN'T LET MATTHEW DIE!* I finally said it, "…Matthew…is…going…to…die. Are you satisfied, God?" There, I said it. *Are YOU satisfied, GOD, because I'm NOT!* And, Matthew…wanted to die…at…home.

TEXT Message to Matthew's Family, August 15, 2017 3 PM

"MATTHEW UPDATE: Matthew is spending more time sleeping, he's at the highest oxygen level they can give him. Urine output is very little, not eating much, he has difficulty feeding himself since his right hand has palsied, I noticed when Diana called that his left hand is starting to do the same thing. Met with hospice, we have your dad scheduled to come home tomorrow. Please call your aunts Bob and Pat to prepare them. Thank you. Can someone call Kathy in California and give her a "heads up?" Aunt Betty needs to know since she's his last remaining aunt."

Based on his nurse's advice, I stopped at Walmart on my way home and picked up items she recommended such as Ensure and plastic sheets for the hospital bed. As I was pushing the cart through the store, I was oblivious to the crowd around me, but I remember one of the cart's wheels was stuck sideways which made pushing the cart noisy and difficult. It's amazing the inconsequential trivia that sticks in your mind when you are numb with fear. I felt like I was walking in slow motion, like you see in movies when they want you to think the character has been drugged. In this case, I wasn't in a movie, and I wasn't drugged. I was numb with shock. I felt nothing. I heard nothing. I saw nothing. Someone could have set the store on fire, and I wouldn't have known or cared. I was sleepwalking with no chance of waking up to any other conclusion than the hand we'd been dealt.

I remember thinking while I was walking through the store, randomly picking up items from my list, "I'll never go shopping with Matthew again. He loved shopping." How can thoughts like this come crashing into your consciousness? He loved shopping. We'd plan a trip to the mall every year at Christmas, splitting up once we got there. We went off in opposite directions, clutching our respective lists to Santa we wrote to each other every year—mine to Santa, Matthew's letter to Mrs. Claus. After completing our Christmas shopping, giddy with excitement and puffed up with pride that we'd found the perfect gifts for each other, we'd meet at a designated time and location and have lunch. These were treasured memories which I had taken for granted, stored in the farthest recesses of my mind, assuming earlier in the year we'd experience this same thing again this year. It wasn't until I found myself randomly, sluggishly sleepwalking through Walmart that it came to me—these shopping excursions would now be a thing of the past.

Matthew's delight in shopping didn't end with the mall. If he was in the middle of preparing dinner and realized he was missing an important ingredient or didn't have enough of something he thought nothing of turning the stove or oven off, hopping in his car, and driving off to our local Publix to get what he needed. It didn't faze him the grocery store was over four miles away. Whereas if this happened to me, I would have discarded any thoughts of the planned dinner and made something else. This was one of those rare qualities Matthew possessed. I envied him that!

When I got home from Walmart, I still needed to prepare dinner for my folks and put Mom to bed. I so longed to have someone I could talk to, someone whose shoulder I could cry on. Someone who could commiserate and provide some form of tender, loving comfort before this last part of our journey ended, Matthew's upcoming death. I never watched someone die before—I wasn't prepared psychologically or emotionally. The closest I'd been was when Casey died in December 2011, but Matthew was with me then. I remembered my uncontrollable crying, keening words of love as Casey took her last, shallow breaths. I was inconsolable at that time, tears flooding from my eyes like Niagara Falls. If I had a hard time then, what would I be like now? I was numb from lack of sleep, nervous tension, trying to care for my parents, tending to the pups, checking on my aunt and uncle, and now Matthew. All I wanted to do was lay down and go to sleep, wake up, and relive the last three years all over again, having the advantage of knowing then what I knew now so I could change the course of history and circumvent this nightmare from happening in the future.

I had so many thoughts cascading through my mind—no wonder I couldn't sleep. It was similar to when I was on prednisone back in January and February. I was wired from heart aching emotions, the weight of too many responsibilities for one person to shoulder, and my inability to communicate with Matthew's family so they could understand what was happening. My parents were no help. My mom couldn't remember who Matthew was, and I couldn't go to her with the expectation of a mother's comforting arms to embrace me and show empathy. My dad was an introvert. He seldom ventured beyond an occasional one or two words in greeting, but he's a master at grunting his disapproval or dissatisfaction. In the past, I could call my Aunt Lou, talk to her, and she'd commiserate and understand and provide a comforting word, but her health had declined within the past two years. Now, she, too, had dementia, which makes having a meaningful conversation a thing of the past. My Uncle Ron, since he'd been taking care of Lou, had lost at least forty pounds and was a bag of bones, weighing just over one-hundred pounds. He had been diagnosed with Parkinson's, which accelerated as a result of the full-time care he was providing Lou. My few friends were busy with their lives, and I didn't feel comfortable picking up the phone and crying in their ear. Matthew had never liked my friends; we didn't socialize with them. As a result of the demands of my job, my parents, and trying to find a few golden moments alone with Matthew, our lives didn't have the time for friends outside of church.

The pups were the closest I had to a living being I could talk to. Kipper would squirm away after a minute of hugging. But Katy, my beautiful little rescue from the streets of Lakeland, provided me all the time I needed to hold her, hug her, and cry into her fur. As I held her, I'd say all the things I was thinking, sharing my thoughts as I cried uncontrollably. Katy's big, brown, Hersey drop eyes would stare back at me with compassion, sympathy, and unabashed love. She was my lifeline. I clutched her soft, fragrant fur with white knuckled hands like I was on the Edmund Fitzgerald on that fateful November night in 1975, as the ship tossed and heaved, eventually breaking up into the angry waters of Lake Superior, knowing that death's grasping tentacles would imminently be claiming more lives.

I woke early on August 16, made breakfast for the pups and my parents, grabbed a cup of coffee, ate breakfast, and quickly scanned the headlines in the newspaper. Being an August day in Florida, it was a sure bet that the sky would be sunny while the temperatures would be swelteringly hot and the humidity unbearable. It was a typical summer day in the sunshine state. Before I left for the hospital, I put clean sheets on the hospital bed, which hospice delivered the night before. Matthew's recliner was sitting two feet from the bed, next to the door wall, in case Matthew wanted to sit in a comfortable chair. Oxygen tanks had been delivered as well, in addition to equipment hospice assumed we'd be needing in the days, hopefully weeks to come. After checking my to-do list one last time, making sure everything was ready for Matthew's homecoming, I left for the hospital as soon as Mary Ann arrived to supervise the folks.

Driving to the hospital, I was lost in thought, like I was most of the time these days. I couldn't seem to erase extraneous details from my consciousness. Everything seemed to be of utmost importance these days. Once in a while, a lyric from a Beatles song would play in my mind, over and over, like a continuous loop. On those occasions, I wasn't sure which was worse, hearing lyrics playing nonstop in my mind, or having a horde of thoughts colliding in my mind, banging into each other like bumper cars at a state fair.

TEXT Message to Matthew's Family August 16, 2017 9:22 AM

"MATTHEW UPDATE: Spent couple of hours with him this morning, more alert, appetite seems better and his speech is easier to understand. Matthew is looking forward to coming home today!"

I spent the day with Matthew at the hospital, waiting to learn when hospice would be having our patient transported on his last ride home, his last car ride while still alive. I asked repeated questions of his nurse, hoping subconsciously she would say, "I don't think you are capable of doing this. He better stay here." Of course, she didn't say that. How could I look competent when in my mind I thought I must have resembled a lost, frightened four-year-old child, stumbling alone in the forest expecting to see a menacing, roaring lion hiding behind each tree. The day slowly coasted along like we were on a raft, floating lazily down the Withlachochee River, with its canopy of tree branches shading the merry makers from the hot, scorching Florida sun.

Finally, the news came. Matthew would be picked up around 4:00 p.m., and he should be home no later than 5:00 p.m. He'd been semi-conscious, on and off all day. When he was conscious, it was hard for him to get comfortable. He still had a bedsore on his coccyx from his last stint at our local hospital. He had two drainage tubes surgically implanted in his side from the Bayonet Point biopsy surgery. He was spitting up sputum regularly, more at night than during the day, and he had a cannula in his nose which did little to provide the oxygen he so desperately needed. He was now a mere shell of the man I grew to love since the day I met him. He was a ghost of the man I had grown comfortable and safe with, journeyed with, loved with, laughed with, and cried with. It's amazing what cancer can do to change, disfigure, and ravage the human body. It's unbelievable what the lack of sufficient oxygen can do to befuddle, vitiate, and annihilate the human mind.

I left the hospital before the ambulance arrived and bid farewell to his nurse. The whole time I wished I could take her home with me. We had a vacant lot next to our house. I parked my car there, and as I went to turn the car off, I couldn't turn the key in the ignition. The car wouldn't shut off. I jiggled the key, hoping it was just a minor glitch. Nothing happened. The car kept running like it was laughing at me. I got out, walked around the car, not really knowing what that would accomplish, but I needed to do something. As the car continued to run, I walked up to our house to unlock the front door and check on my parents and the pups. I put the pups in the pen, so they wouldn't be in the way when the transporters moved Matthew into the house. I returned to the car, got in, and sat there in total bafflement and frustration. This had never happened before.

Any minute now, Matthew would be coming home, and I was in an embarrassing situation of not being able to turn my damn car off! I finally thought to press the OnStar button located in the middle of the windshield. The first thing I heard was a pleasant sound followed by a young woman's voice asking how she could assist me. I explained to her what the problem was. She made several suggestions and nothing helped. Finally, she said she'd send roadside assistance to my location. As I was talking to her, I noticed the ambulance turning the corner onto our street, slowly approaching our house. I still had OnStar live while the ambulance was pulling into our driveway. I felt pulled in two different directions. I needed to assist the transporters on where to move Matthew into our home, yet at the same time, I couldn't let my car continuously run and eventually dry the gas tank. Then, I'd have a problem compounded by a problem. I explained the situation to the calming voice at OnStar, walked up to the two transporters and outlined my dilemma to them. The transporters consisted of a male and a female. The female was kind and offered to check my car. She walked up to it, looked inside, and determined within two seconds what the problem was. My car was still in neutral as I was trying to turn the ignition off. Boy, was I relieved it wasn't anything worse, but that didn't come close to how embarrassed I felt. I let OnStar know to cancel onsite help, put the car in park, turned the key in the ignition, closed, and locked the car door. I slowly walked up to the front door of our home and cautiously stepped over the threshold. I felt relief Matthew was finally home, but at the same time, I was vexed with an avalanche of conflicting emotions. I felt trepidation regarding whether I could take care of his needs so Matthew would be comfortable and pain free. I felt anxiety as I prepared to bear witness to his death. I feared I wouldn't be strong enough psychologically and emotionally to face this daunting challenge, to keep my husband comfortable, and at peace in the face of his looming death.

I know I made dinner for my parents that night and tucked Mom into bed, but I have no recollection of doing so. The only thing I remember was caring for Matthew. The transporters settled Matthew into bed—the bed was situated in the middle of the living room facing the TV—his recliner was to the left of the bed. Hospice provided a bedside table on the right side of the bed, which was extremely useful. The couch was to the right of the hospital bed with the front door a few feet behind. The dining room was located on the left, behind the hospital bed. The dining room table was helpful in catching the overflow that quickly materialized, things not needed on the bedside table, information from hospice, and instructions for his medications, especially the morphine dosage. The TV remote, a large box of tissues, several plastic cups for Matthew to spit sputum into, a glass of water with a straw, a bag taped to the side of the hospital bed for trash, and a pen and paper for taking notes were all taking up the limited space on the bedside table. On a table directly behind the bed, I had placed a CD player, a lamp with dimmer switch, and a stack of Matthew's favorite Irish CDs. There was also a portable commode that got moved around the living room as space was needed.

I remember standing next to his bed after the transporters left, thinking, *Now what?* I was exhausted and couldn't remember the last time I had more than an hour of sleep. I was running not on overdrive but triple-drive. Although I could have a limited conversation with Matthew, he was glad to be home but antsy as well. He wasn't interested in talking, or, perhaps talking was too exhausting for him. I asked him if there was any one he wanted me to call, perhaps his good friend and golfing partner, Wayne. He became agitated when I mentioned Wayne's name. I wasn't sure if he just didn't want Wayne to see him in this condition or if saying good-bye to such a dear friend made the reality that much harder for him to bear.

At some point, I let the dogs in from the pen. Being their normal, curious selves guided by their ever-truthful noses, they made a beeline to the living room in wired excitement, but something unusual happened. Instead of recognizing their daddy by showing their excitement and happiness with their normal, wiggling bodies, both pups stopped dead in their tracks at the edge of the living room just feet shy of Matthew in the bed. They didn't go any further. Matthew called out to them in a weakened voice that sounded more like a hoarse whisper, "Come here, Kipper. Hey, Katy, how's my girl? It's Daddy!" Despite wanting to go to their daddy, something held them back. It was as if they, too, had a premonition that something sinister, something frightening was looming in the air. Matthew so dearly wanted to cradle them in his arms, pet their fluffy, silky fur, and say good-bye to them in his own way. And they, with their sixth sense, felt something apprehensive in the air, something much more powerful than even their love for their daddy. It broke my heart to watch. Matthew loved them so much.

The pups stood stock still, their feet glued to the spot. It seemed to last for seven or eight minutes, reminding me of hunting dogs standing at point as they spot their prey, keeping it constantly within their sight. You could tell they were yearning to run up to their daddy, yet at the same time, they seemed scared to go any further.

Eventually, it was Katy who finally overcame her fear, coaxed to submission by the loving, tender calls being emitted by Matthew. Katy was always subservient to Matthew. He was the alpha to her beta. He could call her name, and she'd come to him and place her snout into his cupped hand and leave it there. Matthew was very proud of this and would do this on a whim just to test her, and she never failed the test. So, it's not surprising she was the first to acknowledge his presence. Katy slowly, cautiously, walked up to the bed, looked up for about a minute, like she had to convince herself that's really her daddy. Then, she sprang up onto the bed, smothering Matthew's face with doggy loving kisses. I wished I had the foresight to video tape this scene of loving embrace, but I was frozen in place watching this show of unconditional love. Kipper, on the other hand, being the more internalizing of the two, continued to stand there. Slowly, he slunk down to his belly and belly-walked across the living room to the far corner, laid down, and buried his head on his paws staring at Katy as she slathered doggy love onto their daddy. I walked into the kitchen on the excuse to get vanilla pudding for Matthew. I searched for a tissue and silently balled my eyes out.

It took about another hour for Kipper to eventually gain the nerve to approach Matthew. By this time, Matthew had indicated his bedsore was hurting, and he wanted to sit in his recliner. It took all my strength coupled with what limited help Matthew could provide to get him moved and comfortable in his recliner. That's when Kipper finally approached Matthew, sniffed him cautiously, backed away a couple of inches, stared back at Matthew for a few seconds than inched forward again. Kipper cautiously sniffed Matthew a third time, stopped, stared, and finally convinced that this was his daddy, he allowed Matthew to pet him. This interlude didn't last long. Within a minute, Kipper ran out of the living room into the family room where he jumped up on the couch and buried his head under a pillow. Turns out, this was the last time Kipper had any interaction with his daddy.

Matthew wanted to watch TV. We'd been having problems with his TV for over a year. You'd turn it on, and within a couple of minutes, it would turn itself off and then immediately turn itself back on. It repeated this sequence for about a half an hour until it warmed up, and then, it would stay on. It was a nuisance. Matthew had gotten into the habit of turning the TV on a half hour before he wanted to watch something. It was now close to ten or eleven o'clock at night, Matthew insisting on holding the remote, as he always regarded it as the man thing. Heaven forbid it was ever in the possession of anyone of the female persuasion! I expected the TV to turn itself off, like it usually did, and then pop back on. But this time, it stayed on. Using the remote was drastically taxing Matthew's oxygen levels. He mumbled incoherent sounds, trying to say something and swayed slightly like a tall pine tree sways with a gusty wind.

As a late-night talk show host was enjoying a laugh from his invisible audience, I lowered the volume on the TV, hoping we could have some time together. I pulled the bedside commode next to his recliner, lowered the lid, and sat on it. We had a few, brief moments when we sat quietly, listening to Irish music as it played softly in the background. All of a sudden, the TV went silent, and the screen lost its picture. It was replaced by a field of solid light blue, reminiscent of a clear baby blue sky on a cloudless day. I never saw anything like that. It scared me. I turned the TV off, seeing this as a sign from God. I believed God was telling us, "Don't waste this valuable time watching the boob tube." I must admit, this never happened since, only on that one occasion.

The TV occurrence was later followed by the bathroom episode. Matthew wanted to go to the bathroom, and he was hell bent on going into our bathroom to relieve himself. I pleaded with him, "Matthew, let's use the bedside commode, walking into our bathroom is too far for you. Plus, I'm afraid you'll trip over the oxygen tube." No matter how often I repeated myself, he was determined he was going to use our bathroom. Finally, having worn himself out, gasping unsuccessfully for breath and sweating from this mild exertion, I was able to convince him to use the commode.

It was worse trying to get him off the commode and back into bed. By this time, he'd taxed himself so much, his oxygen levels were extremely low. His legs could no longer help me. Now, moving him was all on me. It was like trying to move the Empire State Building with nothing but my own brute strength and will power to assist me. Every time I'd try to get him up, he'd fall back onto the commode. If he'd still been in the recliner, I would have had some leverage to work with. I could see this task was going to be a lot harder than I imagined. I searched the room, trying to find something I could use to prop him up against, but nothing looked promising, and I didn't want to go into the garage and leave him alone for any length of time. Then, I remembered we had a second walker with a seat that I'd tucked into a corner of the family room. After retrieving the walker and a rug from our bathroom, I positioned the walker in front of Matthew, locked the brakes, and put the rug on the floor in case I lost my grip and he fell. Because of the drainage tube on his left side, it was awkward trying to get my arms under him. It was difficult to get a good grasp of his body without being afraid of hurting him. No matter how hard I tried, I wasn't successful in moving him. My frustration reached its boiling point. Inches in front of his face, I shouted words laced with venom and hatred, "Matthew, I can't do this! You're too heavy, you can't help me. I need help! I can't do this by myself!" He stared at me with a blank, uncomprehending stare, like someone who had too much to drink the night before and just woke up in a stupor, unresponsive to the situation.

I couldn't understand why he wanted to come home to die. I was frustrated he thought I could do everything myself. Two years ago, he'd helped his sister Bobbi when her husband Franky had been under hospice care in New Jersey. At that time, Matthew voiced to me how hard it was to care for Franky at home. Now, he'd placed me in the same situation, and I was furious with him. He didn't have any deep and abiding attachment to the house we were living in because it was my parent's house, and he hated it. I later came to realize the true reason Matthew wanted to come home to die. He wanted one last moment with his beloved pups, Katy and Kipper, which I didn't realize at the time.

Instead, I immediately felt remorse for having said such hateful words. I was angry at myself for having lashed out at my poor husband when I should have been more compassionate and loving. I was being my worst, and I was ashamed. I had plenty of excuses I could have used, but that still doesn't forgive me of such inexplicable behavior to the one I loved. It's one thing I still can't forgive myself for and being reminded of it now, I can't help but cry. What happened to my compassion, my empathy, and my love for this man? If God was testing me, this was the wrong way to do it. I felt I'd been tested all year, how strong does God really think I am?

After chastising myself for my behavior, I said a prayer and asked for strength. The nurse at the hospital had given me a large band for safeguarding Matthew in bed. I attached one end of it to the bed and wrapped the other end around Matthew, which I used as leverage to lift him up off the commode. I anchored and braced my feet. The first attempt didn't work, so I tried again, and again. By the fourth try, using every ounce and smidgen of strength hidden within the resources of my body, I finally got Matthew up off the commode and sitting on the walker's seat. I was amazed I'd gotten this far. I thanked God and asked him to please help me the rest of the way. I pushed the walker, with Matthew sitting on it, to the edge of the bed. Then, I repositioned the band under his arms without conscripting his drainage tube. I walked to the other side of the bed where I repositioned and retightened the band to the bed. I went back to Matthew and slowly worked at getting him into a standing position and then eased him into a sitting position on the bed. Having the band around him was my safety net to guard against his falling onto the floor. Gradually, I got his legs up and helped move his torso and head onto the bed. I positioned a pillow under his head, one next to his neck, and another pillow under his buttock to help take some pressure off his bedsore. Even though he'd lost over twenty pounds since Christmas, Matthew was now dead weight. He wasn't able to move or use his legs. I don't know where I got the strength from. I barely got him moved into bed. It was awkward and dangerous, but by the grace of God, I got him moved.

I dimmed the light, put another Irish CD on to play, and stood next to his bed. Earlier, I coaxed Matthew to eat some vanilla pudding, but not much. It was difficult for him to drink from a cup, even when using a straw. Not too long after he got settled into bed, that white, grayish foam started running out of his mouth. He wasn't strong enough to help himself, so I worked all night clearing the whitish-gray foam from his mouth and keeping his cannula, which provided him oxygen, in his nose. Sometimes, the foam would run like a river. I couldn't keep up with it. As soon as I'd toss a couple of tissues into the trash, I'd have to reach for more. I emptied the trash bag several times during the night, using at least three boxes of tissues. It was a long night, punctuated sometimes when I'd hear Dad rambling around the house in a sundowner's daze.

TEXT Message to Matthew's Family August 17, 2017 9:22 AM

"MATTHEW UPDATE: Sorry it took me so long, yesterday was hectic, Matthew is home, he had a comfortable night, it's been difficult trying to move him by myself but we've managed. Not much appetite, he's seeing visions of people, currently playing Irish music and looking at family photos and photos from his trips to Ireland, only pain is from his bedsore, at hospice recommendation Matthew is getting morphine every 2-4 hours. His feet are more swollen this morning, a hospice nurse is expected sometime today. I think Matthew thought he was passing during the night, he got real anxious between 3-6 AM, hopefully I can keep his spirits up today."

I couldn't have gotten through this time without the help of my good neighbor, Gail Mattox, a retired nurse, and our dear friend Wayne. Thursday morning, Matthew wanted to sit in his chair. He had some semblance of alertness, and his bedsore was aggravating him. I tried moving him myself, but I quickly realized Matthew was no longer able to assist me by using his legs, and I couldn't hold him up any longer than a few seconds.

I had no choice—I was going to need help moving Matthew and I had no idea who to contact. The first person I thought of was our neighbor Gail, who lived across the street. I tried calling her and resorted to leaving a voice message. In desperation, I thought of Wayne. I knew Matthew had been adamant the night before, but I had no one else to call. I looked Matthew in the eyes and told him I needed help. I couldn't move him by myself, and I was going to call Wayne, and I wanted his blessing to do so. I had to repeat myself three times before he finally acquiesced. I immediately called Wayne, explained the situation, and asked if he could help. Wayne didn't hesitate. He promised he'd be here within the half-hour. After I got off the phone, I looked out the dining room window and noticed Gail in her front yard. I assessed Matthew to make sure he was okay and ran across the street to talk to Gail. Gail took one look at me and knew I needed help. Once Wayne arrived, it took the three of us to move Matthew. The process wasn't any easier now with three people than it had been the night before when there was just me.

Over the next two days, Wayne and Gail proved to be my guardian angels. I'm not sure how I would have taken care of Matthew without their help. Gail organized a schedule for Matthew's meds and dispensed them while she was there. Wayne helped to keep an eye on Matthew and talk with him while Matthew was semi-coherent. When needed, they were both present during the day to lift and reposition Matthew every couple of hours to relieve the pain resulting from his bedsore. Mary Ann was there during her normal hours to supervise Mom and Dad. I was often out of the house at this time, going to the pharmacy to pick up meds, grocery shopping, taking Dad for a doctor's appointment, or checking on my Uncle Ron who was in the hospital at this time.

True friends were there when I needed them most. I will forever be grateful to Gail and Wayne for their selfless help and compassionate understanding during this most critical time in our lives. I learned what true friendship is thanks to Gail and Wayne. Someday, I pray, I can pay forward their kindness, generosity, and compassion when a friend is in need.

TEXT to Matthew's Family August 17, 2017 3:49 PM

"MATTHEW UPDATE: My minister stopped by today to visit with your dad, it's the same church where he sings in the choir with Wayne, his golfing and Stage West buddy. I couldn't get Matthew up from the chair this morning after changing the sheet on the bed so I ended up calling Wayne and tracked down a neighbor to help. I haven't eaten since 11 AM yesterday, my church will start sending meals tonight, which will help a lot, Mom and Dad still need to be taken care of. Hospice nurse just left. His feet still swollen and he doesn't want to elevate them when he's in the recliner. I'm falling asleep as I'm typing this, just fragments of sleep last night. It's hard to lift him, I have help during day but at night there's no one to help. He's not strong enough to help, sorry about this message but I'm sleep deprived, starving and worn out."

TEXT from Diana August 17, 2017 4:22 PM

"Vicki—we are coming, don't say no, you need help!"

TEXT to Diana August 17, 2017 4:23 PM

"I'm sorry, didn't mean to gripe...I've reached my frustration level, as I've told him it takes two sets of hands to take care of him, one set can't do it. Wayne said he'd come back later tonight to help settle Matthew in bed and tomorrow morning."

TEXT from Diana August 17, 2017 5:46 PM

"Arrangements made, we leave bright and early tomorrow morning, should be at your place by noon."

Friday, August 18 was a non-stop day. Wayne arrived in the morning to help, as did Gail. Earlier in the morning, I called 911 for help in moving Matthew. As I watched a couple of firemen gently pick him up and reposition Matthew in bed, they made it look so easy, like they were picking up a feather, I was speechless and extremely grateful.

TEXT from Diana August 18, 2017 6:15 AM

"Delay, mechanical issues, I'll keep you posted!"

TEXT to Diana August 18, 2017

"Fire Department just left; second time called them within 12 hours to lift and position Matthew back into bed, I dozed off and when I woke up this morning he was sitting up on edge of bed and no matter what I did to reposition him he was dead weight (sorry about the pun). He and I had a heart to heart talk that if he doesn't cooperate his wish of being home may need to be changed. I don't want anyone to get injured trying to do what Matthew wants."

An aide from hospice came to give Matthew a sponge bath and change his sheets. Hospice also scheduled a pinning cere-mony since Matthew had proudly served with the Marines from 1957-1960. When this took place, sadly I missed it because my uncle was being discharged from the hospital, and he had no one else to pick him up. As all of this was going on, Diana and I were constantly texting each other with the latest laments regarding their travel plans. Originally expecting them around 1:00 p.m., time kept getting pushed back with the fear they might not get here in time.

TEXT from Diana August 18, 2017

"Poor guy, sounds like a race against time now. Does he know we're coming?"

TEXT from Diana August 18, 2017 10:16 AM

"What a morning! We are stuck, rerouting issues now. Feels like we'll never get there. Hang on, we aren't giving up!"

When I finally got home after dropping my uncle off at his house, I walked into our living room, and it was full of people. Our good friend Betsy Glasson had stopped by to see Matthew one last time and to say goodbye. Betsy had been Victoria to Matthew's Toddy in *Victor/Victoria* at Stage West. They had been friends and theatre colleagues for over twenty years. Another golfing buddy of Matthew's stopped by, Drew and his girlfriend. Everyone was congregated around Matthew's bed. After a couple of minutes, Matthew became agitated. We deciphered from his gesturing he needed to urinate and wasn't able to. Drew tried to help, as he towered over Matthew firmly holding him up while uttering words of encouragement, to no avail. I called hospice, begging them to send someone to cath him. I couldn't stand to see Matthew in so much pain.

TEXT from Diana August 18, 2017

"Finally, some progress! We have a new connecting flight out of NY, hope we make it in time!"

TEXT from Diana August 18, 2017 2:33 PM

"We should be landing in Tampa around 6 pm!"

A hospice nurse came and left immediately after cathing Matthew. Betsy left shortly thereafter followed an hour later by Drew and his girlfriend. It was just Gail and I monitoring Matthew. Gail stayed until I fixed dinner for my folks and tucked Mom into bed. After Gail left for the night, I dimmed the lights. Irish music was playing softly. I resumed my vigil next to Matthew's bed, mopping up with tissues the white, grayish foam that was again flowing nonstop from Matthew's mouth. This was the scene when the front door opened and in walked Michael and Diana. It was 7:20 p.m.

I was both relieved and thankful Michael and Diana finally made it. They'd had such a long day, and words couldn't come close to conveying what I was feeling in my heart. I'd been facing Matthew's inevitable death alone, and I was frightened. I'd been functioning for days on strength I didn't know I had. I now attribute this strength to my SISU, my Finnish heritage helped me face this final chapter of our marriage, *till death do us part.*

Michael silently approached his dad. He gently touched Matthew's head, bent down, and whispered in his ear. Later, when I asked Michael if he thought his dad knew he was here, Michael looked me squarely in the eyes and responded, "He knows." Diana next walked up to Matthew's bed and spent a few quiet minutes with him. I silently thanked God Michael and Diana had a few final moments with Matthew before he died.

Diana always used to say that Michael was a chip off the Matthew block. Not only did Michael follow in his dad's footsteps becoming a police officer with the Philadelphia Police Department, as did his brother Matty, but they were also golfing enthusiasts, beer experts, and could finish each other's conversations along with spouting classic lines from some of their favorite movies like *Caddy Shack* and *Odd Fellas*. Matthew was proud of both of his sons. They meant the world to him, and he loved them more than life itself.

The evening of Friday, August 18 was winding down. Michael and Diana were exhausted, they'd been up since 2:00 a.m. for a 6:00 a.m. flight that never materialized. In a short time, Diana crashed in Matthew's recliner, despite looking uncomfortable, she quickly fell into a deep sleep. Michael laid down in my bedroom, falling asleep in his dad's spot on the bed. I stayed up, standing sentry next to Matthew. The foam running out of Matthew's mouth was even worse now. There were times when I couldn't keep up with it. It flowed like lava erupting from a volcano, out of his slightly opened mouth, onto his pillow, soaking the sheet, dripping down the handrail of the bed, and pooling on the floor. As soon as I'd get done mopping up one mess, I'd turn around, and it was flowing all over again. How could one person produce so much whitish-gray, frothy foam? He hadn't been eating or drinking all day. Was this the interior of his lungs disintegrating and flowing out of his body? I was trying to do what I could for him. I wished, instead, I could have spent that time whispering in his ear, telling him how much I loved him, how grateful I was he was my husband.

After midnight, it appeared Matthew was starting to choke on the foam in his mouth, I tried to reposition his head but moving his neck was difficult. In order to help him, I inserted my finger into his mouth, using my finger like a hook to draw out the thick, whitish-gray foam.

Shortly after 1:00 a.m. on Saturday, August 19, the house quiet except for the softly playing Irish CD, a CD Matthew and I particularly liked, Foster and Allen's *Memories*. The light was dim. I could hardly see Matthew's face. I had dimmed it lower so as not to awaken the slumbering Diana just a few feet away. I started to notice the foam wasn't flowing with as much intensity. Our favorite Irish song started playing, "Red Haired Mary." Until this moment, Matthew had been quietly sleeping, but upon hearing this familiar song we both loved so much, he became agitated, as if he was reacting to our song. "Matthew," I whispered into his ear, "our song is playing, 'Red Haired Mary.'" His agitation continued throughout the duration of the song, like he was trying to body dance to this lively Irish tune we both knew so well.

When the song ended, Matthew quieted down. Within minutes, it appeared he wasn't breathing. I nudged him saying, "Matthew!" He started breathing again. I just stood there staring at him. It was hard to see him clearly in the dim light. After about two minutes, as I was looking intently at him, I came to realize he wasn't breathing. I stood there, just staring at him. My mind was totally void of any thoughts. It was as if my mind had been instantly wiped clean like an erased chalkboard. After a few minutes of numbness, I finally came to my senses and realized I should wake Michael and Diana, but my feet were glued to the floor. I couldn't move. After what seemed like hours, my feet finally synced with my brain, and I silently walked into the bedroom to wake Michael. He woke with a start, and I spoke in a whisper, "I think your dad just passed away." We both quickly walked into the living room. Diana woke and joined us as we circled around Matthew's bed. Michael felt for a carotid and confirmed Matthew had died. Why didn't I cry? I was probably in shock. While part of me knew this was coming, another part of me was still in denial thinking Matthew would regain his health and our lives would resume where they left off before this nightmare began. My mind couldn't comprehend that my husband of twenty-one years had just died. I felt like a pillar of salt, no emotions, no tears, not even a sense of sorrow. I was totally devoid of any feelings.

I called hospice. The hospice nurse came and pronounced Matthew dead. She asked the time, and we agreed on 1:15 a.m. After she left, the undertaker was there within thirty minutes. I put the dogs in the laundry room, not sure what their reaction would be.

Michael, Diana, and I were sequestered in the bedroom as the undertaker prepared Matthew's body. When he called us back into the living room, I was surprised to see a rectangular box covered in a red velvet drape with the funeral parlor's embossed logo prominently displayed. I didn't know what I expected, but that wasn't it. As the undertaker solemnly pushed the gurney out the front door, he stopped on the porch. The lone overhead porch light illuminated the gurney, like a spotlight shining down onto

Matthew's earthly remains. I remember thinking at the time the light looked like God shining his continence down upon Matthew and welcoming him into heaven with outstretched, loving arms.

Facebook Post August 19, 2017

It is with a broken heart that I inform our family and friends of the passing earlier this morning of my husband, Matthew Veasey. My prayers were answered, Matthew passed away peacefully. Funeral will be Monday, August 21 at the Spring Hill United Church of Christ. Details regarding Philadelphia funeral will be announced by his son Matty within the week. Thank you everyone for your heartfelt words of sympathy.

PART II
A Door Opens

CHAPTER 15

Welcome to Widowhood!

The exact moment after Matthew took his last breath, 1:15 a.m. on August 19, 2017, I no longer had a husband. For the past twenty-one years, my life had been defined as the wife of Matthew J. Veasey, Jr. That identify no longer existed. Suddenly, I had a new moniker. I was now a widow. How did that happen? I wasn't prepared for this. Where is the widow's manual? Probably in the same hidden recesses where the manual's hiding on how to be a wife. Where's the switch to turn off being a wife and turn on being a widow? I'm only 60 years old. What do I do now?

I no longer had someone to run interference for me while I was at work—someone to talk to, laugh with, cuddle with, shop with, shop for, cry on, argue with, hang out with, or, most importantly, to love. I kept expecting Matthew to walk into the house any minute carrying grocery bags or dragging his butt after a game of golf. No matter how long I wait, he…doesn't… come…home.

Matthew was larger than life—at least to me he was. How could he get sick and die? That wasn't in the script. The house had never seemed so quiet, empty, or unbelievably sad. The house felt as sad as I was, if that's possible. As I wandered from room to room in a daze, my mind on autopilot. Frozen images popped into my mind—Matthew blowing out the candles on his birthday cake, eating Village pizza and watching a movie, walking into the bathroom seeing him sitting on the toilet working on his crossword puzzles, or going over lines with him in preparation for a new show. Everywhere I looked, I couldn't shake my memories. Images played before my eyes in slow motion like an old-time newsreel. No matter where I looked, I saw flashbacks or things that spoke of our life together. How can all these inanimate objects still be here? How can those memories randomly pop into my mind when Matthew isn't here? It's not fair. How come I didn't get to vote on this?

My life had changed. I was probably in shock. I knew I was in denial, and I was definitely bone-weary tired. All I wanted to do was curl up and sleep. Sleep forever. Aren't I entitled to stay in bed forever from now on? However, I couldn't. I had two parents and two dogs who were dependent on me.

Although I've experienced the death of loved ones before—grandparents, aunts, uncles, friends—Matthew's death was affecting me in ways the others hadn't. Why is that? Because he was my husband? My heart and soul? My best friend? Lover? Soulmate? Confidant? I never realized how much of myself died the night Matthew died.

Realistically, since Matthew was seventeen years my senior, the odds were in his favor that he'd die before me, but those stats never really meant much to me. He didn't seem *old* to me. Oftentimes, when we'd meet people for the first time, they thought I was Matthew's daughter, not his wife. The reactions we'd encounter when those new acquaintances learned the truth were priceless. We'd drive home chuckling to ourselves never feeling we were a generation apart in age, especially as the years melted, and our marriage melded into a solidarity of oneness. When I looked at

Matthew, I didn't see a person old enough to be my father. I saw the man I loved and who I built a life with. After twenty-one years of marriage, I had come to accept Matthew for the person he was, warts and all, and I treasured our life together. It was the same way he'd finally learned to trust me and accept in his heart I wasn't going anywhere. I often told him, "Matthew, you're stuck with me whether you like it or not; I'm in this for the long haul." It took him years to finally believe me.

Matthew and I had reached that phase in our marriage where we trusted each other, depended on each other, and treasured the other person as the one who made us whole. Life was good. Life was feeling right, and we were as comfortable as two old, worn out house-slippers. Of course, the slippers were the ones with holes in the toes and stunk real bad, but you loved them anyway because they felt so comfortable. They were broken in, and you wore them every day. They were your favorites! That's the best way I can describe our life before Matthew died. Now, instead of a whole, I am a half. Yearning for my other half to come home and say, "God changed His mind. He knows how much you miss me and need me."

It's amazing—around the time Matthew died, there were calls, notes of condolence, and well-meaning acquaintances who reached out. Shortly thereafter, it was as if I had evaporated from the face of the earth. I was now invisible! Was it because I was no longer half of a couple? Or did they believe that because I appeared so strong in their eyes, they thought I no longer had need of their friendship, concern, or help. My friend Anne refers to this part of widowhood as *Two Steps Back*. I noticed that couples who Matthew and I used to socialize with all of a sudden disappeared from my life. I'm not sure if it was intentional. Were the wives afraid my widowhood was contagious, and by associating with me, they'd catch what I had, and they, too, would become a dreaded widow? *Heaven forbid!* Or did they feel threatened by having a single female within the confines of their social sphere? Were they afraid their husbands might feel called upon to help the poor widow, and through contact with me, they'd be tempted to stray from their marriage vows? If that's the case, then I guess they were never true friends after all. This was the time I needed my friends the most, to reach out, offer a shoulder to cry on, or to call just to say hello. I felt so lost, alone, frightened, and unsure of myself during those months immediately after Matthew's death. I so desperately needed my friends, yet they didn't seem to need or care about me. Everyone else had their lives, and my life no longer existed, at least the life I was used to—my life as Matthew's wife. I never felt so alone as I did at that time.

I was surprised to recognize how much I had become dependent on Matthew. Before Matthew, I was a loner, extremely independent, a person who felt comfortable within her own skin and had herself as a best friend. Matthew expected me, as his wife, to share the same opinions as him—be dependent, subservient, and obedient—to him. My fierce sense of independence was often a source of heated arguments when we were first married. He expected me to change into his idea of the perfect wife and to extinguish the flame of independence which defined my soul and ran deep within my psyche.

Somewhere during our journey, I changed, and so did he. I am not sure when this change occurred, but I saw myself as a person who had evolved into a partial image of that perfect wife Matthew so desperately wanted. I had evolved into a person who now felt dependent on a ghost, imprisoned within an unbearable craving of need. I was gasping for breath and longing for a person who would never come back. It overwhelmed and frightened me how dependent on Matthew I had become. I didn't recognize the person whose reflection now stared back at me in the mirror.

With time, I understood the difference—I realized I was creating inner turmoil and was reluctant to resort back to my independent self. I didn't want to give up the sense of confidence I'd gained while being half of a whole. As long as Matthew was alive, I felt more confident in my abilities because I knew my safety net would catch me if I fell. Now, I was traversing that wide divide with no safety net. I didn't want to hide behind my independence any longer, like I did before I knew him. Then, I used my independence like a shield. Now, after living for over twenty years with that shield cautiously lowered as each year progressed, my soul was crying out, *don't become an island again.* Yet, it would have been so easy to resort back to a behavior that was second nature to me. Before, I didn't realize the significance of social interaction. Now, thanks to Matthew, I did, and it was this tug of war with my psyche that was creating havoc within my world. It would have been so easy to become an island unto myself again, like I was before Matthew. I was trying to avoid my life coming full circle, and I was hating every single minute of it. I never felt lonely before I met Matthew. Now, I couldn't shake the feeling that there was no one left in my life who loved me. Loneliness was now my worst enemy. Before Matthew, I welcomed being alone like a long, lost friend because I had been raised that way. I always knew I still had my parents in the background. With Matthew gone, even though my parents were still alive, their minds, memories, and emotional support were no longer an issue. I was literally without any immediate family. I felt alone and forgotten.

I didn't expect to feel a physical pain as a result of mourning. However, I felt like I was being eaten alive from the inside out. My heart was consumed with each excruciating bite, gnawing at every fiber of my existence. I heard people talk about this before, never dreaming I'd become a victim myself one day. Once in a while, I wondered if I'd died first, would Matthew have felt any of these same emotions and pain? I doubt it—he would have moved on with his life and continued doing what he normally did. Maybe that's the difference between men and women. Most women feel emotions far deeper, from the very depths of their heart. While men, in general, are often ruled from a physical strength, need, and desire.

As I was struggling with the emotional loss of my husband, I was also concerned about finances. Matthew's pension died with him, since he was retired before we met. I couldn't work and take care of my parents at the same time—Mom needed 24/7 supervision. Plus, I was too young to collect Social Security.

Matthew didn't believe in life insurance except for two very small policies through the City of Philadelphia and the FOP. With my job, I had a 401(k). However, it wouldn't provide the monthly income I needed to survive. Less than two weeks after Matthew died, I received a letter from the City of Philadelphia demanding I return 40% of his pension for the month of August. They prorated what I owed based on the date he died. Fortunately, my job was still held open for me, but I wasn't receiving a paycheck. And I needed time to think and figure out what I was going to do regarding the safekeeping of my parents if I returned to my job. If I didn't return to my job, how would I earn a monthly income while still caring for my parents 24/7?

If I continued my job, all my wages would go for a caregiver nine hours a day, five days a week. I wasn't making the kind of salary where I could sock money away for a rainy day because I worked in a small area north of Tampa on the Nature Coast of Florida. My dad's pension would cover the household expenses, but I had personal expenses each month as well. Plus, and most importantly, I had to take off my blinders and look at the big picture and be practical. My parents were 96 and 89 years old, and they both had Alzheimer's. In all likelihood, they didn't have much time left. When something happens to them what would I do?

After crunching the numbers, I realized it would be cheaper to draw up a caregiver's contract, quit my job, and take care of my parents' full time. When I was working, the hourly rate I was paying for a home health aide wasn't much different from the hourly rate I was making with my job. The caregiver's contract would allow me to earn additional Social Security credits while earning a salary so I could pay my personal monthly expenses. Plus, in the off-chance either of my parents were ever transferred to assisted living, the contract was worded so Medicare or Medicaid wouldn't question the paychecks written to me each month.

My last day of employment was October 31, 2017, with the company I'd worked for since August 2000. I never heard a word of thank you for seventeen years of dedicated service. Now, it was time to adjust my mindset, embrace this new opportunity, and make the most of this new chapter in my life. The hard part, though, was deprogramming my mind of the sense of accountability my previous employer had instilled into my consciousness. It took over a year to finally realize this new chapter in my life didn't have to be as structured as my business life had been. That was easier said than done.

Just weeks after Matthew passed away, during the second week of September 2017, Hurricane Irma roared into Florida. It first appeared in the Naples-Ft. Myers area followed by a northward path along the Gulf Coast. It was bad enough I was trying to deal with widowhood, but now I had to contend with a hurricane as well. I secured our home the best I could. I wrapped precious family heirlooms and photographs in bubble wrap and placed them inside the appliances, hoping to safeguard our treasures. By nature, I would have stayed home rather than evacuate. I didn't believe our home was in jeopardy, but my Uncle Ron had been voicing concern for days, and my Aunt Lou was upset about all the hurricane coverage on TV. I was worried they'd evacuate and get stuck in traffic during the height of the storm. I suggested we stay with them until the storm passed—my parents, the pups, and I. Their home was five miles further inland from our house and sat on higher ground. We had an uneventful couple of days as we sat glued to the TV, listening for updates as Hurricane Irma knocked on the doorstep of Hernando County. We survived the hurricane, something I attributed to Matthew and God keeping us safe from harm's way.

I struggled through each day the best I could. I was busy nonstop. There were numerous phone calls to settle Matthew's estate, trips to banks, mailing keepsakes to Matthew's family, and arrangements regarding his car. I never settled an estate before—it was a true learning experience—and I had no one to help me. This, like caring for my parents, rested squarely on my shoulders.

We were living in a house that held no true significance for me, except it was the house where Matthew died, a memory I didn't want to face for the rest of my life. When I stood in the living room, I could still see Matthew laying in the hospital bed. My mind couldn't shake the image of the undertaker's gurney with the front porch light shining down on Matthew's covered body. It made me think that was Matthew's last performance, his final curtain call. When I took the pups to the pen, my eyes would sometimes play tricks on me, and I could swear I saw Matthew sitting in the gray, plastic chair in front of the door working his Sudoku puzzles. When I walked into the computer room, I encountered remnants from the last time Matthew sat at his computer. Everywhere I looked, I was constantly reminded of Matthew. And with each reminder, my heart ached and my eyes would flood, and I wanted to curse God for making this happen. I wasn't at my best during this time. I just wanted to curl up and die, but I couldn't—I had responsibilities.

God knew what he was doing when He brought the pups into our lives, Kipper and Katy. They joined our family in January 2012, both rescues, just a month after Matthew and I lost our beloved Casey. Kipper is overweight, slightly goofy, a white and buff-colored cocker spaniel with the biggest heart of gold. Katy is the same coloring, smaller in stature, with an unbobbed tail that resembles a skinny princess wand with delicate feathers floating along the stem. She looks more like a Kooikerhonje than a cocker spaniel. Katy can be spunky but is totally devoted to her adopted brother, Kipper. They are inseparable! My heart melts every time I see them. The pups provided me the lifeline I so desperately needed. The pups and my parents—I don't know what I would have done without them. All four distracted me, but only two showed me any signs of love.

Everywhere I looked, I saw worldly possessions that no longer held any significance or were no longer needed. Our home was stuffed with furniture and personal mementos that echoed the accomplishments and lives of four individuals. My mom, when she had her faculties, was always reluctant to part with anything she no longer needed. It made our move into their home back in 2008 much more difficult despite numerous garage sales I held at the time. Add to that a neighborhood and zip code prone to sinkholes, I was afraid we'd become the next victim of a bottomless pit. I had no allegiance to our home and had been planning on selling even before Matthew died. The entire time Matthew and I lived there, we saw it more as my parents' home where we slept, rather than as our cherished home. I was overwhelmed those precious weeks following Matthew's death. I didn't know what to do and when I did do something, I often doubted the decision I was making.

Feeling overwhelmed is a characteristic of being a new widow. I didn't know this at the time. It felt like a giant hand crushing down, trying to smother me. The harder it pushed, the more difficult it was for me to catch my breath, clear my foggy mind, and comprehend what I needed to do. Upon reflection, this must have been how Matthew had been feeling as his oxygen levels started to decline. It's a shame to realize something so important after the fact. If I'd comprehended this earlier, I could have been more help to my husband when he needed me most.

Six weeks after Matthew died, I attended the annual rummage sale at church. Mary Lou, who worked with Matthew on the updated church directory just five months earlier, was stationed at the door as prospective customers arrived to shop. Being a widow herself for several years, she pulled me aside and provided me with some sage advice, "No matter what you do, don't make any drastic changes for a year. That's the best advice I can give you." I didn't have the heart to tell her I'd just sold our home.

CHAPTER 16

We Evolved into a Family

When Matthew and I were first married, I moved into his home in Spring Hill, where he lived with his mom and Aunt Kathleen. I'd never been married before, so not only was I experiencing a difficult time adjusting to married life but also to living with two additional adults, both females. Knowing his pension would die with him and I was seventeen years younger, it appeared that I was probably going to outlive him. Despite his frequent nagging me to quit my job, stay home, and play housewife, I put my foot down. The idea was tempting, but my practical side won out. This was difficult, at first, for Matthew to accept.

Our first year of married life was very nerve-wracking for me. We often argued. I used to run off into our bathroom, locked the door, and cried buckets of tears. This now sounds rather childish on my part, but marriage takes a lot of getting used to. It was particularly difficult for this shy, introverted loner. The perpetual audience of his mom and aunt didn't help. We were from two totally different generations with totally different ideas and expectations about marriage. I learned early on he did not worship the ground I walked on, and he didn't place me on a pedestal. The one at the top of that pedestal was Matthew himself, followed in order by his sons and mom, then his sisters, grandchildren, and daughters-in-law. I was on the bottom rung of the Matthew ladder. It hurt like hell, especially when Matthew was always so insistent we provide a united front for family and friends. On many occasions, I silently wept on the inside as I smiled on the outside. I had family who saw through this charade and were, as a result, always guarded and cautious around Matthew.

Matthew's way of treating a wife was totally different from how my parents behaved toward each other. I seldom observed my parents' arguing, fighting, or angry with each other. Matthew didn't believe in compromise or a truce. Things had to be his way or no way. Once we made plans to do something and those plans changed at the last minute, it wasn't in him to willingly accept the change, especially on short notice. On those occasions when this happened, Matthew would often sulk and be moody.

There were aspects of my earlier life Matthew couldn't accept or comprehend, which shaped how I viewed our life together. When I was growing up, my dad went deer hunting every November, which was a common occurrence for many families living in Michigan. Dad often left Mom and me home alone for a week or two. This was a foreign concept to Matthew, and he wasn't shy in making snide remarks about this whenever we'd have a disagreement. Yet he saw nothing wrong with leaving for Philadelphia once or twice a year to see his family, usually for a couple of weeks at a time. I never begrudged him those trips because family has always been very important to me. We always planned on my flying to Philadelphia for an extended weekend while he was there, which became a norm for us. A couple of years into our marriage, I once joked I saw more of his family than I did of my own; Matthew didn't appreciate hearing that.

Matthew lived by a double standard that was a stumbling block during the first years of our marriage. He never seemed to recognize this within himself, yet he was a master at manipulating an argument in his favor by using that double standard. He found it implausible that a woman could have a platonic friendship with a man. However, he had many platonic female friends who he called on the phone, emailed, and sent text messages to. It was like listening to two females gossiping. If he saw me talking to a male friend at a party, or when I wanted to visit a male friend in Texas who was terminally ill, Matthew got jealous and made nasty, untrue comments. It took years for me to understand, accept, and get over the fact that Matthew lived by a double standard.

I had nightmares about becoming a bag lady one day, living on the streets because I couldn't afford to maintain the household expenses if something happened to Matthew. Throughout the first year of our marriage, I begged Matthew to let me take out a life insurance policy on him to provide me with some peace of mind in case he died. No matter how much I pleaded, he was adamantly against it, even when I promised to pay the premiums myself, and there'd be no cost to him.

About two years into our marriage, I braced myself and approached him once again about life insurance, a topic that became a sore spot for us. I wasn't expecting any change in his attitude, but something compelled me to ask one more time. It was a weeknight. We'd just had dinner, and we were putting leftovers away and cleaning the kitchen.

"Matthew," as I cautiously asked him, "what if you get sick or you're in a car accident and find yourself in and out of the hospital for a couple of months and eventually die? How am I supposed to pay your medical bills? You know I don't make much with my job, and you don't want me to travel over an hour to Tampa for work. How am I supposed to make ends meet?"

At first, he kept putting the leftovers away like he hadn't heard me. After about thirty seconds, he stopped and turned to look at me. I stopped what I was doing. My heart froze as he asked, "Would it be a large policy?"

154

"No, about one hundred thousand, enough to keep me afloat financially for a while until I figured out what to do. You know I'd never be able to keep the house without your pension, and I'd need money to move and resettle. I don't even know if I'd stay in Spring Hill or move back to Michigan."

Mathew didn't say anything for a while. I kept staring at him, holding my breath.

"Alright."

I couldn't believe what I'd heard. Matthew finally agreed that I could take out a life insurance policy on him. I was ecstatic! After almost two years of asking and being rejected, often with no reasoning, I finally had a positive answer. I thanked Matthew profusely and went to bed that night with peace in my heart. Those nightmares of someday becoming a bag lady were, I assumed, a thing of the past. I called the insurance agent the next day and made an appointment the following week so Matthew could sign the paperwork. His agreement lifted a heavy burden off my shoulders. At the same time, it symbolized to me that he truly loved me.

The night before our appointment with the insurance agent, we were sitting in front of the TV after dinner. He had control of the remote, like usual, channel surfing for something that caught his attention. I casually reminded him, "Matthew, I'll get out of work a little early tomorrow. I'll be here at 3:45 p.m. to pick you up. We have the appointment with the insurance agent for you to sign the paperwork for the life insurance policy."

He stopped playing with the remote and slowly turned his head toward me, staring at me with a look of venomous hatred that wasn't there the moment before. He said, "I've changed my mind. I'm not signing."

It took me a moment to realize what he'd said. When I did, I was dumbfounded and shell shocked. I was afraid of his answer, but I needed to know why. I slowly, cautiously, asked in a whisper that was barely audible, "Why?"

He looked at me with revulsion in his eyes that sent arrows into my heart. "I don't want you to have fun money to play with after I'm gone."

Those fourteen words stopped my heart and took my breath away. Those words were the most hateful words anyone has ever said to me. Those words, which have forever been seared into my heart, told me he really didn't love me. The only one he loved in our marriage was himself. I couldn't move. I was in shock. I felt betrayed. I was betrayed not by a mistress but by a husband who cared more for himself than he did for me. Being a Pisces, I'm a dreamer. Before meeting Matthew, I fantasied, like most girls, about one day marrying the man of my dreams. My prince charming, a man who loved me with all his heart and soul. A man who would *want* to take care of me. A man who would make sure I was taken care of if anything ever happened to him. The man I married, as it turned out, wasn't my image of prince charming.

It would have been so easy to turn my back on him and walk out the door. I was tempted to that night. I'm not sure what held me back. Maybe I was ashamed to tell my parents I'd made a mistake. My parents weren't thrilled I married a much older man and now this. I was forty years old. How did I make such a mistake in marrying this man? You'd think someone my age would have been wiser. How could I have been so blind to the truth? I went to bed that night, turned my back away from his spot in bed, and silently cried as I prayed for guidance. I didn't sleep much that night. Matthew never acknowledged me when he finally came to bed. He never kissed the top of my head like he normally did or whispered *Good Night* to me. We were like two strangers, both bound by servitude, both imprisoned within the confines of the same space. I know I didn't budge an inch all night, lost within the tears that eventually dried on my cheeks, each one a crystal of heartache.

The next morning, as I was lying in bed taking a few moments to brace myself for the day, a sense of peace all of a sudden enveloped me, like the arms of God embracing me. I was receiving His message loud and clear: *It will get better. Stay with him.*

Our first five years of marriage were a true challenge. We stuck it out, through good times and bad. It wasn't easy. Everything in Matthew's world was either black or white. There was no gray, no middle ground. We learned to adjust our attitudes, expectations, and our hectic lives. I learned when to compromise, when to give in, and when to stand my ground. I credit Matthew's willfulness in helping me learn how to stand up for myself and not always to stand up to him but others as well. Mathew helped me to develop a backbone, which I didn't have before. I'd never been married, and I had more expectations and illusions about marriage than I should have. Matthew, on the other hand, had two failed marriages to his credit, so it's no wonder he had a damaged psyche that shaped his attitude.

As each year passed, we grew closer and stronger as a couple. Matthew gradually came to realize I wasn't going to walk out on him. As a result, he eased his strict, outdated attitude toward our marriage and me. I, on the other hand, learned to stop feeling like I was being pulled in two different directions—Matthew versus my family. Matthew, with time, came to understand that *both* our families meant the world to me. When I suggested we acquire e-mail, cell phones, skype, and Facebook as a way for him to communicate with his family and friends, he applauded each new technology.

Often, when I was at work, Matthew accused me of not thinking about him. "Why didn't you return my phone call? I sent you a text. You didn't respond back—didn't you read it?" And my favorite, I'd call him immediately after leaving work longing to hear his voice and bring him up to date on whether I had any last-minute errands to run before coming home. He'd say, "You didn't check your text messages before calling, did you? I told you that in the message I sent you ten minutes ago."

"Yes, Matthew," I'd respond, "you're right. I rushed out of work and called you as soon as I got in the car. I didn't want to stay at work any longer than I had to. I called you the minute I got in the car because I wanted to hear your voice."

I didn't understand at first that Matthew's past colored his present and jeopardized his future. He was very insecure in his relationships. As the years went on, I kept telling him, "I'm determined to outlast your other wives; you can't get rid of me if you tried." Gradually, he came to accept that I was committed to our marriage and the imaginary tug of war he felt with my family was in actuality nonexistent. It was all in his imagination.

Today, it's become the norm for couples to give up and part ways after a disagreement or when one doesn't get their way. So many couples don't know how to negotiate a compromise, so both parties feel like they won. A good marriage evolves with time, patience, and respect for each other. People change—that's a part of life. It's up to each person in the relationship to work at evolving together. You don't have to like the same things, have the same opinions, or the same hobbies or desires. What it does mean is you recognize the differences in each other, respect them, and work at keeping your relationship loving and meaningful to each other. It's a receptacle relationship that's built on respect. And you not only have to love and respect each other, but most importantly, you need to *like* each other. If you don't like each other, then the love you're feeling is more lust than love. If that's the case, your relationship was built on a weak foundation. Lust evaporates with time, and your relationship will eventually head for the toilet.

Matthew and I both changed during our marriage, or as I liked to call it, evolved. Life is a constant series of evolving as a result of life events, world events, and the people we interact with—in the short-term or permanent. The first time I told Matthew he was evolving, he didn't know how to take it. It was around our seventh year of marriage, and we'd had Casey, our first pup, for about a year. I told him, "Matthew, you're evolving. You're not the same person today that you were when we first got married. You've grown as a person, and you react to life in a more compassionate way—you have more empathy. You've mellowed, and your edges aren't as sharp and defined as they were before." At first, he was unsure how to respond to this. He wasn't sure if it was a compliment or not, but after reflecting, he came to realize I was right—it was a compliment. I attribute this change in Matthew not so much to my influence on him but more what he came to learn about himself when he fell in love with Casey, our first pet.

Matthew never had a pet growing up and neither did his sons when they were young. Pets were not in Matthew's vocabulary. He often said, "Where does the animal fit in the food chain?" I'd been a dog lover all my life but learned very early in our relationship that a pet wasn't going to be a member of our family of two. So, you could have blown me away with a feather when Matthew surprised me with a card that said he was giving me a puppy for our fifth wedding anniversary. Matthew was prudent enough to realize we needed to select this pup ourselves rather than him select one for me. I was moved by his gesture, yet at the same time, I was hesitant. I didn't rush into getting a puppy right away, I kept putting if off because I had the mindset that in a couple of months, Matthew would forget about this gift or renege on it just like he'd reneged on the life insurance policy. I didn't want to get a puppy and fall in love with it only to have Matthew get mad at it and tell me to get rid of it.

Around seven months after our anniversary, Matthew asked me one day, "When are we getting that puppy?" I didn't have the heart to tell him, "I'm afraid you'll change your mind. That's why." Instead, I told him, "We need to do our homework. We don't even know what type of puppy we want." This appeased him and bought me time!

So, during the next couple of months we did our homework. In January, we went to the Florida Gulf Coast Cluster Dog Show outside of Brooksville. We looked at breeds, compared notes, and got an idea of what size dog we wanted—large, medium, or small, and what type we wanted—spunky, lively, playful, or quiet in temperament. We went to pet stores, consulted the internet, and borrowed books from the local library. Finally, we agreed on a cocker spaniel. Next, the search began for available puppies. Each morning, we scoured the want ads in the newspaper and checked the internet for local breeders. We learned of a breeder in Live

Oak, Florida whose bitch just had a litter of eight puppies, and they'd be ready the end of August. Matthew emailed the breeder who sent photos of the pups and provided information. Every day, we looked at the photos the breeder sent and tried to determine which one of those cuties would be our little bundle of joy. One morning before work, I remember thumbing through those photos one more time. The edges of were becoming frayed and dog-eared as we studied their looks and personalities. There was one that started to stand out from the rest. I'm not sure if it was the cowlick along the top of her head or the impish gleam in her pouty eyes, but I was receiving another message loud and clear. I wrote a note to Matthew and attached it to the photograph, "She's the one. What do you think?"

We agreed upon the pup, confirmed she was still available, and sent a deposit. Then, we had to wait an agonizing five weeks until our little fur baby could join our family. I got into the excitement of puppy shopping right away and so did my parents—they were both healthy then. My parents were going to have a grand-puppy, and they were ecstatic! Our excitement was contagious and before we knew it, Matthew came home from shopping laden down with bags of doggy paraphernalia—all things he anticipated our baby would need. It took us a couple of weeks to come up with a name. We finally agreed on Casey. Or, as Matthew started to call her, Casey the Conqueror.

On the afternoon of August 28, 2002, Matthew and I met the breeder at a gas station off I-75, halfway between Live Oak and Spring Hill where we took possession of our little furball. As I hesitantly reached out my hands to the breeder, she handed me a squirming bundle of fur. I instantly felt like a brand-new mother who just gave birth. This living being would be dependent upon us for the rest of her life. It had been almost thirty years since I had my last puppy, a Great Dane named Brutus, affectionately nicknamed Boo Boo. I was excited when my parents and I picked up Boo Boo in Flint, Michigan. Now, I was even more excited as Matthew drove us home. We were now a family of three. I sat in the backseat with Casey who was safely secured in a box with a blanket and a stuffed toy. As we got closer to home, I noticed Casey seemed to sense something in the air. She started to chew along the edge of the box like she couldn't wait to get free. By the time we pulled into the driveway, it looked like someone had stapled all along the edge of the box and then removed the staples, leaving little holes overlapping each other.

We'd had a thunderstorm the night before we picked Casey up. A bolt of lightning struck the tree outside our dining room window and blasted shards of tree bark into smithereens. It sent a humongous tree branch down on the sidewalk outside the front door of our house. It missed the garage roof by mere inches. Matthew and I were both standing in the living room when the bolt struck the tree. Against a pitch-black, velvety sky, bursting, fiery sparks radiated outward from the strike zone, as beautiful as it was spellbinding. The spectacle reminded me of a riveting firework display on the Fourth of July. The randomness of Mother Nature shocked us and bedazzled us all at the same time. Looking back on it now, we were fortunate it didn't strike the house. I guess we should have seen this as a preview of how our little bundle of joy was going to disrupt, enchant, stymie, captivate, and frustrate our lives. But most of all, she would be loved!

This was how Casey joined our family and changed our lives for the better. She was a lively little ball of fur. She was so small, just five pounds, seven inches from the tip of her dinky brown nose to the end of her bobbed tail. I learned very quickly to look down at my feet before I moved, otherwise I'd trip over her or step on her. When she was a puppy, she loved being right under your feet.

Casey's first night in her new home was a memorable one. We cordoned off the kitchen with baby gates, prepared her bed with a hot water bottle, a ticking clock, blankets, and a toy. The kitchen floor was lined with newspapers in case she needed to relieve herself during the night. A bowl of water and one with puppy chow were within easy reach of her bed. We turned on a nightlight so the kitchen wouldn't seem so dark and scary for her. She looked so forlorn all by herself. Just before going to bed, we checked on our little fur baby one more time. After hours of whimpering and crying in the kitchen, she finally settled down. She apparently was resolved to her fate of sleeping alone for the very first time in her young life. Matthew and I went to bed, congratulating ourselves that the day had been a success, and we finally had our Casey Girl home with us. We were now officially a family of three.

Several hours later, we woke to a loud enough crash that we both sat up in tandem, looked at each other and said at the same time, "Casey!" The house was so quiet, you couldn't hear anything! I strained my ears, turning my head sideways so my right ear was projected closer to the door, hoping the maneuver would miraculously let me hear something. Finally, I faintly heard what I thought sounded like soft footfalls, barely audible, walking on the carpet. I bounded out of bed, and when I reached the door leading into the living room from our bedroom, I looked down and walking toward me on her short little legs was none other than Casey. As I stooped to pick her up, Matthew looked her over to make sure she wasn't hurt. Casey, we determined, didn't like being by herself in the kitchen. She figured out a way to knock down the baby gates, walk around the tumbled debris, and she used her nose to sniff our path into the bedroom. That was Casey's first night with us, and our lives were never the same again. Our marriage was never the same again.

Casey became the glue that cemented our marriage and helped us become a family. Our marriage strengthened, endured, and evolved. The first couple of months after Casey joined our family were a true challenge for Matthew. But once she wormed her way into Matthew's heart, he was hooked, whether he liked it or not.

Thanks to Casey, Matthew became a doggy daddy, proudly exchanging doggy stories and showcasing his latest photos to anyone who was around. Matthew was there to sooth and comfort her whenever Casey got sick, sprained a paw, or was frightened. Something finally dislodged Matthew from that top rung of his Matthew ladder—Casey—and I didn't mind a bit.

CHAPTER 17

So Much Change

B ack during the summer of 2017 when Matthew was ill, I mentioned my plan about moving. Matthew was overjoyed I'd finally be home full time and gave his blessing. This was something he'd wanted our entire marriage, especially the last four years as he witnessed the gradual decline in my parents' health. Matthew understood the logic in moving, namely to downsize and reduce our annual expenses. My dad was all in favor of the move and understood my reasoning as well.

I found an area in southern Citrus County, sixteen minutes north from our home in Spring Hill. It was close enough we could still attend the same church and retain our current physicians. When Matthew died so unexpectedly, it took me a few weeks to rethink my plan. Once I decided to quit my job and stay home with my parents, I went to an attorney and had a caregiver's contract drawn up. In our new community, I decided on a lot immediately in front of the clubhouse. The back overlooked a retention pond, cattails visible within the reeds surrounded by a grove of tall, majestic pine and deciduous trees. It reminded me of Michigan, peaceful and tranquil, just what I needed after the year's turmoil. I visualized Dad sitting in the living room or the screened porch, gazing at the pond as he daydreamed of his ancestral home in Aura. With the clubhouse across the street, it would be easier to take my parents to community events and eliminate the need for a golf cart.

A friend from church recommended a local realtor, whose name I was familiar with and who had a good reputation in Spring Hill. She was personable and enthusiastic. She firmly believed she could sell our home. The exterior had been painted six months earlier and new landscaping was installed. Thanks to Brandon at Unique Landscaping, our friend's son, our home now had great curb appeal. Talk about timing! Within 24 hours of listing our home, the first person who viewed it made an offer, and we accepted. Talk about a prayer answered! When Matthew was in the hospital, he told me, "I'll do anything to help with the move." I thanked God and Matthew that our home sold so quickly. I believe in my heart Matthew had something to do with bringing about this miracle. For weeks or even months, I anticipated keeping the house clean waiting for a buyer, but it all happened within twenty-four hours. Now, I could focus on sorting and getting rid of possessions we no longer needed.

I was busy throwing stuff away, making numerous trips to Goodwill, and trying to find an auction house that would buy rooms of furniture we no longer would need. There were times when I was up twenty-four hours, sorting and packing to be ready for the movers who were scheduled for the end of October. Mom and Dad were real troopers during this time. They spent their days in the family room, watching TV or playing music while I worked. At the time, if I needed to run an errand, I could leave them home for an hour as long as they were together and the doors were locked. Boxes were piling up, and the dining room table was overloaded with items for the auction house. Flat boxes leaned against the door wall in the living room so I could pack more stuff. My thoughts were often on Matthew, asking myself questions I'd never have the answers to.

We were eating a lot of fast food during this time, quick and easy—what a blessing! Friday night was our traditional pizza night, so I called Village Pizza and ordered the *Matthew special*, a large cheese pizza, half pepperoni, extra sauce all over the whole pie, and baked a couple minutes longer than normal. Matthew and I always took the pups with us when we picked up the pizza. These excursions became a family event. I'm not sure who enjoyed these short car trips more, the pups or us. On this particular occasion, after placing a pizza order, I tethered the pups for the trip and told my folks we'd be back soon. Mom was playing a new Phyllis version of solitaire, and Dad was sitting next to her at the breakfast table looking at the newspaper. As I started the car and pulled out of the driveway, I was parallel to the front of our house when the thought struck me, "I should have locked the connecting door." We often locked the connecting door between the garage and hobby room to slow Mom down, trying to curtail her from getting out of the house and wandering. I had closed the garage door but didn't lock the connecting door, figuring we wouldn't be gone long. I almost turned back to lock the door but decided against it.

As I was driving to Village Pizza, I started thinking of Matthew and all the times we made this same trip to pick up our Friday night pizza. My floodgates let loose. I couldn't help it. It was one of those everyday occurrences which we had done so many times in the past. I parked my Equinox outside the pizzeria, and told the pups, "Mommy will be right back with the pie," and walked into Village Pizza. The entire trip took us no more than fifteen minutes.

When we got home, I clicked the button on the remote, and the garage door came up. I opened the passenger side door to take the pizza out, walked through the garage, reached my hand out to grab the doorknob, and turned. The doorknob wouldn't budge. The door was locked. How did that happen? I knew I hadn't locked the door before I left, even though I thought about it. I dug into my pocket for my keys, which was a little difficult since I was holding the warm pizza box in my hands.

After a little juggling and maneuvering, I unlocked the door and walked through the laundry room into the kitchen. Mom and Dad were in their same places where I left them just fifteen minutes earlier, sitting at the breakfast table. I started to ask them why they locked the connecting door into the house when something inadvertently caught my attention. I turned my head to the right and saw something that wasn't there before I left. There was a barricade of the unfolded, flat boxes that had been leaning against the door wall. These boxes were now standing on their edges, creating a baby gate or barricade to hinder entrance into the living room from the breakfast room. I looked at my dad pointing toward the barricade and asked, "Did you do that?" He looked at me and then looked to where I was pointing. "No," he said. I knew my mom wouldn't do it. When she got ensconced in her chair at the breakfast table, it would take a nuclear blast to budge her. My heart started racing. I couldn't figure out what had happened. Everything stood still. You could have heard a pin drop. Then, I noticed my bedroom door was closed. I *never* close my bedroom door, especially now with just the three of us in the house. I kept it open in case my parents called out and needed me during the night.

I put the pizza box down on the table as I contemplated how three strange things could have happened while I was gone. My parents also didn't close their bedroom door at night, so there was no reason why they would close mine. Why would they create a barricade between the living room and breakfast room? I stood there, trying to make sense of this, looking at my parents like they must have seen something. How could they sit there and not see what had happened?

Suddenly, it dawned on me. There was no other explanation despite how implausible it seemed. The only conclusion I could think of was Matthew. He must have done these things, each one represented something he would have done to safeguard Mom at home. I couldn't come up with any other explanation. After Mom's wandering adventure, Matthew was the one who started locking the connecting door between the house and the garage whenever we went out. Matthew was the one who always closed our bedroom door at night, despite my protests. Matthew always guarded our privacy in the living room, maintaining that the living room was our space, and the family room was my parents' space. He got visibly angered whenever Mom wondered into the living room. And don't forget I'd been thinking about Matthew and crying when I went to pick up the pizza. As I contemplated these phenomena, I remembered there had been other times since Matthew died when the connecting door was locked, and I knew I hadn't locked it. A couple of times, my bedroom door was closed when I came home, and I knew I hadn't closed it. On those occasions, it felt a little eerie, but I was too busy with the sale of the house to give it a second thought. This time I couldn't ignore it. Three strange things happened, things I hadn't done, and I was 99.9% positive my parents hadn't done them, either. It was almost as if Matthew was making it blatantly obvious, doing everything in his power to keep Mom safe when I wasn't home. Since I didn't get his other messages, I suppose he felt he needed to knock some sense into my feeble head, hoping I'd finally wake up and pay attention. First, it was the house selling so quickly and now this. It felt good knowing Matthew was watching over us, keeping us safe, yet I wish I could have seen him, talked to him one last time. There was so much I wanted to tell him, one... last...time. Tears of joy gushed from my eyes with thanks he was watching over us. I missed him so much!

October was a busy month. The auction house came to pick up the excess furniture and possessions we no longer needed. A thrift store picked up the furniture the auction house wouldn't take. I rented a couple of storage units to hold odds and ends until we moved, and the movers came the end of the month. For about six to seven weeks, until our new house was ready, we temporarily moved in with Lou and Ron in Wellington. Lou had bought my parents previous home; it became their winter residence. The first time I ran an errand after we moved in, I left Mom and Dad with Lou and Ron. I was gone an hour, and when I came back, I learned Ron had to get in his truck and look for

Mom. She wandered out the front door and down the hill before anyone realized she was missing. After that, every time I left the house to run errands, Mom, Dad, and the pups all went with me.

Before we moved in with Lou and Ron, I surmised that Dad was responsible for taking off Mom's diaper on those nights when he was frisky, a new characteristic of his sundowning. Some mornings, I found Mom's diaper flung all over their bedroom, and her bed would be soaked in urine. Whenever I asked him about this, he'd deny knowing anything and he'd state, "It must be Phyllis." Mom wasn't in the habit of taking off her diaper, so I had a good idea it was Dad. When I was packing, I placed clothes and boxes on Mom's bed and left them there for several nights. I had her sleep on the couch in the living room, and on neither night did she remove her diaper. Once we moved in with Lou and Ron, I lived in constant fear that I'd walk into their bedroom one morning, and her bed would be a mess. Throughout the night, I often made nocturnal visits into their bedroom breaking up their little love fests, telling Dad to get back into his bed. I hated doing this, but I had no choice.

It felt like a mini-vacation staying with Lou and Ron, except I was trying to sleep on a very hard couch with a loud, ticking clock within three feet of my head. That damn clock! I fantasized about throwing it out the window. It felt good to be on hiatus from packing. I was busy shopping for ceiling fans, curtains, and wallpaper borders. And I gave my uncle a reprieve from cooking dinner every night.

Two weeks into our stay with Lou and Ron, I was surprised to find Ron up early one morning. It was so unlike him. He'd just called EMS because Lou was sick. Lou was in the hospital for a couple of days before being transferred to Hospice House where she died a week later. Within three months, I was experiencing another death of someone who meant a lot to me. It didn't seem possible. Thanksgiving was just a week away, and we'd have two empty chairs at our dinner table that year. How could our lives change so much in such a short period of time? I couldn't wait for 2017 to be over.

Shortly after Lou died, I asked Ron if he wanted to move in with us. He couldn't stay where he was. Lou had mentioned on several occasions that her niece would be inheriting the house upon her death. I hated to think of Ron living by himself in an apartment or a facility. The most logical and practical solution was to have him move in with us. He was reluctant at first, but after a few days, he came to realize and accept that this would be the best solution for him.

The folks, pups, and I moved into our new home on December 20, 2017. The furniture had been delivered a couple of days before, basics had been unpacked, beds made, food in the fridge, and the TV was working. At first, it felt like we were camping because we were surrounded by a fortress of boxes. We couldn't move without stumbling into, around, or toppling over a box.

I set up our beautiful, pre-lit Christmas tree I bought two years before. I purchased it knowing Mom would be enthralled by the lights. I could program it for multi-color, or all blue, all red, all gold, all green, etc. The different combinations of sparkling, dancing, flashing, or twinkling light actions always captivated Mom's attention as she sat mesmerized by the tree's brilliant, enchanting light display. The year before, Mom called out the different colors as she sat spellbound, totally captivated as the lights changed color, "blue, blue, green, green, red, red..." When I remembered how much Mom loved those dancing, sparkling illuminations, I couldn't wait to get the tree up and decorated.

After I got the three sections of the Christmas tree assembled, I turned the room lights low and clicked the switch to turn the tree lights on. I was giddy anticipating our beautiful, softly glowing, multi-colored, lit tree. What I saw instead flabbergasted me! The top third lights were shining brightly, the bottom third lights were ever so beautiful, but the middle third of the tree was totally dark. I had worked so hard to get the tree up, hoping to surprise my folks and instead, it was a fiasco. I hadn't had the time or inclination to decorate like I normally do for the holidays, and the one thing I was trying desperately to accomplish wasn't working.

That damn, uncooperative Christmas tree seemed to symbolize the type of year I had in 2017. Full of disappointment and sorrow, no matter what I did, I couldn't fix what happened. I stuck my head inside the tree hoping to find an unplugged cord, scratching my arms, neck, and face in the process. My upper body started looking like a roadmap of dried blood and crisscrossed scratches. No matter how many times I dove into the center of that tree, I kept coming up empty-handed. I contemplated what I should do, and I did the only thing I could think of under the circumstances—decorate that damn tree, despite the middle lights not working. There's something about a half-lit Christmas tree. It just doesn't convey the same holiday cheer and magic that's normally associated with a beautifully lit Christmas tree. I had been hoping for a glimmer of Christmas spirit and came up empty-handed, or maybe I just didn't have it in me that year. How many days until 2017 was finally over? It couldn't end soon enough! I know, I've said that already…but that's how I was feeling…hoping with all my might that 2018 would be a much better year for us.

Christmas Letter 2017

Dear Family and Friends!

Each Christmas I've looked forward to writing our holiday letter, sharing the highlights of our year and letting you know how special you are to us. Since August I've been dreading this letter. These letters were always a "team" effort. My husband, Matthew, my editor, passed away in August. It all started last Christmas Eve when Matthew was diagnosed with pneumonia. I caught a severe case of bronchitis from him which resulted in an adverse drug reaction, I was hospitalized and recovered, whereas Matthew never did. As each month passed his health continued to slowly decline rather than improve. Between Christmas Eve 2016 and August 1, 2017 Matthew was admitted to a hospital eight times. It was frustrating for him to experience the same symptoms month after month followed by repeated rounds of antibiotics and hospitalizations without a diagnosis or any sign of improvement. During his last admission to a hospital they finally performed a surgical biopsy and we learned on August 9 that Matthew had a rare form of lung cancer. By that time his left lung was so compromised there was nothing his doctors could do to help him. Matthew's two sons, Matty and Michael, flew in to surprise him while he was in the hospital. They had a great visit and it turned out to be a blessing in disguise since Matthew was discharged home days later on August 16th under the care of hospice. Matthew died peacefully at home early on the morning of August 19, exactly one week after the surprise visit with his sons. Michael and his wife Diana arrived from Philadelphia just hours before Matthew died. We believe in our hearts that Matthew knew they were there. I feel thankful that Matthew, Michael, and Matty had that last visit when Matthew was in the hospital. They were always very close and I know they and their families, along with Matthew's sisters Pat and Bobbi, are still reeling from the shock of Matthew's sudden and unexpected death, just as I am.

I've been in communication with so many who have voiced their shock and sorrow regarding Matthew's passing. I feel blessed that we had 21 years together. We created so many loving memories which I treasure. Those memories have helped me through these past three months. I want to thank our family and friends who sent cards, called, and/or communicated via Facebook, email, or text message. Each communication has meant so much to me. I treasure each and every one. Thank You!

Paul and Phyllis are doing ok. Phyllis' memory continues to decline and Paul is experiencing memory loss as well. Paul was also diagnosed this year with glaucoma which coupled with the Alzheimer's, macular degeneration, and loss of hearing has robbed him of so many of his interests and hobbies.

May You Be Blessed with Peace and Good Health
in 2018!

Vicki, Paul, Phyllis, Kipper, and Katy

CHAPTER 18

I Now Know
Why I Exist

Being a fulltime caregiver for my parents took a little getting used to. My entire life I was either a student, worked part-time or full time, or a combination thereof. Now, for the first time, I didn't need to set an alarm, dread the day ahead, or anticipate Matthew's reaction when I contacted him to let him know I was working late. I didn't have to answer to anyone—a novel concept for me—one that my thick, Finnish skull had a hard time accepting. *I* was now the boss—get used to it!

When I was working, I often felt my life had no real purpose. I found myself working jobs that didn't interest me, and there was no real appeal. It was a job, perhaps the current one paid more than the previous one or the job was closer to home. Living in the Nature Coast of Florida, good paying jobs close to home are hard to come by. When you do find a decent job, the pay scale is much lower than in other parts of the United States. I often told my friends from *up north* who voiced to me on many occasions, "Oh, how I envy you, living in Florida! I want to find a job there." I'd look them in the eye and say, "Stay where you're at; the jobs pay better. Move to Florida *after* you retire. You'll have a better retirement." These friends would look at me like I was robbing a bank. They just didn't get it!

I felt discouraged and frustrated because I knew I was destined for a more purposeful life—I just didn't know what it was. I felt like the wheels on a car that's stuck on an icy patch. No matter what you try to do to dislodge the car, the wheels only spin and spin, and the car slides sideways and back and forth. That's how I felt about my jobs. There was no real satisfaction, no administrative support, and no room for advancement. How many times can you teach the same computer classes month after month via webinar before you can do it in your sleep? How many catered lunches can you schedule and clean up afterward before you don't give a damn? How many tables and chairs can you move from room to room in preparation for a conference and then move them back again before you just want to roll those damn tables through a plate glass window and walk away? That's the world I walked away from. Now, I entered a new work environment that channeled my focus on taking care of the two most important people in my life, my parents. The problem was it took me a while to figure this out and appreciate how important my new job was.

After Matthew died, when I became a full-time caregiver, I'd meet people and one of the first things they'd ask me was, "Are you retired?" I didn't know how to answer them. I'd mumble an embarrassed response, hoping they didn't hear me, "I'm a caregiver for my parents. They both have Alzheimer's."

"I commend you! My mom had dementia, and my sister took care of her. I give you credit. You're a saint."

I was amazed how often I heard similar responses. Sometimes, instead of their mom who was afflicted, they said their spouse, aunt, grandmother, father, sibling, or even a good friend. I learned I wasn't alone. There were others in this invisible world who were facing the same challenges every day just like I was. Or, they knew someone who had walked in my shoes. I realized I was finally doing something that had a real purpose. I now had a job of the utmost importance. I felt fulfilled. My life had a purpose, to care for my parents as they took care of me when I was younger.

I've had people tell me that few individuals would do what I'm doing, namely care for my parents. This puzzles me. I find it difficult to understand how family members can take such a cavalier attitude towards their family. Why is that? Are people getting so selfish that they can't see beyond their nose and recognize that a loved one could use some help? Has the attitude of my generation, the Baby Boomers (sometimes we are referred to as the *me* generation), consumed the consciousness of multiple generations since us? Has society in general become so self-absorbed, so self-obsessed that the notion of making a sacrifice for a loved one has become as extinct as the West African Black Rhinoceros?[3]

It's so easy to turn a blind eye when you hear or see that someone needs help. I come from a large, extended family, yet only a handful of relatives ever offered words of encouragement or support, and even fewer offered to help. I received more sympathy and kind words from friends and total strangers than I did from my family. Is this how God created us? Is this how God wants us to treat each other? I chose to take care of my parents for a variety of reasons. One reason was I could hear my Aunt Verna, my dad's oldest sister, whispering into my ear from heaven, "It's your responsibility, do the *right* thing!"

For me, the right thing was caring for my parents. Each situation is different. Not everyone can care for their loved one, and not everyone can afford to place a loved one in a facility. However, what is the best thing for the loved one who is afflicted? I truly believe, if it's possible, keeping your loved one home, surrounded by family, is the best solution for them and for you. Interact with your loved one—interaction and engagement is so important for them. Don't rob yourself of those last opportunities with your loved one. It will be challenging at times, but once your loved one is gone, you can't get this time back. In reality, there is no replay button like you see on television. This is real life, a one-shot deal. Make the most of those opportunities with loved ones while they are still alive, even if they don't recognize you. I can't emphasize this enough.

Caregiving Tips from the Heart

Caregiving Tip #11:

Once in a while, your loved one will appear normal. No, they haven't recovered. No one recovers from Alzheimer's or dementia. It's how the disease sometimes plays tricks and provides little pockets of lucid moments. My best advice— treasure those moments—make the most of them and see these moments as gifts from God. They normally don't last long or occur very often.

Caregiving Tip #12:

Accept that your loved one won't be the same person they were before. Accept that your loved one won't be able to rationalize like they used to, communicate in the same way, remember life events, or recognize family or friends. Your loved one will eventually not even know you. *Never* forget that your loved one is *still* a person who is deserving of love, compassion, dignity, empathy, and respect. Your loved one won't be the same person you used to know, but *you* are the same person they used to know. *Never* forget that!

Caregiving Tip #13:

Be vigilant of your loved one's health. Urinary tract infections, or UTIs, can have devasting effects on Alzheimer's or dementia patients. What may appear as a drastic, sudden decline in their cognitive condition could actually be the result of a UTI. Don't be shy in consulting their physician if you see a sudden change in your loved one's behavior.

CHAPTER 19

New Home, New Neighbors, & A New Beginning

January 2018

God does work in mysterious ways. Since Matthew died, I was so busy caring for my parents and selling our home, I didn't have time to crash and burn. And I would have. The sad thing is my parents had no idea what a blessing they were to me at this time in the same way the pups were a blessing as well. We started the new year, 2018, living in a new county, new city, new home, and with new neighbors. Everything a new widow wasn't supposed to do, I did.

Uncle Ron moved in with us the middle of January. He was a good sport. I wasn't always the most congenial person to be around in those days. My callous attitude was bigger than the

Grand Canyon and as nasty as a rattlesnake. In my mind, I was doing great. I was getting out of bed each morning, taking the pups potty, caring for my parents, cooking meals, doing laundry, shopping, paying bills, unpacking, and trying to find places for everything. You name it—I was doing it. My world was nonstop fun. Or, as Mom would say, bullshit!

My new neighbors were a God-send for me just like Mary Ann had been two years earlier. So many offered to help. The sad thing was I often couldn't remember their names or didn't know how to contact them. They meant well and that meant so much to me. The folks, Ron, and I would attend pot luck dinners at the clubhouse and on occasion, after I put Mom to bed, I attended the monthly movies in the theater. Life was taking on a new routine, and I was slowly adjusting to not working a traditional 8:00 a.m. to 5:00 p.m. job. Instead, I was on duty 24/7.

I was trying to do it all, and my all just wasn't good enough. All the literature about caregiving states *Don't try to do everything yourself*, that's the direct route to caregiver burnout. It was annoying me not to have a computer room to store the unpacked boxes. Boxes took up every single available space, especially my bedroom and bathroom. Many nights, I slept on the couch in the living room because I was using my bed as a table to unpack boxes while trying to figure out where the hell to put everything. Other nights, I got out of bed to go to the bathroom and tripped over boxes in the narrow path I created between my bed and the bathroom. Thank goodness I'd gotten rid of what I could *before* we moved.

How can people live with so much crap? But my crap was good crap! Mementoes Matthew left behind, photo albums, incomplete manuscripts he'd written, treasures from his police career, and theatre work. The crap I couldn't get rid of held the passages of my Matthew life. I couldn't part with anything that hinted of Matthew, whether it was during our life together or, as Matthew liked to say, "BV," as in, *before Vicki*. I treasured every single scrap of paper or greeting card, anything he wrote on. I saved it like I was holding onto the Holy Grail. I even came across an old grocery list written in Matthew's distinct script tucked inside a book. I saved that as well. I couldn't will myself to throw anything away with his writing on it. If I did, I felt like I was getting rid of a part of him. Something buried deep within my soul compelled me not to.

For me, it was part of my mourning process. When we moved into our new home, I placed his hairbrush next to my bathroom sink. The last pair of sneakers Matthew wore now sit on the floor next to my bed, and his blue bathrobe found a home on the back of my bedroom door. I use it frequently when I take the pups out. I created a Matthew shrine on top of his armoire. I carefully arranged his treasured keepsakes, including his urn, wooden treasure box, a cross of palm leaves Matthew made months before he died, and photographs of his mom, sisters, and his dear Irish friend, Charlie Cavanaugh.

Each morning, I prayed to this holy shrine. I prayed that this was only a dream, and I'd wake up and Matthew would be snoring loudly next to me. Kipper would be at the end of our bed, and Katy would be snuggled behind my knees. No matter how much I prayed, I woke up to the same realization as I did the day before. I felt like I was in the movie, *Groundhog Day*, repeating the same scene over and over with the exact same conclusion. It was a conclusion I firmly didn't want to live with or accept.

I was surprised at the range of emotions I felt as a widow. One minute I was fine and the next, I had silent tears suddenly erupting from my eyes. I couldn't predict when this would happen. It was like someone flipped a switch. After I put Mom to bed at night, I sat on the screened porch with the pups, listened to Matthew's treasured Irish music, and drank a glass of wine. It was my refuge. Those precious minutes brought me peace, acceptance, and renewal. I did a lot of soul searching during this time. I eventually realized God's plan made sense. If Matthew was never going to get better, it would have been extremely difficult to care for him and my parents at the same time. I never questioned God or got angry with Him, not like I did immediately before or after Matthew died. I was smart enough to realize I needed

His help now more than ever. I didn't want to tempt fate by not trusting in God's plan. He brought me this far. I knew in my heart He wouldn't let me down now.

Every month, on the 19th, I was a basket case. I relived what had happened that same date just a year before and compared it to the present. The 19th symbolized to me I was moving further and further away from the one I loved. Each day, every minute took me farther away from my treasured memories. I came to hate the 19th every month as it loomed its ugly, forbidding head. I felt like I was spiraling into space, totally untethered, forced to face a reality I reluctantly didn't want to face. Nights were the worst when I felt like I was aimlessly floating in a void, an empty orbit of nothingness. I did a great job of hiding these feelings. Whenever someone asked me how I was, my normal response was, "I'm hanging in there; it is what it is." I doubted anyone would have listened if I told the truth.

One morning in January, my new neighbor Nancy Casey brought me the local newspaper, the Citrus Chronicle. She pointed to an article that saved my life. It referenced the Key Center of Lecanto, an adult day respite care for those with diminished memory. It was like I was given a lifeline. After a series of phone calls and evaluations, Mom and Dad were both approved to attend the Key Center one day a week. Talk about miracles. For two years before we moved, Mom had been on a waiting list with Elder Options in Hernando County. We'd been in Citrus County less than a month, and my parents were both approved to attend adult respite day care once a week. I came to treasure this day like it was a million bucks, tax free.

When Fridays rolled around, I was as excited as a jumpy, tail wagging, three-month-old frisky puppy. I came to cherish Fridays. Fridays symbolized that magic day of the week where I had seven whole hours to myself. As soon as I dropped Mom and Dad off at the Key Center, knowing they were in competent hands, I hightailed it out of there like a rocket shot into space and hit the road home. Sometimes, the pups and I stopped at the nearby doggy park so they could romp and run to their little hearts content. Once their tongues started to hang from their opened, parched mouths, we headed home, just a short distance away. As they scarfed up water to quench their thirst, I made breakfast, brewed a cup of Café Carmel on the Keurig, and commenced to read the newspaper in utter peace. What heaven! I met friends for lunch, went shopping, ran errands, read, did needlepoint or cross-stitch, and unpacked. But mostly, I caught up on sleep. It's amazing what one day a week can do to rejuvenate your soul!

I've heard people advise against any major changes for those with Alzheimer's. For my parents, the move to Citrus County had no major effect on them. By now, Mom was so far gone cognitively that she was like a happy, little puppy. She followed anyone as long as someone was close by and paying attention to her. Dad learned quickly where the bathroom was and the screened porch. If he wasn't sitting in his recliner in the living room, then he was usually in one of those other locations. I rarely found him in the carport watching traffic drive by. The only room he had a problem with was his bedroom at bedtime. After I gave him his night-time meds and eyedrops, he got up, looked at me, and asked, "Where do I sleep?" Dad always asked the same question every night. At first, I walked him down the hall and opened the door to his bedroom. After a while, I taped a Santa made of felt to his bedroom door, and when he'd ask his perpetual question every night, my response became, "Look for the Santa on the door." It worked every time. He never again retraced his steps back to me in utter confusion.

When we moved into our new home, I purchased Mom a remote-controlled lift chair for Christmas. Before the move, I noticed she was having difficulty getting up from her recliner. She was losing muscle tone in her arms and legs, resulting in no strength to help propel herself up from a sitting position. The remote had a green light and two buttons. One button lifted the chair up, and the other lowered it. I couldn't get her to understand how to use the remote. However, the green light often attracted her attention and proved to be a great tool to distract her when she was having a bad day. Sometimes I found her with the remote

182

in her hand, not knowing what to do with it. She'd randomly press the buttons totally oblivious to what those buttons were actually doing. Mom's chair and two blue recliners, which became Dad and Ron's designated chairs, were placed in a straight row directly in front of the TV in the living room. The kitchen was within easy viewing of the living room where I could cook and still keep an eye on Mom in the living room. Our new living arrangement was working to my advantage. My only concern was I didn't have enough storage.

Dad was usually the first one up in the morning. He got dressed and turned on the TV. As the year progressed, I started noticing Dad was often dressed in the same clothes he wore the day before. He obviously was grabbing the first thing he saw, which were the clothes he discarded the night before. It didn't do any good to tell him to put his clothes in the hamper. By the time he walked down the hall to the door with the Santa taped on it, he totally forgot what I told him seconds earlier. So, I learned to tiptoe into their bedroom at night to check on them and put Dad's dirty clothes into the hamper. Then, I arranged clean clothes on top of the hamper for him to wear the next day. This worked fine with the exception of those rare occasions when he totally disregarded the clean clothes on top of the hamper and pulled out something dirty to wear. Through trial and error, I eventually learned to put a blanket on the top of the hamper and placed his clean clothes on top of the blanket. The blanket seemed to circumvent his digging into the hamper.

It was also about this time shortly after the move when Mom no longer remembered what she called her walker. For the last eight years, she referred to her walker as Tilly, like it was her best friend. Whenever she got up in the morning, the first thing she did was reach for her Tilly. Now, whenever I mentioned Tilly or her walker, she had no idea what I was referring to. I started to notice by late afternoon she'd get up from her chair, wouldn't reach for her walker, but tottered around like a baby taking its first, tentative, unsteady steps. On many occasions, I heard Ron yell out, "She's on the move!" I immediately stopped what I was doing and raced to her side to grab her, hoping I could catch her in time. Thank goodness for Ron's verbal warnings! Dad sat in his recliner, staring blankly at the TV, totally oblivious to what was going on. Or, he was snoozing because he had been up so much the night before due to his sundowning. Either way, Dad was of no help in keeping an eye on Mom when my back was turned.

Dad's attention span was waning. His beloved Michigan State basketball games, and Detroit Tiger baseball games were no longer holding his attention for more than a couple of minutes. The days were gone when Dad sat on the edge of his chair, his eyes glued to the TV with his MSU cap perched proudly on his head. He used to clap and cheer golden plays, lamented and cussed every missed free throw, grumbled under his breath sound advice for Coach Izzo, and sent positive vibes to the team. I started taping the games hoping to play them back later as an electronic Paul sitter for those more frequently occurring occasions when he got bored and walked away from the TV or was in a funky mood. His Alzheimer's and limited vision were robbing him of his key interests. It was disheartening to watch. Dad's world was quickly shrinking. About all he had left were his memories, and even those were slowly fading.

The only thing I found Dad enamored with these days was Spanish TV. I was amazed to see my poor, befuddled Dad with a lopsided, goofy grin on his unshaven face, eyes glued to the TV like a teenager who accidently stumbles upon a porn channel. He had no idea what was going on. He didn't comprehend Spanish, but he was fascinated by the Spanish beauties wearing the tight-fitting sweaters that accentuated their bulging, swollen balloons. For a guy who was 97 years old, he had the libido of a teenager. No wonder he was taking Mom's diaper off at night and waking her up on a whim!

February 2018

February 3 would have been Matthew's 78th earthly birthday. The year before, we had celebrated Matthew's birthday with dear friends as we were trying to recover from our respective illnesses. Now, a short year later, Matthew was gone, and my life didn't come close to resembling what it had been just 365 days before. I spent that Saturday reliving our past, staring at photos and crying until my eyes were red and swollen.

The next day, February 4, was Super Bowl Sunday, and Matthew's beloved hometown team, the Philadelphia Eagles, were playing the New England Patriots in Super Bowl LII at U.S. Bank Stadium in Minneapolis, Minnesota. His family in Philadelphia were circulating texts and Facebook posts, buzzed and excited about the big game. I hinted that I knew the Eagles were going to win. I knew it as well as I knew my own name. How did I know this? Because I knew Matthew would work his new found heavenly magic to secure an Eagles win, something he had hoped to see one day himself. I believed with all my heart the Eagles were going to win. Was it just a coincidence that the Eagles were playing in the Super Bowl just months after Matthew died? Five months before, three strange things happened at my Spring Hill home. Were those mere coincidences too? I didn't think so. Some things you just know are going to happen. The Eagles did win, as I predicted. They beat their arch rival the New England Patriots, 41-33, one of the few bright spots during an otherwise sorrowful and heart aching six months.

Shortly after the Super Bowl, I had a meltdown. What started off as an occasional occurrence became a daily one. Mom woke up in the morning without her diaper on. Her bed and nightclothes were soiled. Sometimes, I had a devil of a time trying to get her poopy, peed nightgown over her head to get her cleaned and dressed. And there were a few times I searched high and low for her missing diaper and couldn't find it. Despite being awake so much during the night, I never caught Dad in the act of removing her diaper. Stripping her bed and washing her soiled clothes and sheets was becoming a morning ritual. *And I didn't like it!*

On this particular overcast winter morning, I discovered Mom's diaper was missing. Her bed was filthy, the worst I've ever seen it. That's when I lost it. I detonated like a stick of dynamite.

One moment I was calm and collected, looking forward to a new day. The next second, I exploded like a pop bottle that'd been shaken too much. A string of curse words—some I made up—peppered the soundwaves like a TV with its volume jacked up to the loudest decibels. I ranted! I raved! I cursed Matthew, and I even cursed God! I was ready to do battle, and my arsenal of choice was every single swear word I could think of. Nothing I tried to circumvent this from happening worked. Dad was turning into one sneaky, little devil each night, and I was tired of cleaning up his mess every morning. Poor Mom had no idea what was going on. And of course, he never remembered removing her diaper. His standard reply was, "It must be Phyllis."

I'd put multiple diapers on her, but the next morning, I found each diaper flung around their bedroom. When I put Mom to bed with her pants on over her diapers, those pants, along with the diapers, looked like they'd been tossed willy nilly throughout their room. I tried adult plastic pants over her diaper with regular pants over those. Regardless, I found the same crime scene every morning, diapers and clothes tossed all over like a teenager's bedroom. I didn't have an extra bedroom for Phyllis to sleep in. We had just enough beds for the four of us. The couch would be too uncomfortable for her, and I didn't want her sleeping in my bedroom with all the boxes piled up waiting to be unpacked.

I must admit it felt good to reach my boiling point. I didn't realize I had so much pent up rage locked up inside of me. I didn't know what to do, and I knew I didn't want to be washing her sheets and nightclothes every day. Plus, I was concerned about the effects on her skin of sleeping in urine and sometimes feces-soiled sheets. After a few minutes, I cooled down and a thought occurred to me. I attended an Alzheimer's conference about a month ago and mixed in with the literature was a flyer that talked about the Alzheimer's Hotline. Their phones are manned 24/7. I was in utter desperation. I had never called a hotline before, but drastic measures called for drastic actions. It took me a couple of hours to finally make the call. I was grappling with myself, feeling foolish about my dilemma. How do I explain what's going on? They're going to think I'm making this up. I'm going to feel foolish, let alone embarrassed, complaining about my dad's over-excited libido. But that little voice inside my brain kept asking me, *Do you really want to be washing clothes every morning?* That practical side of me won out. I called the Alzheimer's Hotline.

Now, I wish I had called the Alzheimer's Hotline sooner. It would have saved me months of aggravation and turmoil. The first person I spoke to was kind and sympathetic. I explained my problem, and she connected me to a specialist. The specialist was knowledgeable and made several suggestions. After each recommendation, I stated, "I already thought of that, tried it, and it didn't work," or "I don't have another room or bed for Mom to sleep in." After an hour, the specialist admitted she was stymied and wanted to speak to someone else. She promised she'd call me back within an hour, and she did. We spoke for another hour. There was no time during our two phone calls that she rushed me or made me feel like I was an incompetent caregiver. She actually commended me on how I had approached this problem. Her final recommendation was adult onesies. Adult onesies are pajamas with a zipper in the back rather than in the front, an adult version of baby onesies. I'd never heard of those. She recommended an online catalogue, and I thanked her profusely for her recommendation and her time. The next day, I contacted Buck and Buck catalog sales, ordered four onesies for Mom, which arrived within days. The first morning after I dressed Mom in her new onesie pajamas, I said a silent prayer as I walked into her bedroom, wondering what I'd find. Miraculously, her bed was clean, dry, and most importantly, her diaper was still securely wrapped around her little fanny. The case of the disappearing diaper had been solved. Thank you Dr. Watson, aka the Alzheimer's Hotline!

Both pups reacted to Matthew's death in different ways. Then, with the move shortly thereafter, their world once again changed. I didn't anticipate Katy would change like she did. Before Matthew died, she was carefree and frisky. She was the alpha dog to Kipper's beta, and Matthew was alpha to her beta.

Now, she was more subdued like she was trying to be a good girl so her beloved mommy wouldn't leave her like her daddy did. Several days after we moved, Katy stopped sleeping behind my knees. Instead, she curled up like a little bundle of fur and slept on Matthew's pillow. Kipper, who I took to the emergency vet twenty-two hours after Matthew died because he suffered from bloody vomit and diarrhea, appeared to accept Matthew's dying differently. Kipper no longer sleeps in bed with me, but instead, sleeps in the hallway outside our bedroom doors, like a sentinel who is guarding his castle from marauding invaders.

Now, every time I walk the pups and they see a person of the male persuasion, they run up to him, dragging me along as their tails wag looped-d-loops. Kipper leans against the guy's leg, begging for attention and hopefully some belly rubs. Katy is more subdued. She stands quietly, almost reluctantly, as if she knows this isn't her daddy. But she plays along since her adopted brother Kipper loves this game so much. Whenever I press the key fob for my car, the pups perk up. The sound mimics what they used to hear every time their daddy came home and locked his car. They are still mourning their daddy; their actions speak volumes. It's as if every male they see is their long, lost daddy. How do I tell them their daddy isn't coming back? On those occasions when I leave them home to run errands, Katy stares at me with such sorrowful, big, brown eyes like she doesn't expect to ever see me again. Meanwhile, Kipper scratches the door, beseeching me to reconsider and take them with me. After a couple of months, they relaxed a bit and accepted that mommy has to leave them once in a while, but they obviously don't like it.

Dad's world continued to decline due to his diminished eyesight from macular degeneration and glaucoma. He was no longer able to create beautiful stained-glass objects of art, read his treasured books, do needlepoint, or counted cross-stitch. When Mom and Dad first moved to Florida in 1992 and they were living in a two-bedroom rental waiting for their house to be built, Dad taught himself counted cross-stitch. He was bored and needed something to keep him busy. One day, he went out to the garage, found the box with the craft kits, selected a Christmas sampler, and taught himself how to do counted cross-stitch. That was the first of many kits he worked on through the years. Dad did beautiful work; several have become treasured family heirlooms.

Dad came to enjoy counted cross-stitch and needlepoint so much, he'd spend hours in his hobby room stitching intricate designs, sometimes with over thirty colors. I came home from work one day in 2015, went out to the garage to put trash in the bin, lifted the lid, and I found an opened cross-stitch kit in the garbage. I was furious and knew who the culprit was. Mom hadn't worked on kits for several years, but at that time, Dad was in his element stitching. I had a drawer in his hobby room where I kept kits I hoped to work on one day. I'd given Dad cart blanche to work any kits he wanted. I walked up to him and asked, "Why did you put this in the trash? It's a new kit." Dad looked sheepish, turned his head away from me, and refused to answer. I wasn't sure if he didn't remember putting it in the trash—his dementia was making it difficult for him to comprehend and work the stitching charts—or, did he decide he didn't like the design and discarded it on a whim? I wasn't sure if his temper got the better of him when he realized the kit intimidated him, or was there something within his psyche he was battling within himself? In all probability, it was a combination of a too challenging kit, decreasing eyesight, and diminished comprehension as to why he no longer had it within himself to do something he enjoyed so much in the past. It's things like this that helped bring the truth home to me. Dad's Alzheimer's was progressing, and his quiet, introverted persona wouldn't admit to having problems or acknowledge he needed help. The SISU that was inbred in him was creating internal strife he didn't know how to circumvent, acknowledge, or understand.

Since Dad still seemed to have the desire to do counted cross-stitch, I ordered several quick point kits for him. I selected kits with simple designs that consisted of large blocks of limited colors. This worked for a while until he completed the simpler kits in their inventory. Then, I started designing kits for him, using hooked rug canvas, large ply yarn, and a larger-eyed needle. My designs consisted of geometric shapes. I painted the canvas in their respective colors so it would be easier for Dad to distinguish which yarn to use. Dad could easily see the design on the canvas since hooked-rug canvas has larger holes, and he could decipher which yarns to use with the limited number of colors I chose. For a while, he was happy. I created ten kits for him. As soon as Dad completed one, I had the next kit ready for him. It reminded me of an assembly line. Just before we moved to Lou and Ron's in the fall of 2017, I created two kits for him, knowing he'd have lots of free time until we settled into our new home. I wanted to circumvent Dad getting bored. However, it was during this time when he lost total interest in stitching and never again worked another counted cross-stitch kit.

Once we moved to Citrus County, Dad fell in love with the screened porch. I purchased porch furniture that required me to assemble it. I will forever be thankful I was a farmer's granddaughter as a result. When Dad wasn't in the swivel chair gazing at the retention pond, he was stretched out on the loveseat snoozing to his heart's content, enjoying an afternoon siesta. With his compromised cardiovascular system, Dad survived a AAA rupture in 1998, he was always cold. Dad ventured out to the porch on the hottest days, reveling in the sultry temperatures as they warmed his tiring and freezing soul.

Dad had three locations he often congregated to in the house, and he had specific things he did at each location. He gravitated to the screened porch for his naps. His blue recliner in the living room, flanked on both sides by Phyllis' and Ron's chairs, was his TV chair. A rust colored chair in the living room next to the window overlooking the retention pond became his favorite place to spend hours thumbing through family photograph albums. Mom created these photograph albums when they lived in Aura. Dad would sit there and stare at those photographs. He must have been reliving cherished memories of his youth living on the farm, thinking about his siblings and childhood friends who were long passed, lost in his thoughts which only he could relive. I felt sorry for him. You could tell he was perplexed and confused. Dad still remembered some of his family and friends, yet at 97, almost all of those individuals were no longer alive. I saw this same, silent lament portrayed by my grandfather Miller during the last couple of years of his life. As his male friends passed away, he was the lone male in their circle of friends. Most of my dad's family and friends were now long-lost ghosts of the past. They were ghosts to remind him of the inevitable agony of still being alive. He would live with the uncertainty of not knowing when he himself would become a ghost of someone else's past. That person, years from now, will stare at photographs and reminisce about familiar events so hauntingly long ago.

Dad still had his teeth and consistently took very good care of them. He always had dental floss in his pocket, and on many occasions, he pulled out his dental floss, yanked off a string, and started flossing his teeth. It didn't matter who was around or what he was doing. I found used strings of dental floss laying on the floor. I'd grab a tissue, pick up the string, and dispose of it. No matter how often I brought this to Dad's attention, it didn't mean a thing. In his mind, someone else dropped it or he responded, "I didn't know where the trash can was." One afternoon, I picked up five strings of used dental floss found on the floors of the screened porch, living room, hallway, their bedroom, and even the carport. I hated seeing these mangled, white, waxy, strings littering the floor. They looked unsightly, unhygienic, like little stringy worms. But mostly, I was concerned about the pups. I didn't want them to lick the strings up and swallow them.

Dad seldom acknowledged Mom, even though their chairs were side-by-side in the living room. Dad was often bored, while Mom played with her toys. When he did talk to her, it was usually chastising her for her behavior. At least he appeared to know who Mom was, whereas she had no recognition of who he was. Dad and I were people she seemed to know belonged in her world. She couldn't put a name to either of us, and she couldn't remember who we were in relation to herself. As long as you talked to her or interacted with her, she was satisfied and talked gibberish to us. The words that came out of her mouth made no sense, except on those rare occasions when she was evaluated by her case manager and then, miraculously, she could string together a three or four-word sentence that made some sense based on what she was asked. The rest of the time, she made up words. She couldn't identify what she was eating, wearing, or doing. She said words like *buap* or *mugie,* when looking at her shoes, sitting on the toilet, or during Phyllis conversations.

Often, I had no idea what Mom was saying, but I realized that as long as she talked, that was a good sign. Someday her voice will be silent, a signal that she was transitioning to the final stage. Now, her gibberish was welcomed because Mom was communicating, and that's what counted. She wasn't perturbed that I didn't know what she was saying. I responded to her with, "Are you sure about that?" or "I didn't know that." She'd look at me, smile an angelic smile, and we continued our conversation. Mom talked about imaginary images and stories only she could relate to as I nodded along and interjected generic comments at will.

I learned to keep my communication with her to short sentences of three to five words and to give her directions one step at a time. Once she'd complete the first direction, then I gave her the next one. It is impossible for someone with Alzheimer's to comprehend steps all at once. I also started using hand signals, touching her and saying her name to get her attention, followed by pointing in the direction where I needed her to go.

Another key development at this time was I started referring to my parents by their given names. My mom hadn't known who I was for several years. If I called her Mom, she didn't know who I was referring to. She automatically thought of her mother. When I started to call her Phyllis, or used her childhood nickname, Fi Fi, that was when Mom recognized her name and knew I was referring to her. For consistency sake, I started to call my dad Paul at this time as well. It was difficult to tell if he still knew who I was, especially at night when he was sundowning, a time when I definitely knew he had no idea who I was.

Using their first names separated me from my role as their daughter. I shrugged off my daughter role and replaced it with my new caregiver role. Psychologically, it made the changes in their conditions easier for me to deal with. Otherwise, I would have spiraled down into a deep depression as their inevitable futures began to tandem with Matthew's ghost. I wasn't ready for this, but I knew at some point this was inevitable.

Caregiving Tips from the Heart

Caregiving Tip #14:

> When you communicate with your loved one, keep your words to a bare minimum. Use as few words as you can to get your message across.

Caregiving Tip #15:

> When communicating with your loved one, I recommend using hand signals or pointing. For example, I would point to my mom to get her attention, then state, "this way" as I'm pointing to where we were going.

Caregiving Tip #16:

> When giving verbal directions, only give one direction at a time. Once your loved one completes the first direction, verbally give them the next direction. Your loved one no longer has the ability to listen, retain, and follow through on a long list of directions. Providing a long list of directions will only confuse and frustrate your loved one and you.

Caregiving Tip #17:

> There will be times when you are tempted to argue with your loved one to make your point. *Don't* argue! It's pointless. You will only frustrate yourself. On those occasions, find something to distract your loved one's attention or take them on a short car ride.

CHAPTER 20

One Last Birthday Gift

March 2018

When married to an Irishman, it's hard not to become a little Irish yourself. As March roared in like a lion in 2018, I looked forward to St. Patrick's Day more than my birthday. With Matthew gone, my birthday didn't seem to have much significance anymore. It felt like any other day. There was no one to help me celebrate, no one to bake a birthday cake for me, no one to wish me happy birthday, or give me a birthday hug. My parents didn't know it was my birthday. Even their birthdays were lost to them. I felt alone and abandoned, adrift, floating along with no clear destination. I was wandering at a slow, tedious pace, following the eb and tide like a person blindly going through life with no feelings or emotions. I existed day by day. In other words, I was basking being the center of attention at my pity party of one. Whereas with St. Patrick's Day, I could wave my

Irish flag, immerse myself in Irish music, and relive our trip to Ireland, enjoying memories that warmed my soul.

The night before my birthday, I had been reminiscing about some of the trips Matthew and I had taken through the years. We planned many trips in conjunction with my birthday or our anniversary. Some were forgettable while others, like our trip to Ireland in May 2011 to celebrate our 15th anniversary, was unforgettable. I remember the nights we sat around the dining room table, giddy like two school children as we planned that trip. It was a trip Matthew had been wanting to take me on since the day we were married. I pointed to places on the map of Ireland. I dog eared pages in tourist books extolling the historical significance of places I dreamt we'd visit. I hoped their historical significance in Irish history and the volumes these locations spoke of Irish culture would convince Matthew we needed to add these Irish landmarks to our must-see list. Matthew smiled, and in that voice I loved so much, he said, "I don't know if we'll have time to do that."

Matthew's idea of touring Ireland was to hop in a car bright and early every morning and just drive all day. My idea was a little different. I preferred some of the touristy places like touring the House of Waterford Crystal, country castles, museums, and churches. We both agreed upon the Cliffs of Moher, the Ring of Kerry, and the towns of Killarney and Dingle. Matthew laughed when I told him, "And we have to go to at least three pubs to hear Irish music!" Yes, we were ecstatic planning that trip. The planning is sometimes just as exciting as the trip itself.

In this case, the trip was everything I'd imagined and much, much more. The scenery was breathtaking—panoramic rolling fields and bubbling brooks, rugged coastlines, and an endless expanse of so many shades of green. The people were friendly, we were together, I was spellbound by everything I saw, and most importantly, we were very happy with no interruptions to get in the way. Those two weeks in Ireland were some of the best weeks of my life. We were destined to take that trip! I fell deeper in love with my husband, and I also became enamored of Ireland. The last two years he was alive, we talked about taking another trip to Ireland. We looked forward to seeing more spectacular Irish scenery and making countless additional memories to reminiscence about later on. But he got sick, and then...time...just...ran...out.

Sunday morning, March 11, my birthday, whoop-de-do, big deal. Who was I kidding? I could have stayed in bed with the covers pulled over my head. Bah humbug was how I felt about this day. If not for the pups and my folks, I would have done just that, stayed in bed. My neighbors, Nancy and Shirley, stopped by with greetings, flowers, and cupcakes. I was touched by their thoughtfulness, but I'd rather still be in bed feeling sorry for myself.

Later that morning, as I checked Facebook acknowledging birthday greetings from my family and friends, I saw a post from Matty, Matthew's oldest son. Matty was at the Emerald Society's St. Patrick's Day Parade in Philadelphia. I had forgotten that the parade is always held the Sunday *before* St. Patrick's Day. This year, the parade fell on my birthday, March 11. Talk about a coincidence! A minute later, I read a post from Debbie, Matty's wife, "Dad's mentioned in the parade." Reading those five words caught my attention. Deb also included a video, which I immediately clicked on. One of the first people I saw in the video was Matty proudly walking by the camera, with a big beaming smile on his face. He waved enthusiastically to the crowd, decked out in green, white, and orange. I could also hear the voiceover of a female commentator telling her television audience, "This year's parade is in memory of a past president, former Board member, and a Philadelphia police officer who passed away last year." My eyes instantly welled up with tears when I heard those words. My heart pounded within my chest with unexpected adrenaline as my mind soared with pride. I couldn't focus on anything else but what I just heard. I knew who she was referring to; I knew who the parade was being dedicated to...my Matthew...oh, how I wish he was alive to enjoy this honor!

Matthew was very proud of his years as the President of the Emerald Society of Philadelphia. He treasured those memories, achievements, and accomplishments, which he held dear. His Irish descent defined his soul. I listened to that video over and over throughout the day, crying each time. My emotions ran the gamut from joy to sorrow to happiness for this posthumous honor of the one I loved. I reposted the link on Facebook so my friends and family could learn of this momentous honor. As tears bathed my face, cascading like a waterfall of love, I couldn't help feeling I'd received one final birthday gift from Matthew. I had been dreading this first birthday without him. Now, I couldn't believe he was being honored on this day of all days—my birthday. This particular parade falling on my birthday couldn't be a coincidence.

After the episode the previous year before we moved, I no longer believed in coincidences. I could feel Matthew's arms embracing me, holding me tight, whispering softly in my ear, telling me he loved me and missed me. I envisioned reaching my hands up to his face, where I could feel the silkiness of his hair as my fingers caressed the back of his neck. It was the most wonderful birthday gift I could have received. Later, Debbie posted another video which identified Matthew by name as the person the parade was dedicated to. Thank you, Harry Marnie, President of the Philadelphia Emerald Society, for the most wonderful of gifts. You will never comprehend how much this honor meant to this Finnish-born/Irish-adopted colleen to have the parade dedicated in memory of her Mo fhíorghra.[4] I know Matthew was watching from a heavenly front row seat, smiling from ear to ear, his chest puffed outward brimming with Irish pride, a Jeffie jauntily perched upon his head as he merrily waved an Irish tricolor! Erin Go Braugh!

Later that night as I crawled into bed, I looked at a photograph on my nightstand. It was a photograph I look at each night of a time when Matthew was healthy. It's a photograph that captures our radiant smiles, never dreaming in a few short years our lives would forever be changed. Looking at the photograph,

I also couldn't help but reflect upon this day, a day I had been dreading. It was a day I couldn't help but compare to other birthdays in the past. Yet despite everything, this day turned out so much better than I expected. I received one last, wonderous birthday gift from my beloved, a birthday gift that the whole city of Philadelphia was witness to. But they had no idea how much it meant for someone over a thousand miles away. As I looked closer at the photograph, my eyes focused on the words encircling the frame, an Irish blessing Matthew loved to recite. I closed my eyes, smiling as I relived this day. I could have sworn I heard Mathew's voice whispering those words I knew by heart, words that warmed my soul, words I came to love and hold dear since the day we were married.

> May the road rise to meet you.
> May the wind be always at your back.
> May the sun shine warm upon your face.
> May the rains fall soft upon your fields.
> And until we meet again,
> May God hold you in the palm of His hand.[5]
> —Unknown

CHAPTER 21

Don't Underestimate the Value of a Support Group

Before I became a caregiver, I didn't have much respect for support groups. I didn't see the point of them and being a stubborn Finlander that I am, I didn't think I needed one. Hospice and my church both offered grievance support services after Matthew died. I declined them both. I was too busy, didn't have anyone to watch Mom when these scheduled group sessions took place, and based on my way of thinking, support groups were for sissies, and I was no sissy. I was brought up to believe we don't air our dirty laundry to anyone. We can handle our problems, so why talk to someone else? And that's how I handled the mini-crises that invaded my life from time to time. By the time my birthday came around in 2018, Matthew had been gone for seven months. I was busy taking care of my parents, trying unsuccessfully to get the house in order, feeding and loving the pups, and doing all the other household chores. With Paul's sundowning at night, I wasn't getting much sleep either.

The highlight of my week was Fridays when Paul and Phyllis went to the Key Center of Lecanto. I lived for Fridays! We were getting by; it wasn't perfect but nothing ever is. In other words, I was going non-stop like I did before I quit my job. The only difference was I now felt there was a true purpose in what I was doing. Before, I grudgingly went to a job every day for a paycheck without feeling any sense of satisfaction in what I was doing. I knew in my heart I was doing the right thing. That's why I moved from California to Florida in 1993, in anticipation my parents might need me one day. The time came when my parents needed help and with no one else to help them, who better than me to provide the help they so desperately needed? And most importantly, it was the *right* thing *for me* to do!

It was sometime in March when I learned of a dementia caregiver support group a few miles from our home in Citrus County. Two groups meet at the same time. Caregivers meet for two hours, providing a forum to ask questions, lament to the group, and sometimes even getting a shoulder to cry on. At the same time, those who we care for meet in a room across the hall. Volunteers provide supervision, activities, and once a month sing-a-longs. The support group is called Memory Lane, and it proved to be another God-send for me. It soon won over the non-believer I was. A support group is a must for anyone who has a problem or is in need of information to help make their world a little easier.

Memory Lane is sponsored by the First United Methodist Church in Homosassa, run by the caring soul of Karen Kline and her troop of smiling volunteers. Karen has been responsible for providing numerous opportunities for caregivers, like myself, to gain valuable information about Alzheimer's, dementia, and caregiving. Thanks to Karen, I completed and graduated from a Savvy Caregiver course, provided by Elder Options for Alzheimer's and dementia caregivers. Karen always informed our group of upcoming lectures by such knowledgeable Alzheimer's experts as Debbie Selsavage and Gary LeBlanc. I could not have gotten through the past year of caregiving if not for the help, encouragement, and friendships of my loving Memory Lane support group. We celebrated triumphs, cried when members passed away, and supported each other when in doubt or confusion. We shared the information we gleaned through the school of hard knocks. Several of the *Caregiving Tips from the Heart* contained within this book was information my support group shared with each other.

Attending our respective Monday afternoon meetings, Phyllis was always gung-ho because she loved car rides despite never having any idea where she was going. Paul, on the other hand, was always disgruntled when I pulled up to the church. As soon as I parked the car, he took one look at the building and asked, "Where are we?" I replied, "We're at a church. I have a meeting inside, and it's too hot for you to sit in the car for a couple of hours. You can sit inside where it's cool and comfortable." That reply placated him, and Paul grudgingly got out of the car as I got Phyllis' walker out and assisted her inside. I guided them down the festively painted hallway into their meeting room as the volunteers warmly welcomed. Then, I walked across the hall to attend my caregivers' support meeting.

Paul and Phyllis always enjoyed the sing-a-longs. It's amazing, those with Alzheimer's can remember lyrics and songs from times past yet can't remember who their loved ones are or identify the foods they ate. The magic of music proved to be a soothing lullaby on many occasions when Phyllis was having a bad day or when Paul was so bored all he wanted to do was curl up and sleep. Music, at those times, was an elixir that regained, if only for a short time, the losses that haunted their evaporating memories.

As I alluded to earlier, it was helpful to know I wasn't the only person going through this journey of caregiving. There are so many others, like myself, who are caring for a loved one. And despite the vast information that is now available at our fingertips, thanks to the internet, there are still persons who are caring for a loved one with limited information and with no one else to assist them. Or, as I like to refer to it, "caregiving as an island." I can understand their dilemma. I was there myself, especially during those early years shortly after Matthew and I moved in with my parents in 2008. I was working full-time, and for two years I travelled for my job. I was coordinating fundraising events, trying to provide Matthew some *us* time, and squeezing in family time with my parents, errands, housecleaning, and preparing for holidays and family events. I did all of that while caregiving for my parents. It wasn't easy. Most of the time I felt like I was suffocating. When I could, I tried to educate myself, but I was in denial regarding Mom's condition. In those days, it was so easy to pretend that this would all go away, that it was a passing phase. I thought after a couple of months Mom would get better, be her old self, and we'd laugh about it later over a glass of wine.

If you are a caregiver, don't underestimate the fact that you need help, whether you want to admit it or not. Sometimes caregivers aren't aware there are resources available to them. My advice to anyone reading this book: if you know someone who is caring for a loved one, please reach out to them. They need your help whether they realize it or not. You can help them with caregiving, researching services available in their area, providing information on Alzheimer's or dementia, and giving them the contact number for the Alzheimer's Hotline. You can also provide information and phone numbers for local support groups, research respite care services in their area, or, most importantly, be available to provide a friendly, reassuring smile and friendship.

A common malaise of caregivers, which can be circumvented, is a feeling of being overwhelmed where they reach the point they don't know what to do or how to do it anymore. Some of these individuals are older, less in-tuned to modern technology, and don't have the vast information that's now available through the internet. Others may feel a stigma of shame regarding the issues they face each day as caregivers. Shame or embarrassment are two of the worst enemies a caregiver can face. Caregivers need a break throughout the week. Respite care is essential so caregivers can feel normal, less stressed, and less overwhelmed of their responsibilities.

Believe it or not, there are still older people in this world who follow the ancient dictates adhered to from the beginning of the twentieth century. They believe if someone has dementia, they should be sequestered in a room and their presence should not be acknowledged to others. This is one of the worst things to do to a person with Alzheimer's or any form of dementia—they need social interaction. I believe social interaction on a daily basis coupled with exercise will slow down the cognitive decline in a person with Alzheimer's. Mom blossomed when Mary Ann was a constant in her life, between 2016-2017. Mary Ann talked to her and took Mom for walks around the block. When I took over Mom's care 24/7, I didn't always have the time to spend with Mom like I should have, and her daily walks ceased around this time as well. I was mourning my husband, trying to sell our home, sorting and packing, and then unpacking once we moved to our new home. It took me longer to do everything because I was trying to juggle watching Mom while trying to accomplish other things each day. I should have done more for Mom at that time, but there wasn't enough of me to go around. I will forever chastise myself for not doing enough to try to slow down the progression of Mom's disease.

If you know someone with a therapy dog, I encourage weekly visits for your loved one. This type of interaction is very helpful. I've seen stories on TV about individuals with Alzheimer's who were not *dog people* before. However, once afflicted with Alzheimer's and introduced to a therapy dog, their attitude toward dogs changed. They started to look forward to the dog's weekly visits. If you have small children, perhaps a weekly visit will be beneficial for your loved one as another form of social interaction. As the disease progresses, our loved one's regress to an earlier age—oftentimes small children and Alzheimer's patients are socially at the same level of cognitive development.

I've learned through my journey of caregiving that once that first door of support is opened, other resources, with time, become available as well. Sometimes, we just don't know where to look. Our minds aren't always attuned to recognize these as resources, or we ignored any reference to these resources before because we had no immediate need of them at the time. Situations change, just as life changes. Don't be afraid to network with your friends, family, acquaintances, physicians, and church. You never know what resources they may be aware of that could provide information and assistance. I learned not to be shy. Admit your situation loud and clear. Someone will hear you, listen to you, and point you in the right direction for help and valuable information. Don't be an island. Instead, grasp the resources available to you like you're holding on to a life preserver. Each encounter along your caregiving journey will help make your world of caregiving a little easier to endure, accept, and appreciate.

Caregiving Tips from the Heart

Caregiving Tip #18:

Once you become a caregiver, you need as much help as you can get. Don't be shy about letting family and friends know about your loved one's condition. Don't hesitant accepting their help no matter what they offer.

Caregiving Tip #19:

Your attitude as a caregiver is so important. If you are resentful, angry, or feel put upon as you're caring for your loved one, your loved one will pick up on your attitude. Try to remember they are slowly dying, that's the only outcome for anyone with Alzheimer's. Try to be kinder and more understanding. Try to put yourself in their shoes. The old adage, "How would you want to be treated if that was you," might help you with an attitude adjustment, if needed.

Caregiving Tip #20:

Always remember, your loved one didn't ask to get dementia or Alzheimer's. They are the *victim* of this disease. Their illness has created lots of problems and letdowns for them as well as it has for you. Be kind and help them with their disappointments, their outbursts of frustration, and their neediness.

CHAPTER 22

Alzheimer's and Caregiving

A Caregiver's Bill of Rights

I have the right:

- To take care of myself. This is not an act of selfishness. It will give me the capability of taking better care of my loved one.

- To seek help from others even though my loved one may object. I recognize the limits of my own endurance and strength.

- To maintain facets of my own life that does not include the person I care for, just as I would if he or she were healthy. I know that I do everything that I reasonably can for this person, and I have the right to do some things just for myself.

- To get angry, be depressed, and express other difficult feelings occasionally.

- To reject any attempts by my loved one (either conscious or unconscious) to manipulate me through guilt, and/or depression.

- To receive consideration, affection, forgiveness, and acceptance for what I do, from my loved ones, for as long as I offer these qualities in return.

- To take pride in what I am accomplishing and to applaud the courage it has sometimes taken to meet the needs of my loved one.

- To protect my individuality and my right to make a life for myself that will sustain me in the time when my loved one no longer needs my full-time help.

- To expect and demand that as new strides are made in finding resources to aid physically and mentally impaired persons in our country, similar strides will be made towards aiding and supporting caregivers.

—Jo Horne, *Caregiving: Helping an Aging Loved One*, 1985[6]

Every 65 seconds someone in the United States develops Alzheimer's, the most common form of dementia.[7] One in three American seniors will die as a result of Alzheimer's or another form of dementia, that's more than the number of deaths combined of breast cancer and prostate cancer.[8] After diagnosis, the average person can live between four to eight years, maybe even longer. Currently, there is no cure for Alzheimer's. It's the sixth leading cause of death in the United States. Pretty scary statistics, aren't they? As a caregiver, I had a front-row seat to what this disease is capable of, how it affects a person's life, and how it pulverizes dreams for an innocent victim's future. And yes, as I write this, there is the underlying thought in the back of my mind that I, too, may become another Alzheimer's statistic one day. For these reasons, I can't help but reflect upon the future of Alzheimer's and dementia. Specifically, I have three main concerns. First, the quality of life for those with Alzheimer's and dementia. Second, the quality of life for those who care for a loved one with Alzheimer's or dementia. Third, the lack of short-term respite care facilities available in many areas of the United States.

According to the Alzheimer's Association, there are currently five million Americans afflicted with Alzheimer's. But there are people who have Alzheimer's who haven't been diagnosed or counted, so the numbers of Americans currently living with Alzheimer's is in all probability higher. For years before my mom was diagnosed and while I was her caregiver, she was living with Alzheimer's, but we didn't know it. During those early undiagnosed years, Mom was an undisclosed statistic. How many in the United States and throughout the world unknowingly have Alzheimer's or dementia, and thus are undisclosed statistics?

By 2050, the Alzheimer's Association predicts there will be 15 million Americans afflicted with Alzheimer's. That correlates to a new case of Alzheimer's every 33 seconds by 2050.[9] It could be your mother, father, grandparent, aunt, uncle, beloved friend, or neighbor. Maybe it'll be that person you see each Sunday at church in the third pew from the front. It could be a co-worker, boss, former teacher, or your favorite sports star. Alzheimer's doesn't discriminate against income, ethnicity, race, age, health, wealth, or education.

No one is immune from Alzheimer's or dementia. Alzheimer's is a disease that doesn't play favorites. A person's credentials or achievements won't buy them a *Get Out of Alzheimer's* card. If only it was that easy, so many individuals might still be with us today. The list of well known, accomplished people who have succumbed to Alzheimer's or dementia is staggering. In all likelihood, you will recognize several names from the following list: Ronald Reagan, Robin Williams, Gordie Howe, Rosa Parks, James Stockdale, Patty Berg, Malcolm Young, Janet Lee Bouvier, William Asher, Eni Blyton, Archer Martin, Imogene Coca, Vincent Minnelli, Robert Kearns, Briggs Cunningham, Dean Smith, Barry Goldwater, Don Cornelius, Margaret Rutherford, Claude Shannon, Etta James, Neil Simon, Enoch Powell, Perry Como, Otto Preminger,

Floyd Patterson, Norma Shearer, Molly Picon, Abe Burrows, Dana Andrews, Darlanne Fluegel, Margaret Thatcher, Omar Sharif, Pauline Phillips, Adolfo Suarez, Willem DeKooning, Peter Falk, Rita Haworth, Alfred Van Vogt, Aaron Copeland, Pat Summitt, Louis Feraud, Thomas Dorsey, Irving Schulman, Ross MacDonald, Tom Fears, Jack Lord, Raul Silva Henriquez, James Brooks, Joyce Chen, Bill Quackenbush, Iris Murdoch, Harold Wilson, John Douglas French, Edmund O'Brien, Terry Pratchett, James Doohan, Betty Schwartz, Mabel Albertson, Marv Owen, Rudolph Bing, Joe Adcock, Arlene Francis, Sugar Ray Robinson, Carroll Campbell, Burgess Meredith, John Mann, Mervyn Leroy, Eddie Albert, Glen Campbell, Kay Swift, Norman Rockwell, Mike Frankovich, James Stewart, Estelle Getty, Charles Bronson, Charlton Heston, Casey Kasem, Sparky Anderson, David Cassidy, and E.B. White.[10]

All of the above led productive lives in their chosen fields. All made credible contributions to life. Their names are etched in history books, sports lists, and many have won prestigious awards. They laughed! They loved! They enjoyed their distinguished careers. They spent time with their family and friends. And each left behind loved ones whose lives were shaken, disheartened, and traumatized by the disease. Add the name of a person you hold dear in your heart because we all know someone who has fallen victim to Alzheimer's or dementia. We cannot help but be humbled, saddened, and disheartened. These diseases rob the affected person of their memories, accomplishments, achievements, and recognition. At the same time, there is no cure. The only certainty is death.

Anyone and everyone is a possible victim of these diseases that rob the innocent person of their capacity to function, rationalize, communicate, empathize, sympathize, and love. I'd like to believe that my memories will be what comforts me as I ease into my golden years. If my body slowly fails me and it's no longer possible to enjoy hobbies, activities, or associations with loved ones, then if my mind erases my memories, too, will this be quality of life? It's the only quality of life someone with Alzheimer's or dementia has. The saving grace is they either are so confused they aren't aware of what's taking place, or they've advanced into the later stages of dementia whereby they no longer have any memories to reflect upon.

Quality of life for a person with Alzheimer's, or any form of dementia, is defined in different ways, depending on the person directly involved. For those with Alzheimer's or dementia, many continue living in their homes cared for by family or friends. If this means the caregiver adjusts her or his life to care for their loved one at home, I commend you. It's a difficult but rewarding journey to undertake. Sometimes, we need to make sacrifices in order to look ourselves in the mirror at night. For others, their only option is to place their loved one in a facility, and hopefully the family doesn't shut the door on their loved one's existence in the process.

For many who care for a loved one with Alzheimer's, we do so because the high cost of memory care at a facility is cost-prohibitive, even with Medicare assistance. The *average* cost per person for those with Alzheimer's or dementia receiving Medicare assistance for assisted living, age 65 or older, in 2019 dollars, was approximately $49,000 annually, of this amount almost $11,000 was out of pocket expenses, an amount most Americans cannot afford.[11] It's estimated that 27% of these Alzheimer's or dementia patients, who receive Medicare, also receive Medicaid assistance as well.[12] Those Alzheimer's patients transitioning into the final stage of Alzheimer's often require greater care, ranging from nursing home, semi-private room, or private room, and those average costs range between $85,775 to as high as $100,375 per year.[13] Looking nationally the cost for the care of individuals with Alzheimer's and dementia, age 65 or older, in 2019 was $290 billion.[14] Of this amount, $195 billion was paid by Medicare or Medicaid accounting for 67% while American families shelled out approximately 22% or $63 billion in total out of pocket expenditures.[15] By the year 2030, all Baby Boomers, those born between 1946-1964, will have reached age 65 or older. Baby Boomers, currently, comprise the largest population who serve as caregivers for someone with Alzheimer's or dementia. With life spans increasing, the Baby Boomers will be the majority population the Alzheimer's Association is targeting when they project the cost of Alzheimer's care by 2050, in the United States alone, will be a staggering $1.1 trillion.[16]

Who is going to care for these Baby Boomers with Alzheimer's or dementia? Will the United States have enough caregivers, memory care facilities, or short-term respite care facilities to accommodate this growing need? I don't have to guess at an answer, because all I have to do is look around me. *We do not!* So, America, we need to take our blinders off and acknowledge that we have a problem that's going to bite us in the butt real soon, and do something about it. Our legislators, local, state, and federal, along with our esteemed elected officials have to finally learn how to work together, in bipartisanship, for the betterment of the American people. My fellow citizens, we need to let our voices be heard to let our nation know this problem is looming in the horizon. We can't wait until the problem becomes obvious, like the homeless situation in most of our large, metropolitan cities from coast to coast. At that point, it's impossible for an agreeable solution, and the costs to implement those changes are exorbitant.

Not everyone can sideline their current lives to care for a loved one. However, I recommend if you place your loved one in a facility, place them in a facility close to where you live. Don't drop them off, close the door to their existence, and never visit. That's the coward's way out, the family that doesn't want to be bothered. It would be so easy. But ask yourself, if your roles were reversed, would your loved one help you? I've often wondered if my parents were healthy and I was the one with Alzheimer's, would my parents care for me? Definitely—it would never have occurred to them not to. I would have become their number one focus—I knew my parents well! The mentality these days is *I can't be bothered.* People view their lives as more important than anyone else's. That's a sad excuse for living. I can only imagine what the social mentality will be like in twenty to thirty years.

Has society lost its compassion and empathy for its fellow man? Has society chosen to turn a blind eye to those in need, choosing instead to ignore the plight of others? Have they replaced their consciousness with blinders, adopting the theory *everyone for himself?* What a sad state of affairs, if that's the case.

There's an image that will haunt me until the day I die. It is an image of my aunt who was in an assisted living facility in New England. My parents and I visited her a couple of months after she was admitted. Her family was not in the position to care for her at home, and she was no longer able to care for herself. We arrived at the facility, gained access to her secured unit, but she wasn't in her room. I searched for her and finally found her, snoozing in a wheelchair, tongue hanging out of her mouth. Her wheelchair was one of many encircling the nurses' station like a group of Conestoga wagons making camp for the night during the height of the westward migration. I softly called her name. The minute my aunt woke up, her mind slowly cleared of its fog, and she recognized me. She instantly started to cry, tears of relief bathing her face because she believed I was there to take her home.

After our visit, as my parents and I walked down the hall to exit the secured unit, my aunt trailed after us in her wheelchair. As we said our final goodbyes, she looked at us with such desolate sadness emanating from her eyes. Her eyes looked like she recognized this occasion for what it was. With tears running down her round, little cheeks, she beseeched us, "Aren't you taking me with you? I want to go home to the farm." I didn't know how to tell her we weren't going to Aura, to the farm in Michigan she yearned for. We were going home to Florida. That's the last image I have of my aunt. It broke my heart to leave her. I felt so inadequate not knowing how to ease her anguish and her pain. She died less than a year later. I wish I lived closer so I could have visited her more often. Distance was a huge factor for me. I wasn't in the position at that time to quit my job, uproot my husband and parents, and move over eighteen hundred miles to live closer to her, but I wanted to. I wish I could have, and there are many others who find themselves in this same quagmire. Now, when I relive this scene with my aunt, I can't help but cry. My aunt shed her copious tears when we last parted because she couldn't understand why we weren't taking her with us. She was fun-loving, naïve, and always the life of every party. She was my dad's younger sister, the one who, as a child, used to cut the buttons off her brothers' trousers when they were sleeping.

I encourage you to be an active participant in your loved one's life. Visit them, encourage other family members to do the same, even if it's just for a few minutes. Use the time to make sure your Alzheimer's loved one is fine and the staff are caring for them with respect and dignity. And if you can't visit your loved one due to distance, then I recommend you communicate weekly with your loved one via phone call, skype, letters, cards, or videos. Consistency is the key to helping your loved one maintain some recognition of you. They may not recognize who you are in relation to being their spouse, daughter, son, niece, nephew, or friend, but the more often you visit them, something in their memory will sometimes trigger a sense of familiarity. Do what you can so that trigger mechanism doesn't fail because once it fails, it normally doesn't come back. Also, since you know your loved one will never recover, don't you want to do what you can while they are still alive?

I found from experience with my mom, when I was with her every day, she recognized me not as her daughter but as that consistent person in her life who cared for her. She seemed to develop an innate sense that I was the person who kept her safe in every sense of the word. When I was lucky enough to take a short break and I picked her up afterward, there was still something buried deep within her that recognized me as her caregiver. It took a few days to readjust to our old routine, but she always readjusted with a smile on her face, which conveyed to me she was content and happy to be back where she subconsciously knew she belonged, home with me.

Quality of life is so important for those with Alzheimer's or dementia. It means maintaining contact with your loved one and being concerned about their welfare. It is important to make every effort to provide them with cognitive stimulation and social interaction, anticipating their needs since they are no longer capable of doing that. Talk to them soothingly and lovingly. Provide a gentle touch, an understanding gesture, and take the time to be with your loved one no matter how busy *your* life gets. Learn about their disease. Spend time with your loved one by listening to music or singing songs they are familiar with. Recognize your loved one is different with different emotional needs than they had before.

I wish assisted living facilities would realize Alzheimer's patients do not need luxury accommodations with crystal chandeliers, granite countertops, and four course gourmet meals. Instead, they need kind souls, people who aren't overworked but are dedicated to their care. These surrogate caregivers need to recognize and appreciate our loved ones as individuals who used to be productive, loving souls rather than the unrecognizable shell of the person they now see. Our afflicted loved ones need clean accommodations, nutritious food, a safe environment, social interaction, cognitive stimulation, daily exercise, and souls with loving and compassionate hearts. They need caregivers who are trained to deal with dementia and care about the people they care for. Our loved ones may not recognize what they need, but they respond to the loving care they are provided.

If you are a caregiver for a loved one with Alzheimer's or dementia, applaud yourself because the job of caregiving is not easy. The published statistics speak volumes to the unpaid contributions you provide indirectly to the taxpaying citizens of the United States of America. Your unpaid labor is saving the American tax-payer billions of dollars every year as the following statistics attest to. According to the Alzheimer's Association in 2018 approximately 18.5 billion unpaid caregiving hours were provided by 16.2 million families and friends.[17] The value of these unpaid caregivers was estimated at $234 billion US dollars.[18] Of these figures at least 86% have been caregiving for a year and over half of these individuals have been taking care of their Alzheimer's afflicted loved one for at least four years, if not longer.[19] Add to these figures an estimated one-quarter of dementia caregivers care for not only their Alzheimer's loved one but also someone else, like a child or grandchild.[20] These caregivers are referred to as the "sandwich generation" of caregivers. Women account for two-thirds of dementia caregivers,[21] a third of these are daughters, and 34% are 65 years of age or older.[22]

The above statistics are estimates. As I mentioned earlier, it's next to impossible to get exact counts of Alzheimer's and dementia cases in the United States. However, the numbers published by the Alzheimer's Association regarding the official number of Alzheimer's and dementia cases in the United States provides us with a target to use for comparison purposes. I've never completed an Alzheimer's survey on either my mom or myself as her caregiver. Anyone who may have included us in a survey would not have had the most accurate information. Specifics regarding my caregiving hours have never been discussed or shared with any survey or governing organization—only general information at the most. And like I mentioned earlier, several years passed when my mom was never diagnosed but the symptoms were evident. She simply didn't have a physician at the time who provided a diagnosis for treatment.

The world of caregiving for a family member or friend is totally different than the average job. You don't get weekends off, earned vacation days, sick days, benefit packages, job security, or a chance for promotion. Caregiving for most of us is twenty-four hours a day, seven days a week. You can't leave early for a doctor's appointment or take time off to see your child in a dance recital without carefully orchestrating someone to watch your loved one. It's challenging to have even a few hours of normal life, let alone take a vacation.

Alzheimer's caregiving has its challenges. Approximately 59% of caregivers view stress as a highly charged aspect of their daily life.[23] No kidding! Some of you are probably laughing and thinking, *What an understatement!* Caregivers often experience hypertension, anger, exhaustion, anxiety, guilt, sleep problems, eating or digestive issues, 30-70% are depressed,[24] shy away from family and friends, feeling overwhelmed and underappreciated, fatigue, uncertainness, excessive use of alcohol, irritability, feeling hopeless and helpless, and experiencing weakened immune systems with a 15% lower level of antibody responses and 23% higher level of stress hormones than non-caregivers.[25] More than 51% of Alzheimer's caregivers have no prior experience caregiving nor have any trained nursing skills.[26] These characteristics have now become synonymous with Caregiver Syndrome, a phrase that was coined by Dr. Andree LeRoy.[27] I doubt there isn't an Alzheimer's caregiver who hasn't experienced at least half of the above symptoms sometime during their caregiving career.

Alzheimer's and dementia statistics have been gathered for decades. However, it's taken a little longer for physicians and researchers to realize that statistics on caregivers are equally as important. Slowly, these statistics are gathered and analyzed. There is one grievous statistic that can't be ignored, and that is the correlation between Alzheimer's caregiving and the early death of the caregiver. Approximately 40% of Alzheimer's caregivers die before the person they take care of.[28] You read me right, a staggering 40%! I first learned of this sobering statistic when I started attending Memory Lane support meetings. I never questioned this statistic, but I distinctly remember thinking at the time, *If that's 40% for taking care of one person with Alzheimer's, what are my odds of dying sooner since I'm taking care of two with Alzheimer's?* And, if you are an Alzheimer's caregiver between the ages of 66 and 96 your chances of dying before your Alzheimer's loved one is 63% higher than for non-caregivers.[29]

How can Alzheimer's caregivers circumvent caregiver syndrome? Your best defense against caregiver syndrome or burnout is to learn as much as you can about the type of dementia your loved one has. The more you learn, the easier your job will become. Thanks to the Internet, there is no excuse not to educate yourself. It's something you can do when your loved one is sleeping or engrossed in some form of entertainment. Don't be afraid or reluctant to speak up about your loved one's condition. The more people you talk to, you will be amazed at what you learn and discover, and the connections you will make.

As an Alzheimer's caregiver, you need to eliminate any embarrassment or reluctance to divulge the problem to others. Most people can tell just by looking at your loved one that they have Alzheimer's or dementia. So who do you think you're fooling keeping mum about your situation? The more people who know, the greater chance you'll find help, learn useful information, and perhaps even learn of services available in your community. Spread the word about your situation to friends, family, church, co-workers, and neighbors. Create a networking group who can provide you support, information, and respite care. Learn to market your situation. You may be surprised at the resources available to you.

Another concern that's been generating red flags in the press is the possible correlation between lack of sleep and the possibility of developing Alzheimer's. Several sleep studies hint that a lack of quality sleep over time can increase the production of beta-amyloid in the brain, even in healthy individuals, and thus put a person at a higher risk for developing Alzheimer's.[30] Beta-amyloid is a protein that's prevalent in the brains of Alzheimer's patients clumping together to form amyloid plaques. Amyloid plaques, coupled with tau tangles, act like mini-munching machines randomly destroying the various components of an Alzheimer's riddled brain. Lack of sleep in Alzheimer's patients causes tau tangles to increase in number. Quality, deep sleep helps to eliminate beta-amyloid buildup in the brain. To date, there is no definitive answer to the possible correlation between lack of sleep and developing Alzheimer's. However, twenty-five to thirty years before my mom developed Alzheimer's, when she was in her productive years, she didn't sleep well. Consistently during those years, my mom only slept between two to three hours every night. My dad's Alzheimer's was diagnosed later in his life. For years before his diagnosis, he didn't sleep well due to restless legs syndrome. By the time he was finally diagnosed with Alzheimer's, my dad's nightly sundowning had gotten so bad that he was lucky to get a total of two on and off hours of sleep throughout the night.

After reading the above statistics you are probably wondering, *Why would anyone take care of someone with Alzheimer's if there's a 40% chance of dying before their loved one?* My first response, "Hell yes, you're right! Let's hitch our pony and high tail it for the hills and never look back!" That's the easy way out. Life isn't always easy, as I alluded to in the Introduction. There are times when life happens. We find ourselves in a situation which, in our wildest dreams, we never would have placed ourselves. But our hearts tell us one thing while our conscious tells us something entirely different. That's when you, the unsuspecting family member, have to dig deep within your soul and ask yourself some very important questions. I know I asked myself those questions when Matthew died. I didn't know what I should do. Should I quit my job and be a full-time caregiver? Or, keep my job and shell out almost my entire paycheck every other week for a caregiver to do what I could do myself.

It was the hardest, yet the easiest decision I made. *For me,* I made the right decision. It doesn't mean that's the right decision for everyone. Each situation has its own uniqueness, its own characteristics which define the problem, and ultimately, point the person in the right direction *for them.* After two years of full-time, 24/7 caregiving for my parents with Alzheimer's, would I make the same decision again based on what I now know? Unequivocally, yes! I'm not the same person now that I was when I quit my job and became a full-time caregiver. I'm a *better person* for having experienced caregiving for my parents. And based on a national poll appearing in the *2019 Alzheimer's Disease Facts and Figures* published by the Alzheimer's Association, 45% of caregivers found caregiving for someone with dementia very rewarding.[31]

For some, like myself whose mother and maternal grandmother were both afflicted with Alzheimer's, there can be a genetic link that predisposes some of us to Alzheimer's. I'm not sure if this was one of the reasons I subconsciously decided to care for my parent's full time, but I'm glad I did. If I find myself in their shoes someday, I pray the advances in Alzheimer's research will find a cure. And if not a cure, then maybe a plan of care to delay or slow down the onset of symptoms to buy me and others afflicted a few more weeks, months, or perhaps even years of lucidity. Maybe this is what God intended all along, for me to care for my parents as an eyewitness to what they were experiencing—to learn, understand, and help others as they, too, journey along this same path. I believe it was my destiny to experience caregiving so I could become an advocate and recognize the symptoms if one day, I, too, develop the disease.

I've grappled with the question of genetic testing because I'm conscious of the fact I could be a third generation Alzheimer's victim. I'm torn between wanting to know so I can perhaps help scientists develop a cure versus staying ignorant and letting my life unfold without the anxious worry. In my heart, I believe Alzheimer's may very well be in my future. However, those who have been tested and receive word that they are at high-risk don't always develop the disease. Again, it's the randomness of Alzheimer's that's so puzzling and makes developing a cure so difficult. If you get tested for Alzheimer's, be aware that timing is the key. Get tested *after* purchasing life insurance, long term care insurance, or updating your health insurance since any communication of the results with your physician will ultimately affect whether you can obtain any of those insurances afterward.[32]

When Matthew died, it was his decision to have both a Florida funeral in my church and a Catholic funeral in his hometown of Philadelphia. He'd even prepared, the year before he got sick, a list of scriptures to be read, hymns, and Irish songs to be sung. He prepared CDs with his favorite Irish songs and a DVD with his most treasured photographs.

Two months before he died, Matthew and I sat down, and he explained his wishes for his funerals. "Matty will help you with the Philadelphia funeral. He'll be there to help you," Matthew told me in a hoarse voice. I looked at him and replied, "Matthew, I won't be able to go to Philadelphia for your funeral." He looked at me with a blank stare, like this was something he couldn't fathom.

"Why?"

"My folks, you know I can't leave them. Who will care for them when I'm gone?"

When Matthew died, his Spring Hill funeral took place two days later on Monday, August 21, which coincidentally, was also the original scheduled date for his appointment with his new pulmonologist, Dr. O. When I asked Dr. O. for an earlier appointment back in June 2017, I said to him at the time, "I don't think he'll be here by then." And I was right.

According to Matthew's wishes, a funeral was held in Spring Hill, which I attended, with his adopted church family who he loved as much as they loved him. His Florida friends were there, who had been an integral part of our lives. The undertaker knew Matthew had served with the Marines for three years, yet did nothing to provide a military color guard or military honors. He never even asked about it, and I was so numb at the time when we made the arrangements, I didn't even think to inquire about it. I simply assumed he'd make the arrangements, which he hadn't.

Matthew's Philadelphia funeral took place the following Monday, August 28. This was the funeral with all the pomp and circumstance befitting a respected individual who served his city with distinction. He was a thirty-year veteran of the Philadelphia Police Department who retired at the rank of captain. He was a past president of the Philadelphia Emerald Society, and he proudly served in the Marine Corps. There was a 21-gun salute, taps, and his family and friends all attended. I, being his widow, wasn't there. I should have been, but I didn't have anyone to care for my parents. I couldn't just leave them, even at that time they were beyond being able to care for themselves.

When I picked up Matthew's ashes later in August, they casually handed me a folded American flag, like it was a loaf of bread, then his urn. I felt like I was at a used car lot, receiving the keys to a beat up, dirty, old car that I'd just purchased. I selected this undertaker because my neighbor assured me he respected veterans. However, in our case, the undertaker showed very little respect in honor of Matthew's service to his country.

This is a very real concern for caregivers, short-term respite care, and other places where caregivers can make reservations for their loved one so they themselves can take a much-needed break from caregiving. Or, in the above instance, I needed to make a reservation so I could attend my husband's funeral in Philadelphia. When I go out of town, I call a kennel and make a reservation for my pups. There are several good kennels in my area. If we have facilities for our pets, why don't we have short-term respite care facilities for our elderly with Alzheimer's or dementia? I've heard there are some short-term respite care facilities in the United States, but hardly enough. There are a few assisted living facilities that will take reservations for Alzheimer's short-term respite care, but not many.

Some caregivers are fortunate because they have family or close friends who can assist them with caregiving. If you are one of those fortunate few, consider yourself blessed! And make the most of this opportunity. Do not try to take on caregiving by yourself *if* you are fortunate to have assistance. If you ignore this gift from God, you will only set yourself up for caregiver burnout. Ultimately, you are not helping your loved one or yourself.

I've met caregivers who say they have grown children who live merely miles away from their home, but they don't use them for help. My response to them, "Get your family involved since they live so close. Talk to them. Schedule them each week to help you so you can get some time off. You can't do it all yourself." Some have listened, and some were very stubborn and reluctant to listen to reason. At the beginning, I believed I could do it all myself, too. Now, I know from experience that you need all the help you can get if you are a caregiver. My Finnish SISU pride, though, often got in the way. What's your excuse?

It's difficult to find short-term respite care, whether it's for one night or several weeks. In 2018, when I was looking for short-term respite care for my parents so I could attend two family events later in the year, I couldn't find any short-term respite facilities anywhere in my area. I broadened my search to assisted living facilities, and I toured many of them. I repeatedly heard facility administrators throughout Citrus and Hernando counties tell me, "Based on availability." And my response back to them was, "How can a caregiver make travel arrangements ahead of time if they can't make a reservation for their loved one now? I'd hate to make plane or hotel reservations only to have to cancel just a day or two before I'm scheduled to leave because you don't have a bed at your facility." I had many heated discussions with facility directors who thought I'd be a soft sell, all extolling the wonders and amenities provided at their facilities. Assisted living facilities, as I learned, don't want to commit their beds for temporary patients. It all boils down to money. They are in the business to make money, not necessarily to satisfy short-term needs of the community. They also boasted to me how much better their facilities are as a permanent home for my loved ones as opposed to the unskilled care I was providing my parents at home. I never wasted my breath telling them, *I disagree with you because I only have two people I'm caring for whereas your nurses and aides have many more patients to care for each day. Plus, I know my charges much better than your aides ever would, because I love them with my heart and soul!*

If caregivers don't have a chance to take a break once in a while, a vacation to recharge their batteries or attend to health issues, there's a greater chance the caregiver will burn out from their responsibilities of caregiving. They may become ill and eventually need to make other arrangements for the permanent care of their loved one. Or worse, they may die from the stress of caregiving. I've seen the worry, exhaustion, and resentfulness etched on the faces of those who attend my support group. There were changes I periodically saw on their faces, body language, and deep within their souls that said more than any words could convey. Caregiving for a loved one comes from the heart, but there are times when your heart feels like it's about to wear out and you desperately need a break. Without the accessibility of short-term respite care facilities, the statistic of 40% of caregivers dying before their charges will only increase with time. What this means, ultimately, is that the United States government will end up footing a greater percentage of the care for more Alzheimer's and dementia patients because there's no one to accept the caregiving responsibility or afford the cost of caring for Alzheimer's or dementia patients if a caregiver dies of stress-related caregiving.

Short-term respite houses are a solution to this dilemma. They would serve two purposes. First, as short-term respite care, a caregiver can make a reservation for their loved one so the caregiver can take a break. Caregivers would be able to reserve a bed for their loved one. Each facility would set a maximum stay, and the daily charge would be reasonable since most caregivers do not get paid to care for their loved one. After all, many, like myself, quit their jobs to do so. Second, short-term respite houses would also be used as adult day care. Respite day care could provide caregivers the opportunity to maintain their jobs while at the same time enroll their loved one in a safe, nurturing, and secure environment during the day.

Ideally, it would consist of three to five bedrooms, each bedroom with two to three twin beds. It would have a large common area, kitchen, dining room, several handicap bathrooms, secured fenced in backyard with a covered patio area, and attractive landscaping. This blueprint for short-term respite houses would serve a community need. Staffed by competent, trained individuals who understand the needs of Alzheimer's and dementia patients is of utmost importance. There would be a variety of daily activities each day. They'd have three meals a day plus snacks, daily music with sing-a-longs, and comfortable furniture, too. Some communities have facilities like this, but not many. Collaboration with community leaders like physicians, churches, elder care services, local and state governments, assisted living facilities, parent-teacher organizations, and civic service organizations coupled with proper networking and advertising could allow short-term respite houses to be profitable assets that many communities are in dire need of.

If the Alzheimer's Association is correct in its projection of at least fifteen million Americans with Alzheimer's by 2050, the necessity for short-term respite care needs to be addressed now, rather than later. I'm praying an entrepreneur, group of civic minded individuals, or single-minded people will recognize and acknowledge that this exigence is justified and warranted. Most of us know someone who has Alzheimer's or dementia, and someday you may find yourself as a caregiver for a loved one with Alzheimer's or dementia. Until you walk in the shoes of a caregiver, you truly have no idea how important it is for caregivers to have the opportunity to take a break from caregiving. And the only way a caregiver can do this is either with short-term respite care or the assistance of family or friends willing to help when a caregiver needs to take a break. Not everyone has family or friends willing or able to help. I know I didn't when I needed someone to care for my parents so I could attend my husband's funeral.

Our first thoughts when we learn a loved one is afflicted with Alzheimer's or dementia usually isn't about quality of life, but it should be, just like short-term respite care is pivotal for the quality of life of the caregiver. Without quality of life for our loved one, our loved one will soon wither and die before their time, just like a parched flower will droop and die without proper nourishment. Short-term respite care, so a caregiver can take a break from caregiving once in a while, is crucial for the wellbeing of the caregiver. Without short-term respite care, the only option for caregivers to take a break is to rely on family or friends for help. If there is no one available to help, then the caregiver has no opportunity to take a break. This can lead to caregiver burnout, or they sacrifice their health to care for their loved one. Caregiving shouldn't be an all or nothing arrangement. There needs to be balance in the caregiver's life. Otherwise, there's no quality of care for the caregiver, and there will be more Alzheimer's patients in facilities at government expense. Or more Alzheimer's patients will live by themselves because caregivers have either burned out, became ill, or didn't want to care for their loved one anymore. Alzheimer's patients living by themselves isn't a viable option. The quality of life for Alzheimer's loved ones and caregivers comes full circle when both have the opportunity to nurture and rejuvenate their souls. The patient can benefit from the care of loving and compassionate souls. The primary caregiver can benefit from the chance to take a break from caregiving which reignites the spark in their loving and compassionate soul. Unpaid Alzheimer's caregivers are a national treasure that saves the American taxpayer billions of dollars each year. It's up to us, past and present caregivers, to let our voices be heard so caregivers of the present and future won't become statistics of caregiver burnout. Short-term respite care solves this national crisis by providing a practical, logical, financial, and viable solution.

Caregiving Tips from the Heart

Caregiving Tip #21:

Consistency is important in developing a schedule for your loved one who has Alzheimer's or dementia. Don't assume because your loved one used to go to bed at 11:00 p.m. that they should still go to bed at 11:00 p.m. Adjust their schedule, and put them to bed earlier. This will provide you some much needed downtime to take a break, complete some last-minute chores, and have some *me* time each night.

Caregiving Tip #22:

Keep your loved one's wardrobe to a few basic outfits, a couple of shirts, pants, sweaters, socks, and shoes. If you give them too many choices, they can't make up their mind and become overwhelmed. They no longer need a large selection of clothes since their life has changed, and it will never improve or return to normal. Accept that your loved one can no longer make decisions for themselves. As a result, don't expect them to open their closet door and select clothes that match, are clean, or even know what you expect them to do. Select their clothes for them. Don't have any other clothes within reach while they are dressing, and be there to assist them in dressing. They may not need your help now to dress, but get them in the habit of you being there to assist them. This will make it easier for you later when they digress to the next phase and you will need to dress them yourself.

CHAPTER 23

Where's the Nearest Bathroom?

Paul and Phyllis were always game for a car ride. It was impossible to save all my errands for Fridays when Paul and Phyllis were at the Key Center. Since I couldn't leave them home with Ron—he had no control over Phyllis, I turned errands into family events. I put the pups in the car, followed by Phyllis who would sit in the back seat with Kipper and Katy. Next, I helped Paul, who was my co-pilot. On cold days, I warmed up the car first. On those unbelievably hot summer Florida days, we went out extra early in the morning to beat the heat and hibernate at home the rest of the day.

Since I was their caregiver and they both had Alzheimer's, that meant I was the parent to my parents, and they were now my children. Every good parent makes sure their children go potty before cramming everyone into the car and hitting the road. I was responsible and took my parenting responsibilities seriously. I always made sure Paul went to the bathroom before we left.

Potty etiquette wasn't as crucial for Phyllis since she wore a diaper. As the year progressed, Paul needed more frequent potty breaks while we were on the road. Sometimes, even five minutes after we left the house, I started to read Paul's squirmy body language, a tell-tale clue that something was about to erupt from his body. I'd ask him, "Do you need to use the bathroom?" As soon as he replied in the affirmative, I frantically searched for the nearest fast food joint, gas station, or grocery store. Once I parked my SUV as close to the front door as possible, I'd get out, open Paul's door, instructed Phyllis to stay put, locked the doors, and walked Paul into the establishment as I helped him locate the restroom.

While Paul was in the restroom, I positioned myself between the restroom and the front door so I could keep an eye on both locations, rotating my head back and forth like a metronome keeping pace with the music. Every couple of seconds, I made sure Phyllis didn't get out the car and wander away, and every couple of seconds I stared at the restroom door waiting for Paul to come out. Back and forth, back and forth, back and forth. I'm lucky I didn't get whiplash! When the restroom door finally opened, I waved to Paul to grab his attention and escorted him back to the car. If I didn't keep an eye glued for him, Paul wouldn't know how to get back to the car. Some of those men's restrooms are located right next to an *exit* door. I could visualize Paul walking out of the restroom, see that door with the exit sign above it, open the door, and all hell would break loose with sirens, bells, whistles, and a loud menacing voice booming over the PA system, *Warning, warning, someone is leaving the building. The cops are coming. The cops are coming, help!"*

I got used to the suspicious, cautious looks the staff always gave me as I stood guard in my self-designated location. I got in the habit of explaining my situation to the staff, sometimes this appeased them; sometimes it didn't. There was one particular occasion which stands out in my mind. We stopped at a Burger King in Spring Hill. As a female staffer walked up to me, I started my monologue, which by this time, I could recite in my sleep. Before I could finish, she piped up saying, "Don't worry, I'll keep an eye out for your dad. I'll recognize him when he comes out. You go stay with your mom; I'll bring him back to your car." I was very grateful for her kind words and understanding demeanor. She's the only person who ever offered to help. Her assistance meant so much to me, and she definitely went above and beyond the norm. That female staffer's customer service skills epitomized a characteristic of customer service that's been forgotten or dismissed from the lexicon of most new hire orientation. I dread to think how future generations will interpret customer service in the years to come.

There were times, too, when I got back to the car after shopping and I saw Paul standing with his car door open. The first time I saw this I asked him, "What ya' doing?" His response, "Just needed to stretch my legs." On another occasion, when I was returning to the car, I was approaching the car from a different angle than normal. I saw a stream of liquid under the car that wasn't there before. The day wasn't hot, so the windows were open to provide ventilation, and the air conditioner wasn't running. I walked over to where Paul was standing, in front of his opened car door. I was *appalled* at what I saw! Paul was *urinating*! He thought if he opened his car door and stood in front of it, he could pee, and no one would see him. How do you explain to a 97-year-old man that he can't urinate in public? No matter what I said to him, he didn't see anything wrong with this. I'm not sure if he thought since he was 97 the laws of public exposing or urinating in public didn't apply to him, but *I didn't want to find out!* I knew his Alzheimer's was advancing, but I didn't think he'd gotten *that* bad.

As the year progressed, I continued to see Paul with his car door open standing with his back to the world, facing the car door and in all probability peeing on the parking lot. He obviously needed to relieve himself while I was in the store. Months later, as I was cleaning my car, I noticed a discoloration on the mesh that appears on the lower inside portion of the passenger front door. I looked at this, about a foot in width and two feet in length. I scratched my head a bit. Where the heck did that come from? Perplexed, upon closer inspection, I noticed it had a slightly yellowish tinge to it. I tried to clean it, but no matter what I did, I couldn't get the stain out. It finally dawned on me! Obviously, Paul's aim wasn't always very good. It appeared that rather than peeing on the pavement near his feet, he may have peed on the inside of the car door. I'm not sure how I'm going to explain that when I turn the car in.

As long as Paul was in the car with Phyllis, I didn't have to worry about Phyllis. She stayed put. While I was driving, I often checked the driver's mirror on the visor, keeping tabs on her. Sometimes, she chattered away non-stop to imaginary friends. Other times, she silently gazed straight ahead, not responding to my questions. I placed magazines in the backseat for her, so she had something to look at when she got bored.

When Phyllis transgressed to being very kinetic, she reached and played with anything she saw. There were times when we got home that I helped Phyllis out of the car, assisted her into the house and came back for the pups only to discover that one or both pups didn't have their leashes on. They came bounding out of the car, raced around the house, excited like two little magpies—so happy Grandma had unleashed them. There were times when we stopped for a fast food lunch, and we ate our sandwiches in the car. Later that night, when I put Phyllis to bed, I found the sandwich wrapper tucked inside her diaper. One time, after errands, I opened her car door and found her tightly holding a plastic bag over her head. Why she decided to do that, I have no idea. I quickly removed the bag from her face and explained in an excited, high-pitched voice, "No, don't do, Fi Fi will get hurt!" She must have found the bag in the back seat, saw it as a play thing, and did something I never expected her to do. The bag was normally in her diaper bag, in the cargo hold beyond her reach. I took it out a couple days before, didn't need it, and tossed it back in the car never thinking that she'd do that. After that, I made sure there was *never* anything within her reach that could harm her. This is a good example of how important it is to be *proactive* at all times when caring for someone with Alzheimer's or dementia.

I also learned you have to keep your sense of humor. It was hard sometimes, especially on those occasions when Phyllis was sitting on the toilet. I'd be removing her diaper, and liquidly, brown crap would be drip out from around the leg holes of her diaper. Puddles of poop, the consistency of gooey, chocolate pudding would ooze onto the floor, drip from her legs, and cake the front of the toilet. Feces smeared between her legs, excreta hiding behind her knees, caca in her crotch, and ordure hiding in her bum. There was number two everywhere! She started to point to it, touch it with her fingers, and then there was crap everywhere she touched. Wherever Phyllis touched there was little shit marks, which reminded me of little brown puppy paw prints creating random patterns on any surface she touched.

At first when this happened, I got mad, I swore and I cursed in anger. It took so long to clean her up, and afterward, I usually had to take a shower and change my clothes. And the smell was nauseating! It lingered in the air, meandered up my nostrils, and no matter how much air spray I used, nothing could eliminate or camouflage the stink. There's nothing like an overpowering, odiferous, noxious odor to stop you in your tracks.

That's how I reacted in the old days, when I didn't know any better, in what I now refer to as my *ignorant years*. My ignorant years proved to be a training period of trial and error, research and study. The first couple of times I helped Mom into the bathroom, I felt embarrassed and didn't want to be in the bathroom with her. I had the mindset that bathrooms are sacred, private places. Yet when Phyllis had her accidents, I quickly came to realize she needed help cleaning up when she was in the bathroom. Once I got over my reluctant embarrassment, I steeled myself to help her. With time, helping Phyllis in the bathroom became as easy as a walkin' and a talkin'.

I finally brightened up, or shall I say, I finally smartened up. I came to understand Alzheimer's and dementia. I now know Phyllis had no control over her actions. If she did, she would have been mortified. I learned when I got mad, it didn't help anyone. Later at night after I put her to bed, I felt guilty and remorseful. I wanted to kick myself in the ass. How could I react that way to my mother even though I knew she had no memory of my outbursts two minutes after they happened. There was nothing wrong with my memory, the lingering after affects haunted my psyche, and I had a hard time forgiving myself. I tossed and turned in bed at night; sleep would elude me. I got up in the middle of the night, looked myself in the mirror, and didn't recognize the person staring back as me. I hated the person I became. How did I become such a terrible monster? When morning came, I started the new day, hoping I miraculously matured during the night into a kinder, more compassionate soul. I came to forgive myself, with time, but it was a slow process. When I reflect on this now, I believe in my heart I was reacting to the frustration of the job I had at that time. I felt pulled in so many directions by my employer, and no matter what I was trying to accomplish, there were never enough hours in the day. I felt as if I was spiraling into a bottomless pit with no way out.

Through time, I've transformed. I learned to quietly talk to Phyllis and anticipate possible messes before my sense of smell jumped ahead with confirmation. Sometimes, there were false alarms, and other times, I wish I could have called in a Haz Mat squad. I'd love to have had an emergency kit on hand for those occasions when I encountered an oozing, stinky diaper. This kit would have included a protective gown, facemask, protective booties, and long gloves that would reach from my hands to my shoulders like hospital nurses wear. Most importantly, it would have a hose I could turn on to thoroughly wash her tushy. And don't forget a clothespin for my nose!

I've adopted one of Matthew's favorite expressions, something he learned in the Marines, "Proper Preparation Prevents Piss Poor Performance." Prior to bringing Phyllis into the bathroom to change her diaper, I learned to have all my supplies ready so I'm not grabbing for things while trying to clean her up. I also learned not to have *good* clothes on when I change her diaper, especially if I have plans to go out afterward. This helped a lot in keeping me cool, calm, collected, and *clean*, while helping tremendously with my attitude. I learned better techniques in removing her diaper as she was sitting on the toilet. I had the wet wipes to clean her, and the Clorox wipes to clean the floor already out and grouped on the counter, so they were easy to grab. All dirty items were deposited into a small plastic bag; thank goodness for those Walmart and Publix plastic bags. I had the new diaper ready, which I'd give to Phyllis to keep her hands occupied—tricks of the trade I learned the hard way.

Another thing that helped me was to look at the situation as if I was standing on the sidelines watching a movie. Some people might be grossed out by dirty diapers while others would laugh their heads off, thankful it wasn't them cleaning up such an explosive mess. Either way, bowel movements are a part of life, and as Matthew also used to say, "If you don't shit, you die!" Well, I didn't want Phyllis to die, so I guess it was better to have a messy poop to clean up, rather than no poop at all. On the other hand, caregivers also have to keep track of their loved one's bowel movements to make sure they don't get constipated. It's difficult to get older people to drink water, so I always added a fiber supplement to Phyllis' breakfast coffee. It's helped a lot; she'd been hospitalized once for an impacted bowel, and I didn't want to travel that road again. Keep in mind, if your loved one is on a lot of medications, it's even more important to monitor their bowel movements since medications are one of the leading causes of constipation. In most cases, your loved one either won't remember having had a bowel movement, or they'll have no idea what you mean when you ask them, "Did you do a poo poo today?" A sense of humor, by all means, is a prerequisite for being a loving and nurturing caregiver.

Thus far, our move to Citrus County had been advantageous for us. Paul and Phyllis were attending the Key Center one day a week, which provided me a day of respite from my charges. We were attending Memory Lane once a week, which provided Paul and Phyllis with another social outlet and me with a support group. Plus, we didn't have a mailbox in front of our house. At our old home, at least once a day, Phyllis dutifully went to the mailbox to check for the mail. She'd been doing that for years; our mailboxes and several neighbors' mailboxes were located in front of our house. As her memory declined, she forgot when she'd gotten the mail already and went out again. As her disease further progressed, she occasionally opened our neighbors' mailboxes and attempted to take their mail, thinking it was ours. Either Mary Ann or I would restrain her by shouting, "No, Phyllis!" We learned we had to keep a close eye on Phyllis whenever she attempted to head toward the front door or the garage. When I was cleaning out the garage when we moved, I found bundles of mail hidden in different places, even past-due bills. In our new home, our mailboxes are centrally located in the development and require a key to open. Sadly, by that time, Phyllis had forgotten she ever used to pick up the mail. She didn't even remember what mail was. It was one more sign of how she was declining.

Caregiving Tips from the Heart

Caregiving Tip #23:

Your loved one's sleep pattern may change, whereby they start to sleep during the day and stay up at night. Try to avoid this, since this change in sleep pattern will affect you as well. If they appear to be sleepy during the day, try to stimulate them cognitively with conversation, games, puzzles, or music. If you can keep them awake during the day, they should be tired at night.

Caregiving Tip #24:

Prepare for the unexpected. Dementia, especially Alzheimer's, has no clear, cookie-cutter set of criteria. Each person reacts to stimuli differently and digress at their pace. Keep your eyes and ears open and alert to the needs of your loved one. Be cognizant of their changes; be proactive rather than reactive.

Caregiving Tip #25:

You'll get mad; you'll lose your temper from time to time. You're human and at times, you'll react like one. On those occasions, recognize your emotions, stop yourself, admit you need to cool off, and regroup. Once you do that, you won't feel so guilty afterward. You will be able to look yourself in the mirror with a better attitude and with some forgiveness.

CHAPTER 24

Healing Trips for My Soul

After a stressful year without a vacation plus the previous two years without one, it was no wonder I was a bit testy. To put it mildly, my attitude was like that of a lion in mating season. I needed a break! With two family events on the horizon, I was determined; I was going to go to both. The first trip was a family reunion in Michigan the second weekend of August. The second trip was for my youngest granddaughter's wedding in October in Philadelphia.

In January, I started checking for short-term respite care facilities in my area. I could not find even one facility in the surrounding three counties. That realization didn't bode well with me. So, I broadened my search to assisted living facilities near me. With time, I found an assisted living facility that took short-term reservations. Their marketing director was not only a sympathetic soul, but it turns out we had recently become Facebook friends, though we hadn't realized it at the time. I hadn't had a chance to privately mourn Matthew since he died, so I added a third trip to the schedule with the pups. We went to our special place, Cedar Key.

The pups and I stayed at the Old Fennimore Inn, where Matthew and I had always stayed when we vacationed at Cedar Key. I booked a unit Matthew and I had stayed in. Even though every room, all the furniture, and the heavenly view from the balcony triggered an avalanche of memories and tears, I needed to be somewhere where Matthew had been. I didn't live in the same house anymore, and I had donated all but a few items of his clothing. This was the first trip I took since Matthew died. It felt surreal, strange, like I was sleepwalking back in time.

I timed the Cedar Key trip in conjunction with what would have been our twenty-second wedding anniversary, May 17. The day dawned bright, beautiful, and peaceful. The sky was a clear, beautiful blue, a shade too difficult for a painter to duplicate because it is impossible to reproduce the softness or purity as seen in heavenly color. Birds were soaring overhead, zigging and zagging through the treetops, singing and chirping. I brought Matthew's urn with me to celebrate our anniversary in Cedar Key. If people knew this, they'd probably want to commit me. But this wasn't a vacation in the true sense of the word. It was my first real opportunity to mourn my husband's death.

With Matthew's urn on the balcony table along with a bouquet of flowers, I poured myself a glass of champagne and made a toast, "To what would have been twenty-two years, I love you Matthew. I miss you, and I'm so thankful we had our time together." Matthew's favorite Irish music was playing softly from his cellphone. The pups were sitting on the balcony, gazing outward, totally captivated by the flying birds. After a while, I switched to a recording of Matthew singing his signature song, Kelley Mooney's version of "Hallelujah."

Whenever I heard "Hallelujah,"—Matthew's version or any one else's, my tears always welled like a roaring, deafening waterfall. On this occasion, amidst the balmy, serene surroundings, with palm trees gently swaying and the azure water lapping lazily against the shoreline, was no exception. Birds squawked and chirped as they soared majestically against the pastel baby blue skies. I needed that trip. It helped me to grieve, mourn, and slowly start to heal.

It sucks to be a widow; I can't say it any other way! Widowhood is the most difficult thing I've had to face. Before I was married, I was extremely independent—a loner, and I didn't mind it because that's how I was brought up and didn't know any different. Then, when I married Matthew, my eyes, mind, and heart opened to a different way of life. I thought about Matthew all the time, despite his laments, "You never think about us when you're at work." No matter how much I tried to convince him otherwise, I did think of Matthew whenever we were apart. Though he's gone, he still dominates my mind. I know my life will never be the same; I am missing half of what made me whole. The life I knew and cherished died on August 19, 2017.

Every year, Matthew took his annual trip to Philadelphia to see his family. I treasured those times because I knew how much those trips meant to him, and I enjoyed the mini breaks from married life. I enjoyed the novelty of skipping dinner if I wasn't hungry. Matthew was a stickler about a hearty dinner every night. Life with Matthew was very structured. I missed him during those times, of course. We phoned, sent text messages, or emailed. But I knew when he was coming home. Now, he's *never* coming home. There are no text or voice messages. It's so unbearable to endure the lack of communication. I still wait for a text, hoping he's found some way to communicate with me from heaven, but alas, nothing.

At night, I look up at the sky. Some nights, shining, sparkling ten-carat diamonds plaster the sky while other nights, there's hardly a hint of stars. On those nights, it's as if God forgot to roll the dice; only satiny black brushstrokes punctuate the nightly canvas with the most minuscule specks sparsely dotting the sky, smidgens that the naked eye can barely see. I often wonder if Matthew is looking down from heaven. Can he see me? Does he know what's going on here on earth? I call out his name and ask him questions, hoping I'll hear a response, but I never do. It's become my nightly ritual since the night he died. That same satiny black sky looms above, in mute silence. Almost as if its laughing at me, knowing a secret it refuses to divulge. But I do it anyway, because in my heart, I truly believe he can hear me. Matthew can't answer—his lips forever silenced of a voice I loved so much.

In August, I made my first trip back to Michigan alone. It felt so strange. My flight arrived in Detroit in the late morning. I picked up a rental car and paid a visit to my maternal grandparents' graves at Glen Eden Cemetery and then to a cemetery in Royal Oak to visit an aunt's grave. My last stop was to visit Paul's friend, Jim Ferguson, at an assisted living facility in Rochester. I had a nice, brief visit with Jim. Jim and Paul met during Coast Guard boot camp at the beginning of WWII and remained friends. I remember Jim and his wife Mildred fondly from my childhood. Jim's mind was as sharp as a tack despite his slowed-down body. I'm not sure who appreciated the visit more, Jim or me.

The next day, I visited Phyllis's best friend, Laura Mills Stach, in Grand Blanc. Laura was with Phyllis when she met her Paul in Aura back in 1946. Every trip to Michigan includes a visit to see Laura, although this was the first time without Phyllis. The whole time I was there, I felt like I left something valuable back at the hotel. In my heart, I vowed to do everything I could to maintain these two precious friendships, with Mom's best friend Laura, and Dad's dear friend Jim.

I also visited my aunt and uncle, Peg and Jim Bailey, in Port Hope, in Michigan's thumb. Peg is Phyllis' younger sister. I have fond memories of watching their two sons, Jimmy and Jeff, grow up and become strapping young men. I was an active participant in their childhood as their mom was pivotal in mine. Peg and Jim took care of my grandma when she developed Alzheimer's. Even though our conversation mostly shied away from the challenges of caregiving, it seemed to be lurking in the shadows like a devil waiting to claim a new soul.

Mackinac Island was a magical place Matthew and I both treasured, so I treated myself to a two-night stay. One of Matthew's favorite movies was *Somewhere in Time,* which was filmed on Mackinac Island. Released in 1980, it starred Christopher Reeve and Jane Seymour. I have a photograph of Matthew standing at the rock where Reeve's character, Richard Collier meets Elise McKenna, in the scene, "Is it you?" Whenever we watched this film, Matthew and I would reminiscence about our visits to Mackinac. We laughed about biking the 8.2 miles around the island, enjoying mouth-watering, leisurely meals overlooking the Big Mac Bridge, sightseeing, and shopping. Matthew loved to shop! I felt blessed I was able to share my favorite place on earth with Matthew and that he loved it just as much.

Months before, when I made my reservations for the Island, I chose the inn with the Irish name, Cloghaun Bed and Breakfast. I had been married to an Irishman. In my heart there was no other choice!

The ferry ride to Mackinac Island was memorable. It included a detour under the Mackinac Bridge, which was a treat for me because these bonus excursions only occur a couple of times during the hectic summer tourist season. After the ferry docked on the island, I retrieved my bag and moseyed along Main Street to Hoban Street, carrying my bag being jostled along the way. My accommodation was located at the summit of Hoban and Market. As I approached the property, the beautiful, colorful flowers lining the walkway welcomed me. Flowers lined the covered porch, too, and I could see the Irish tricolor flag proudly fluttering in the faint summer breeze. The Irish flag brought back fond memories of our trip to Ireland in 2011. The inn keeper was hospitable and helpful. My room was comfortable and clean with a balcony, the perfect location to stand at the railing, sip a glass of wine, and people-watch. I listened to the clop, clop, clopping of the horses and carriages as they leisurely made their way down Market Street. It was easy to daydream, imagining what life must have been like back in the 1900s.

For me, the island was heaven on earth, my happy place! The second day, my cousins Katy and Breanne joined me. We had a leisurely lunch overlooking the harbor, catching up, laughing, and having fun being in each other's company. It meant so much to me that they made the four-hour trip from their homes in suburban Detroit. Later that night, after we parted, I enjoyed another glass of wine on the balcony, people-watched, and tried to soak up every sound, every vision, every unique nuance that makes the Island so special to me. I didn't even mind the earthy, uniquely aromatic, pungent steaming whiffs of freshly dropped horse dung since four-legged transportation was the most common mode on the Island.

After dusk transitioned into midnight blackness, I walked back into my room, locked the doors, selected Irish music on Matthew's cell phone, and dimmed the lights in the room to prepare for a shower. The bathroom light was on, and as I showered, my mind wandered to thoughts about the next day. I'd return to St. Ignace and continue on to Aura for the family reunion. Even though I love Mackinac, I looked forward to seeing family.

After my shower, I dried off in the bathroom, put my pjs on, and walked into the bedroom. I stopped midstride. The lights were blaring brightly in the bedroom, not dimmed like I'd left them! I couldn't move; my feet were glued in place. I distinctly remembered dimming the lights before going into the bathroom. How did this happen? After a few seconds, I convinced my feet to move. I checked both doors, the one leading out into the hallway and the other one exiting onto the balcony. Both were still locked. It was impossible for anyone to have entered the room while I was in the bathroom. Then, it hit me. I was at the only Irish inn on Mackinac Island; Matthew loved Mackinac Island! He was so proud of his Irish ancestry! When we stayed on the island before, Matthew asked me, "Why didn't we stay there?" referring to the Cloghaun Inn. Did Matthew pay me a visit while I was in the shower? Was it possible? I no longer believe in coincidences. I couldn't forget what happened in Spring Hill. That still haunted me. In my heart, I wanted to believe. All the signs pointed to

Matthew. I felt so loved and believed Matthew sent me a sign. I felt special, believing that Matthew communicated with me in his now subtle way. I prayed that Matthew was enjoying the Island as much as I was. Oh, I how I missed him!

CHAPTER 25

First Heavenly Anniversary, August 19, 2018

Days after I got home from the family reunion, the first anniversary of Matthew's death approached. Months earlier, I racked my brain to figure out how to commemorate Matthew's first heavenly anniversary. I wanted to do something which spoke of the man I loved. I found a couple of ideas but nixed them due to the environment or aviation rules in Florida.

Earlier in the year, I had a hot pink crepe myrtle tree planted in the front yard of our new home outside my bedroom window. The first summer Matthew and I were married we planted a hot pink crepe myrtle tree in the back yard of Matthew's home to celebrate our new life together. We named our tree *Honey Do*. We took a photo in front of *Honey Do;* she came to our shoulders. Every couple of years, we took more photos in front of *Honey*

Do, always amazed at how much she had grown in a few short years. Matthew sold the house in 2008. On those rare occasions now when I drive by hoping to get a glimpse of *Honey Do* to see how tall she's grown, I'm disappointed because the new owner erected a large shed that blocks the view of the back yard from the street. I hope our *Honey Do* is still blooming her beautiful, bright, pink blossoms.

So, when I moved to Citrus County, it seemed only logical to plant a hot pink crepe myrtle tree at our new home. As the first anniversary of Matthew's death approached, I had the same type of tree planted in the memory garden at our church, the Spring Hill United Church of Christ. My friend Brandon, from Unique Landscaping, planted both trees. Brandon understood how important this was to me. At both locations, I inserted commemorative plaques, *In loving Memory of Matthew J. Veasey, Jr, February 3, 1940–August 19, 2017*.

For an entire month after this solemn anniversary, I flew three flags on our flagpoles behind our home—Irish, Pennsylvania, and Marines—in honor of the ancestry Matthew was so proud of, the state where he was born, and the branch of service which Matthew honorably served. I watched many of Matthew's favorite movies each night leading up to the anniversary—*The Quiet Man, Good Fellas, Somewhere in Time, Caddy Shack*, and *The American President*. I listened to Matthew's favorite Irish music. August 19 was a Sunday; the altar flowers at church were in Matthew's memory. I also requested the Music Director, Kurt, to include Matthew's signature song in the service; Chuck did a great job singing it. After church, I picked up a Matthew Special at Village Pizza, our favorite Spring Hill pizzeria. That night, I had dinner at our favorite restaurant, Nouvelle Cuisine.

As I got out of my car at Nouvelle Cuisine, something told me to look up to the sky. Above my left shoulder was a beautiful rainbow, its colors so clear and distinct. It felt like Matthew was smiling at me, trying to help me through this night, letting me know in his silent way he was with me.

245

As I walked into the restaurant, Isabelle greeted me; she knew how hard this night was going to be for me. We hugged, exchanged a few words, and I motioned to her to follow me to the door. I silently pointed to the rainbow. We looked at each other and she nodded. We didn't need to exchange any words.

It was the first time I went back to our favorite restaurant since my birthday the year before. I ordered the same meal we always ordered, chateaubriand. I recalled lots of memories and shed copious tears. I brought the photo of Matthew and I. Isabelle had taken it the last time we were there. I propped it against a wineglass across the table from me and took a photograph. I had been dreading this anniversary but wanted to memorialize this day for the one I loved.

The next day, I stopped at Dr. Abskhroun's office. Dr. Abskhroun and his staff had been so compassionate and caring when Matthew was sick. So many times, Matthew called when he either reached his pain threshold or had difficulties breathing. They never turned him away, and I will forever be grateful and appreciative of their compassionate care.

When I entered the office, Mary sat in her usual place with her usual smile. "Mary," I began, "yesterday was the first anniversary of Matthew's death." Her smile slowly faded into a solemn frown as she replied, "I was thinking of him yesterday." Extending the bouquet toward her, I tried to convey what was in my heart, "These flowers were on the altar at church yesterday in his memory. I want Dr. Abskhroun's office to have them as thank you for everything he, you, Kelly, and the rest of the staff did for Matthew last year." Mary nodded. I turned and walked out the door.

Once the first anniversary of Matthew's death passed, it was easier to face the 19th of each month. There were even times I didn't realize, until later, that the 19th had come and gone. I still think about our life and marriage and still cry, but it's a little easier. I asked friends who lost their husbands, "Does it get any easier?" All of them said the same thing, "No, not really. You just move on with your life."

Both my grandmothers outlived their husbands. I had never considered what it must have been like for them without their soulmates, but now I had an idea of the heartache, sorrow, and misery they must have felt. I'm determined not to let this thing called grief rule my life. I knew I needed to accept this new chapter and be brave. I had to walk through that opened door with my head held high, knowing God had some pleasant surprises in store for me. But it was so difficult to walk through that door. Of course, I was anxious about what I might find on the other side. A part of me didn't want to relinquish my former life while the other part of me warmed to the idea of what might be lurking on the other side. Taking that first step, though, was so hard!

When I started to feel the tug of war between anxiety versus doubt, I kept thinking about a word exercise we did at church one Sunday. Pastor Robin passed around a bowl and instructed everyone to select one piece of paper as it went by. My yellow, star-shaped piece of paper had one word printed on the back, *Trust*. Our next instructions were simple—think about our word, reflect on how it relates to our life, and think about how it guides us as we go through the motions of our lives. How does that word impact how we live? I didn't think much about it at first, but I taped that piece of paper onto my bathroom mirror. I couldn't help but see it every time I went into the bathroom. Then, weeks later, a revelation hit me. Trust in the Lord. God won't let me down. I couldn't have picked a more appropriate word. Since Matthew passed, I was forced to make so many decisions. There were times when I was exhausted and doubted myself and asked myself, *Did I make the right decision?* I had no one to ask for advice, no one to help. Everything was up to me, which was so daunting and frightening. I had to trust in myself and accept that I was making the best decisions for us. When in a relationship, it's easy to depend on your spouse to provide comfort and confidence. Once I grasped the idea to trust in the Lord, that He's watching over me, and He will guide me based on His will, life started to get easier. It took a while but gradually I didn't feel so frustrated, angry, or lonely. *Trust.* Such a simple word that conveys so much when you relinquish your worries and anguish to God. *Trust in God; He won't forsake you, forget you, or let you down.*

CHAPTER 26

Reconnecting with Friends

As fall approached, our lives coasted along pretty comfortably. Around that time, an extra day was added to Paul and Phyllis' schedule at the Key Center. My cherished days of soulful refuge were Thursdays and Fridays, and nothing made me happier. Once or twice a month, I reconnected with friends. It was wonderful to reestablish friendships that meant so much to me. At first, I couldn't shake the feeling that I was playing hooky from work. When I walked away from my previous employer of seventeen years, I felt brainwashed because I had to account for every single minute of every single day. The feeling of accountability never totally evaporated from my soul. Sometimes, I still feel as if I have to prove my worth by showing how much I've accomplished during the day.

I became addicted to Facebook, posting photographs and responding to friends' posts. I'm not sure what I would have done my first year of widowhood if not for Facebook. Years ago,

Matthew discouraged me from establishing a Facebook account, saying at the time, "You're too busy; you don't have time for that." But that was then, this is now. I craved human interaction, because though caring for my parents kept me fulfilled, it limited my opportunities to socialize. Facebook became an accessible means to achieve that without sacrificing caring for my parents. When tending to someone 24/7, it's easy to lose all contact with friends and family. A loved one becomes the caregiver's whole world, which is not necessarily good for the caregiver. Like a seesaw, it required balance. For someone who, by nature, was a loner most of her life, I started to see the importance of friends and family, treasuring those rare moments when I could feel normal and connected with others. Despite my limited, confined world, Facebook provided enough of a glimpse into the lives of my family and friends that I felt like I still belonged, and someone still cared.

Via Facebook, I was able to get better acquainted with my family. Most of my cousins are married with families, and I now look forward to photos and posts of Luke's cute little kids, Jeff and Katy's jeep weekends, Tessa's astronomical accomplishments as a Girl Scout, and the escapades of Holly's little boys and her journey to China to adopt another child. I reconnected with friends from my past, Kris, Lora, Shawna, and Kilty. I missed these friends. Thanks to Facebook, I finally had the chance to reconnect and reacquaint myself with these long, lost friends.

Several years before, I met Anne Brewer when I traveled to east Florida for the company we both worked for at the time. We lost track of each other, and several years later, thanks to Facebook, we discovered we lived in the same county in Florida. So, we've since shared many lunches with beaucoup bottles of wine. Anne has an objective way of listening and an uncanny ability to commiserate with my caregiving escapades. Her *tell it like it is* attitude helps to keep me grounded, reminding me this is but a brief chapter of my life. New adventures are waiting for me to discover and enjoy.

My family and friends have become a lifeline for me and even though they aren't aware of this, their communications, whether directly or via Facebook, have helped me to heal, move forward with my life, and accept my new life as a widow. I am eternally grateful.

During my first year of widowhood, people often said, "I don't know how you do it." I had to be truthful and tell them I had no choice. Who else was going to do this? *Yes, it was at the top of my Wish List to chuck a good job and take care of my parents.* Or, I gave them a generic answer, "Yes, it's tough sometimes. I'm hanging in there; it is what it is." I said it so often, it became my mantra. "That was some rain we had last night. I'm hanging in there; it is what it is." If you asked the pups, they'd probably even tell you I say it in my sleep! *Hey, it is what it is!*

I realized my mantra satisfied my friends and family's concerns about me, and they were none the wiser of how I really felt. How could I tell someone when I opened a book the other day and saw my husband's written comments expounding his opinion about the book, I cried for hours and my eyes got red and swollen. Or, could I tell them about the time I was driving south on Highway 19 on my way to Spring Hill to run errands and meet a friend for lunch. All of a sudden, I thought about Matthew's Stage West performance as Toddy in *Victor/Victoria*, my favorite of all his shows. I cried so hard I had to turn around and go back home and texted my friend, "My mom's sick, and I can't make it, sorry."

Thanks to Matthew, I finally understood and appreciated the value of friendship. Before I met him, I didn't know how to be a friend. I had friends, but I was a loner, too wrapped up in my own sequestered, solitary world. Matthew opened my eyes. He was my husband and my best friend. I can't help but think, if Matthew hadn't come into my life, my life would be so empty, and I would never have known what a true blessing a friend is.

Since Matthew died, I've reached out beyond my comfort zone, kept an open mind, and learned how enjoyable it was to make friends. Sometimes, it's friends I've known by association for years, like my friend Sharon's daughter, Katie. I watched Katie grow up and blossom from a softball loving tomboy into a beautiful, kind souled young woman. Katie's uplifting Facebook posts frequently appeared at the right time when I felt low. Some of my new friends are also widows and therefore, we understand and comfort each other as we traverse through healing and recovery. Two such new friends are Joyce Cotton and Cheral Riddick. We met through mutual friends and discovered our common ground of recent widowhood. What a blessing and gift from God to have these two wonderful ladies in my life. They provide friendship, comfort, and laughter.

Thanks to Matthew, I truly appreciate my friends. Maybe I've lost my best friend, but my life is so much richer and more fulfilled for having known Matthew. And most importantly, he helped me to be a better daughter and caregiver for my parents. I value the friends I have and will not squander the value and love they add to my life.

> There is no wilderness like a life
> without friends; friendship multiplies
> blessings and minimizes misfortunes;
> it is a unique remedy against adversity,
> and it soothes the soul. [33]
> —Baltasar Gracian

Caregiving Tips from the Heart

Caregiving Tip #26:

> There will be days when you want to pull your hair out. And there will be days when you smile and enjoy being a caregiver. If you give yourself some **ME** time each day, you will find those challenging days a little easier to deal with. **YOU** need balance in your life, otherwise your attitude will be affected, as will your sense of self-worth and respect for yourself. **KEEP BALANCE** in your life, the best way to do this is to accept help from others.

Caregiving Tip #27:

> Always remember, **YOU** are the caregiver, and **YOU** are in control. Don't let your loved one try to control you. **YOU** now call the shots, **YOU** coordinate their schedule, feed, clothe, manage finances, provide transport, and love them.
>
> In other words, **YOU** are now the *parent* to your loved one, they have now become your child, even if it's your spouse. This change in perspective takes a little getting used to. Your role in your loved one's life has changed, and you need to understand this and accept it.

Caregiving Tip #28:

> When your loved one no longer recognizes you or knows who you are, don't take it personally. They have no control over this. Somewhere buried within the quagmire of their brain, I'd like to believe they are mourning this loss of recognition just as much as you are.

CHAPTER 27

A Trip to Philly

October 2018

October was a tough month for me. I was excited about my granddaughter Meghan's upcoming wedding, but at the same time, I was anxious because it would be my first trip back to Philadelphia since Matthew died. In my mind, Philadelphia and Matthew were synonymous with each other. With the exception of the three years Matthew proudly served with the Marines, he spent the first fifty-four years of his life in Philadelphia, including his thirty years as a police officer. Matthew raised his family in Philadelphia. His sons and their families still live there. Philadelphia is a beautiful city with a patriotic history. The day I married Mathew; it became a third home to me.

The mere thought of being in Philadelphia without Matthew traumatized me. I wasn't looking forward to this trip, but I had to go. The advance notice about the wedding helped me to find respite care for Paul and Phyllis, as opposed to when Matthew died. I had no excuse not to go; it was my inner demons pulling me in so many emotional directions. It would have been so easy to give an excuse, be a coward, and not go. I knew in my heart if

I didn't make this trip *now,* then the next time the opportunity arose, it would have been even more difficult. No matter what, I was determined to go to Philadelphia, and I *wanted* to be a witness to Meghan's wedding. My determination gave me courage.

The last time I was in Philadelphia was November 2015, a couple of months after our great-granddaughter MacKenzie was born. Now, MacKenzie was three years old and had a baby brother, Michael. So much changed in three short years. That trip, like this one, was a short, extended weekend jaunt. I enjoyed the flight; it's always exciting to look down onto a place you know well and try to determine the landmarks. As the plane taxied to the terminal, I saw passengers all around me texting their arrivals to friends and family, something I used to do so many times in the past. The realization hit me hard and heavy. I was afraid of my reaction to Matthew's absence in Philadelphia, the city he knew so well, the city of brotherly love.

I never felt so lonely as I walked through the familiar terminal at the airport. I used to walk that path with a spring in my step and a smile in my heart knowing Matthew would be there to welcome me with a big, warm bear hug. I seemed to move in slow motion this time. There was no spring in my step or smile in my heart. Instead, with every trepid step, I dragged my bag, lost in thoughts. The inevitable finally caught up with me. The enormity of that realization was overwhelming. I wanted to sprint to any plane that was leaving within the next five minutes and get out of that city as fast as I could. I was even willing to go to Timbuktu! I would have gladly been a coward at that moment, but my mind propelled me forward. I had to face the ghost of visits past.

It was not only my first trip to Philadelphia after Matthew died, but it was also my very first time driving in Philadelphia. Matthew always did the driving since this was *his* city. He had an imprint of the map emblazoned in his mind. He knew all the shortcuts and byways like only a city born and bred kid could. I, on the other hand, had my heart in my throat as I consulted the map one more time and started to coax my little, red rental onto the road heading toward I-95 and the city. I arrived in

Philadelphia at the height of rush hour traffic. Cars zoomed by at the dangerous, breakneck speed of 2 mph. I had never been as thankful for bumper to bumper traffic as I was then. I saw the logjam as a blessing, whereas I'm sure everyone else around me cussed a blue streak. As I got closer to Michael and Diana's home, my trepidation eased, and I began to get excited about the wedding. I thought to myself, *So far, so good. Easy peasey, Veasey!*

I was almost there, less than a block from my destination. The street seemed so quiet, devoid of its usual traffic and cars parked along each side of the road. I pulled up to the house. There were no other cars around. That was strange. Their cars weren't parked in the driveway or on the street like they normally were. It looked like no one was home. Diana knew what time I was expected to arrive. Something seemed odd, but I couldn't put my finger on it. As I got out of the car, I looked up at the window above the garage. The window looked different. Did they replace the old bay window? I loved that bay window and Diana's seasonal window displays! She never mentioned replacing it. I pondered the mystery of why her house and those around didn't look familiar. After a couple of seconds, it dawned on me. I was in the wrong driveway! *Dammit, how did I do that!* I felt sheepish, embarrassed, and after a few more cuss words, I scanned all around to see if anyone was looking. I hoped not. I didn't think so. I quickly got back into the car, backed out of the driveway still shaking my head, and thought, *How did I do that?*

Only two houses further down the street I glimpsed the house that's so familiar to me. This time, I pulled into the *right driveway* knowing I was at the *right house* this time. I saw the familiar bay window above the garage. It felt like a welcoming beacon, my home away from home. I turned my head and saw the multi-story house across the street I'd seen hundreds of times before. I felt pretty stupid but thankful I'd made it. It felt like I was home. That sense of anxiety I'd been feeling for months started to abate like a faint, crisp, rustling autumn breeze.

I walked up to the front door, knocked, and walked right in. Diana greeted me with a warm smile and a hug. I believe she, if anyone in Matthew's family, knew how hard this trip was for me. I could have kept my secret, no one would *ever* have been the wiser, but the first thing that blurted out of my big, fat mouth was, "I feel stupid, I pulled into the wrong driveway. Can you believe that!" It broke the tension and opened the door so I could enjoy Philadelphia and feel excited about Meghan's upcoming nuptials. I was thankful to be back home with family! I still couldn't believe I pulled into the wrong driveway; *it is what it is!* Matthew must have gotten a good laugh out of that!

The day before the wedding, I had lunch with Grace Croke, a friend of Matthew's, at the Dining Car Diner. The Dining Car was always our favorite diner. Whenever Matthew and I were in town, we *always* managed to squeeze in a trip to the Dining Car. I hadn't met Grace before. She and her husband, along with Matthew and a couple of their friends, formed a group many years ago, known as the Potato Soup Gang. They met periodically for potato soup and to catch up on each other's lives. As the members dwindled through the years, Matthew continued to keep in touch with Grace and have lunch with her whenever he was in town. Every time Matthew returned home to Florida, he regaled me with tales of who he visited. I felt like I already knew Grace, even though we'd never met. Grace and I had a delightful lunch. I especially enjoyed hearing her stories about Matthew and his life BV, *before Vicki.* BV was a time I only had snippets of through Matthew's occasional stories.

After lunch, I went to the cemetery to visit the graves of Matthew's family. I prayed and dispensed a portion of his ashes at his mom's grave and his stillborn oldest son's grave, Joseph. Matthew and I often visited the graves whenever we were in town. I thought he'd appreciate a part of him resting with his family. I was proud of myself. The night before, I navigated from the airport to Michael and Diana's home. Then, I found my way to the cemetery. I could almost see Matthew beaming with pride over my accomplishments.

The wedding was beautiful, as all weddings are. Meghan looked stunning! Fran was handsome! Both had that special look in their eyes only two lovers have for each other. When they were pronounced "Man and Wife," I held my hands and squeezed them together. In my mind, Matthew and I were holding hands. I remembered when we were that bride and groom twenty-two years before, and our family, friends, and God bore witness to our declaration to stay together in sickness and in health, till death did us part.

Twenty-two years ago, Meghan was the flower girl at our wedding, a cherubic three-year-old brimming with the promise of a wonderful life. Now, Meghan was the bride. Her life represented the length of my marriage. Her marriage represented a new chapter in my life as a widow. How could time go by so quickly? Like a nanosecond. So much living took place in the past twenty-two years. Yet there were times when life seemed to stand still. I wish there was a *relive button* I could push to select a date or occasion to relive one more time. The problem is, I wouldn't know how to narrow the list down to one or two occasions, because thankfully, there were too many wonderful memories to choose from. If I learned anything from widowhood, it's never to take the ordinary, everyday things for granted. Life goes by too fast. It changes in the blink of an eye…and you can't get it back. What may seem like every day inconsequential things are memories, especially when they include the one you love.

Meghan and Fran's wedding reception was lively, and everyone had a great time. Michael, Meghan's father, made a stirring speech that made me cry. I knew in my heart this day was just as hard on Matthew's family as it was on me. I remembered when Matthew and I first learned of Meghan's engagement. Matthew was so happy; he was looking forward to attending her wedding. Instead, he got sick and died. I watched the dancing, saw the comradery, heard the laughter, and witnessed the merriment. I tried to fit in but felt like an outsider looking at the action from the sidelines, as if I was at an Eagles football game, and they were playing at New England. I felt like I was sitting at the 50-yard line, mesmerized by a beautiful Hail Mary pass thrown by Nick Foles in a repeat performance of the Super Bowl. As the ball reached its mark and scored a touchdown for the Eagles, I was reluctant to cheer too loud because I was sitting in enemy territory.

I kept looking for Matthew to show up any minute or indicate he was watching from above but sadly, nothing. In the back of the room, there was a display table with two photographs in memory of family who passed away much too soon. One photo was of Tina, Diana's sister, and the other was of Matthew. Even though they were not with us on this happiest of days, in my heart I knew they were together holding hands, smiling down from above with so much love in their hearts for this remarkable couple on their very special day, the wedding of Meghan and Fran. I walked up to that table several times during the reception. I stared at Matthew's photograph. It should have been Matthew here with me rather than an inanimate object. I blew a kiss to his likeness, tenderly touched the frame, and walked away. But I kept returning to the photo throughout the night like a moth that's attracted to a flame.

When I returned home, despite the feelings of trepidation and anxiety I'd felt for months, I was proud of myself. I faced my fears and came home a victor. I conquered the roads of Philadelphia and the ever daunting I-95. I tackled the demons of being back at Michael and Diana's home where I had so many Matthew memories. Their home represented the only physical place left where Matthew and I spent any significant time together. Everywhere I looked, I saw Matthew. He was at the dining room table talking to Michael, sipping his morning coffee and reading the morning newspaper. He was sitting at their computer, checking his email and Facebook, or snoring in Michael's recliner as a PGA tournament played on the TV. The vivid images are memories I hold close to my heart. Although I suspected this visit would challenge me, I knew I'd have to face it sooner or later. What better time than a wedding, with its sense of busyness, allure, and excitement? Mentally, I was able to check off three more milestones from my Matthew List—the return to his hometown of Philadelphia, a visit with Matthew's sons and their families, and conquering the ghosts of visits past.

Caregiving Tips from the Heart

Caregiving Tip #29:

It's human nature to select what looks like the most comfortable chair to sit in. For older individuals, especially those with mobility problems or dementia, soft-cushioned seating becomes a nightmare. It's difficult for them to get up from deep cushioned seating. Instead, select chairs or sofas with firmer cushions and with arms, to help your loved one to leverage themselves up.

Caregiving Tip #30:

Trying to keep your loved one engaged can be difficult; however, there are simple, everyday items in your home that can help. Give your loved one a pile of towels or clothes, and ask them to fold them. Once the towels or clothes are folded, you can move the items out of their sight, tangle them up again, and give the items back to your loved one to be refolded.

You can do something similar with old, discarded mail and some envelopes. Ask your loved one to stuff the envelopes with the old mail. Once done, you can do the same as mentioned above with the folded towels to have them re-stuff the envelopes.

CHAPTER 28

Only Mom Would Have Understood

Since Matthew died and I cared for my parents' full time, I hadn't had either the time, desire, or inclination to go out much except an occasional lunch with friends. However, a month after Matthew died, a friend at church asked me, "Did you see *The 39 Steps* at Stage West?"

"No, Lynda, I haven't."

"Larry and I went last night. The director dedicated the show in Matthew's memory." That caught my attention. A couple days later, I stopped at the box office and inquired of my friend, Sue, who worked there.

"Sue, I heard Saul dedicated his show to Matthew. Is that right?"

"Yes, he did. I'm so sorry about Matthew, my condolences."

"Thanks, Sue. Are there any tickets left for Saturday night? I'd like to go. If you see Saul, please give him a big hug from me,

261

and let him know how much I appreciate his gesture. It means so much to me."

I attended the second to last performance of *The 39 Steps* at the Forum Theater at Stage West. Before each performance, the show's director walks out on stage and addresses the audience. The director of *The 39 Steps* was Saul Leibner, a good friend of ours for over twenty years. He and his wife Roz attended the dinner the year before on February 3 that turned out to be Matthew's last birthday. I sat in the audience and listened as Saul provided insight about the play. I started to choke up when Saul informed the audience that the run of the show was dedicated to the memory of a long time Stage West member who graced their stages in many memorable productions in the past. Saul also acknowledged my presence in the audience. I was moved with emotion, inwardly crying tears that wanted to rain down my face, liquid crystals I was trying desperately to contain with little success.

Stage West was where I met Matthew. His stage debut was Bill Ray, the dentist, in *On Golden Pond*. I actually saw one of those performances. I'm sad to say his acting on that occasion didn't stand out in my mind. A year later, I sat in the audience at the same theatre watching an entertaining performance of *My Three Angels*. There was something about one of those angels that caught my attention, specifically a particular angel's voice. It was soothing, gentle, and comforting. I sat spellbound, enjoying every single minute of that show.

Several weeks later, November 1995, I watched a rehearsal for a show in preproduction at Stage West. I was going to do props for another upcoming show, *The Essence of Molly*. I never worked a show before, and the props mistress thought it might be beneficial if I watched a rehearsal. As I sat toward the back of the theatre, taking mental notes, a door opened to the left of the stage, and an older gentleman walked in. He had a jaunty walk like he was dancing on the balls of his feet, walking on air. Everyone seemed to know him. I stared at him, mesmerized, but I didn't know why. After a couple of minutes, he looked my way. I was in partial darkness and thought I was invisible. Our eyes

262

met and the next thing I knew, he walked up the aisle, turned down the row directly in front of me, and stopped within two feet of me. When he introduced himself, I instantly recognized his voice. He was the same person I saw in *My Three Angels*, that particular angel whose voice I found so appealing, the voice I wasn't able to get out of my mind.

During the years, we both worked many shows at Stage West. Matthew was either on or off the stage. I, on the other hand, always worked behind the scenes. Matthew even appeared in shows at other venues in our area. It was bitter sweet to sit in the audience that night after Saul dedicated the run of the show to Matthew's memory. It reminded me I'd never see Matthew on stage again. So much of our married life revolved around Stage West, and it was hard to accept this chapter of my life was over. I made so many good memories and numerous dear friends as a result of my life with Matthew, a life that's never more.

I looked forward to a concert on November 18, 2018. It all began the winter of 1966. My mom drove me to my grandparent's house. I remembered how dark and bone-chilling cold it was both in the car and outside. The car's heater blasted on that wintry January morning with very little success. Mom had the car radio on. I was familiar with the local Motown bands because the airwaves played The Supremes, The Temptations, and Smokey Robinson and the Miracles. When an unfamiliar song started to play, I noticed it sounded so different from what we normally heard on the radio. Something about this song captivated the attention of this shy, introverted eight-year-old. Suddenly, the car felt warmer, and the outside appeared brighter despite the predawn hour. The lyrics, coupled with this singer's voice, made me feel happy and cheerful. Every time I heard that song on the radio, I asked Mom, "Turn up the volume!" My reaction was always the same whenever I heard those distinctive first bars of the music. I loved that upbeat melody of sunshiny love. This song became my happy song and knocked the Beatles' "We Can Work It Out," from the coveted number one spot on the Billboard Hot 100 the weeks of February 5 and 12, 1966.[34] The masterful Tony Hatch wrote the song, which brightened my soul and painted a smile on my face, still, over fifty years later. The song is "My Love" sung by Britain's top female singer, Petula Clark. I was an instant fan and have been ever since.

The sixties were known for long hair, bell bottoms, tent dresses, paisley prints, the Rolling Stones, The Beatles, drugs, marijuana, and free love. It didn't take much coaxing on my part to convince my mom to buy me the latest Petula Clark album. Mom was probably relieved that her young daughter was a fan of someone contemporary, not to an extreme. Clark was someone her young daughter could look up to with respect without wondering if some dangerous influence would warp her young child's mind.

Birthdays and Christmas were especially happy times for me when I spied a wrapped, square-shaped gift with my name on it. Nine times out of ten, it was a new Petula Clark album, in the good old days of vinyl. I knew all the lyrics. I lip synced to every song. And as I moved around the country when I became a working adult, my Petula Clark vinyl collection always traveled with me. When I was sad, my favorite Petula songs always brightened my melancholy mood. Some of my Petula favorites, aside from "My Love," are "I Couldn't Live Without Your Love," "I Know a Place," "This Is My Song," "Round Every Corner," "Kiss Me Goodbye," "Downtown," "Sign of the Times," "The Other Man's Grass Is Always Greener," "You're The One," and "Don't Sleep in the Subway." These songs became my best friends like my favorite Beatles songs became life-long friends, too. There was one song I fondly remember, a song Petula sang in the film, *Goodbye, Mr. Chips*, written by Leslie Bricusse. It was a song I always loved hearing but even more so since Matthew passed away, "You and I." The poignant lyrics of sentimental love between a husband and wife never fail to make me cry.

I remember my very first concert like it was yesterday. It was Friday, May 16, 1969, a balmy, warm spring evening. I was still dressed in the clothes I wore to school that day, a vest and culotte set, white with large, brown circles, and a white pullover. As soon as my dad came home from work, my parents called me to the car, and we left immediately. They didn't tell me where we were going. All I could tell from looking out the car window was that we were heading to downtown Detroit. I knew Petula was scheduled to perform two concerts that day. I had asked my mom weeks before if we could go. She was noncommittal. It wasn't until we parked the car, walked around a corner, and I looked up to see the Masonic Auditorium. It was at that moment I knew where we were. I was ecstatic!

By nature, my parents weren't ones for surprises, but they sure surprised me that night. It was my first concert ever, and it spoke volumes of how wonderful my parents were to take me to see my favorite singer. I still have the ticket stubs and the souvenir program. Since then, I've attended other Petula Clark concerts. I remember each one fondly, but that very first concert, thanks to my mom, was the concert that meant the most.

Concert day in Clearwater finally arrived. I'd never been to the Nancy and David Bilheimer Capitol Theatre, but GPS got me there within a respectable time. The concert was great. I loved seeing my favorite singer, and it made my day to hear my favorite songs. Petula's voice was just as beautiful and strong as the first time I heard her on the car radio back in 1966. The only problem was the woman directly in front of me with her wide shoulders and big, bouffant hairdo. It was extremely difficult to see the stage. I kept bopping side to side to catch a glimpse of Petula with very little success. Despite the giant sitting in front of me, I enjoyed every single minute of the concert, and I couldn't ask for anything more, or so I thought.

I could have listened to Petula sing all night, but that wouldn't have been very fair to her. As the house lights came back on in the theatre, the patrons started to get up and leave. I held back for a few minutes. I wanted to record in my mind every emotion and magical moment of this night so I could replay it later, absorbing the atmosphere of that beautiful theatre and the concert I enjoyed.

I finally stood up and started up the aisle. I was about halfway up the aisle, glancing around as I slowly inched my way toward the back of the theatre. My eyes strayed to the tech booth. I saw several people in animated conversation, and something about two of those persons looked awfully familiar. I blinked, thinking my eyes were playing tricks on me. I looked a little closer. No, it couldn't be, but it sure looked like my friends from church, Cynthia Haring and Katia Valdeos. I started to wave my hands, trying to capture their attention. Finally, Katia noticed me, and she nudged Cynthia. As I got closer to the back of the theatre, I cut into a row closer to where they were. We were surprised to see each other and talked excitedly about the concert. I mentioned my life-long appreciation of Petula's singing.

Cynthia asked, "Can you stay a while?"

"Sure," I responded, "I can stay a few more minutes."

"I read in the paper Petula had a birthday a couple days ago. I'm hoping I can give her our latest CD; I think she might like it."

Cynthia and Katia are founding members of the Sue Sue Sisters, a female singing group that records original music. We sat and talked. After a few minutes, a guy walked up to Cynthia and asked her to follow him. Of course, Katia and I tagged along. I was directly behind the guy, with Katia and Cynthia bringing up the rear. We walked behind a curtain, through a dimly lit corridor, and we entered a brightly lit hallway. I looked up, trying to get my eyes adjusted to the sudden brightness when I noticed my idol, the one and only ever diminutive, Petula. I'm not one to get easily tongue-tied. Afterall, I grew up in Lathrup Village in a neighborhood populated by the greats of Detroit's professional athletes. My neighbors consisted of Red Wings, Tigers, and Lions. But this was totally different, this was Petula Clark! In my eyes, she's in a class all by herself. And I was close enough to touch her! She looked at me, a little perplexed, extended her hand, and we shook. Her first words to me, "Your hand is cold." Four simple words that meant a lot. My friends soon met her, and we chatted briefly. Cynthia presented her gift, and we left. What a stroke of luck to see my friends immediately after the concert. If not for them, I never would have met my favorite singer. What a night I will never forget!

As I was driving home after the concert, I couldn't help but think about my mom. Oh, how I wished I could tell her about this night, to share my feelings and emotions about this wonderful concert and chance meeting Petula. Mom used to be as familiar with Petula's songs as I am. She would have been enthralled about this night, especially if she heard about seeing my friends, which ultimately led to a thrill of a lifetime. As I thought about what I couldn't tell Mom, emotions triggered an avalanche of pent-up tears as I reflected on what Alzheimer's has robbed us of. My mom would have understood what I felt that night, but she didn't know who I was anymore, let alone remembered who Petula Clark was. My mom helped nurture my interest in Petula's music every time she bought me an album. It was Mom who surprised me with tickets to my first Petula concert. Mom always took me to see Petula's films when I was a child, *Finian's Rainbow* and *Goodbye Mr. Chips*. Mom was the most pivotal person in my life who could understand how much this special night meant to me, but I couldn't share it with her.

I was crying so hard; I had to pull off the road. Salty tears cascaded from my eyes faster than Niagara Falls. Everything I kept locked up inside me imploded that night. I sobbed with bottled up rage. I keened for the loss and sorrow I felt for Matthew, and I bawled and cursed what Alzheimer's robbed us of. I thunderously wailed from the bowels of my soul. My mom was the one person who could have understood the value of this night, but I couldn't share it with her. I couldn't stop my thunderous balling. It spilled over to a new round of uncontrollable, heart-wrenching emotions and agonizing wailing. I never cried like that before. I didn't recognize the sounds emitting from within me. I felt each new wail as it reverberated up from my toes, traveled through my abdomen, and slowly exploded from my mouth. Each outburst and every tear I shed that night helped to cleanse my soul and heal my heart of the loneliness and grief I felt since the night

Matthew died. It helped me assimilate and accept that the parents I treasured were inwardly mourning who they used to be.

My mom was alive yet dead to me in so many ways. If only Alzheimer's didn't rob loved ones of precious memories for sharing later in life. There have been times since Matthew died when I yearned for my mom to envelop and cradle me in her loving arms, hopeful her embrace would help ease my heartache. I needed my mommy that night, like a child who skins its knee and goes wailing in desperation for its mommy to provide love, comfort, and a motherly kiss. Mom was physically there, but she wasn't alive for me in the way I needed her. So, I sat alone in my car on that isolated roadside drowning in my tears, crying for everything that had happened during the past year. Most of all, I cried for all our simple, everyday memories which I used to take for granted.

That night, November 18, 2018, was a golden night of memories for me, unexpected thrills, and heart wrenching sorrow that cleansed my soul. From that point on, I dedicated myself to be kinder, more understanding, and more loving to my parents. Even though they didn't know who I was anymore, it was important for me to remember who they were to me. They weren't only Paul and Phyllis, two people I cared for. They were still my parents who deserved to be loved and cherished for the wonderful parents they had been to me. That night, I promised myself I'd do everything in my power to always remember our cherished memories. I vowed to do everything I could to never forget, since I now have to remember for four—Matthew, Mom, Dad, and myself. I have a lifetime of cherished memories. I pray they're never erased from my consciousness as my mom's memories have been.

Christmas Letter 2018

Merry Christmas!

I feel blessed! Despite being the second worst year of my life, it's been a healing year for me as well. A continuous year of firsts: first holidays without Matthew, first year to celebrate birthdays and anniversaries without him, first time as a patient in a hospital without Matthew holding my hand and giving me strength, so many firsts! With each first I've cried a ton of tears and with each tear my soul continues to heal. From what friends have told me, you never get over losing a spouse. My goal, to be able to look at photos, hear Irish music and reflect upon memories with a reflective smile rather than a sudden onrush of tears. I'm not there yet, but I am improving!!!

Paul and Phyllis are hanging in there. Paul has issues remembering, difficulty sleeping at night, and his restless legs provide daily problems as well. His macular degeneration and glaucoma continue to decline, despite treatments every six-eight weeks. Phyllis enjoys her Peg-A-Pattern, baby doll, and sewing board. They both have diminished appetites and sleep more during the day. I'm thankful for the services they receive through the county, two days each week at the Key Center in Lecanto and an aide who started coming to the house twelve hours every week. God blessed us with the move to Citrus County, otherwise these services would not have been available to them. Phyllis' brother Ron still lives with us, he has Parkinson's and is rail thin. The pups provide unconditional love, they are my little gifts from God. I don't know what I'd do without them!

In August I reconnected with family and friends in Michigan for the Heltunen family reunion, in honor of the 100th anniversary of the family farm! Also visited with my aunt and uncle, Peg and Jim, in Port Hope, that's in the thumb of the mitten. My cousins Katy and Breanne met me on Mackinac Island, and cousins John and his crew drove up to the U.P. and we shared a few pizzas.

October marked the wedding of my youngest granddaughter, Meghan, to her beloved Fran. Met great-grandson Michael for the first time and was mesmerized by the antics of his older sister MacKenzie. I also met Matthew's dear friend Grace for the first time, what a delightful lady!

May the Blessings of this Holiday Season Continue
into 2019
& Bring You Peace, Happiness, Love, and Good Health.
Vicki, Paul, Phyllis, Kipper, & Katy

CHAPTER 29

Ready to Embrace
the Holidays

November & December 2018

Shortly after returning from Meghan's wedding, the county notified me that Phyllis was now eligible for a new program that would provide in-home respite hours. It felt like an early Christmas present; *thank you, Santa*! I started to notice Phyllis was having difficulty getting in and out of the car. It was a safety issue to lift her left leg into the car. I anticipated it was only a matter of time before I could no longer take her anywhere, which meant I'd be a prisoner at home. Having an aide come to the house was going to be blessing. Plus, it was the added benefit of another person to provide social interaction with Phyllis. She still enjoyed people around her and chattered away in her Phyllis language of mostly made-up words.

We welcomed Leroy Hill, Jr. into our home. Leroy was a quiet gentleman with a heart of gold and a kind, gentle soul.

Phyllis took to Leroy like a child takes to a new toy. Even though Phyllis was no longer capable of remembering who he was, she did enjoy Leroy's company. She was happy to have someone to talk to her and help her. Of course, Paul resorted to his usual demeanor like he did when Mary Ann started with us two years earlier. After an hour or so, Paul told Leroy, "You can go home now." Despite my little talks with Paul regarding his dismissing Leroy like he tried to do, it took months before Paul finally got used to having Leroy come to our home. And with time, Leroy became a member of our family, just like Mary Ann had several years before.

Leroy and I discovered that we had many things in common. We were both from Michigan, and he was even familiar with Lathrup Village. We still cheered for our home town teams, the Tigers, Pistons, Lions, and Red Wings. And our work ethic, love of family, and respect for each other bonded us as family. In the same way I felt fortunate Mary Ann entered our lives back in May 2016, I felt just as blessed we had Leroy, a gentle giant who watched over Phyllis with loving, compassionate care. In the following months, there would be many times when Leroy's help was greatly appreciated and so needed.

For me, November is the beginning of the holiday season of Thanksgiving and Christmas. Last year, the holidays didn't exist for us because my Aunt Lou passed away shortly before Thanksgiving, and it was the first of those holidays since Matthew died. My heart was numb and raw from pain. With my crushed mood and the busyness of the move, I was devoid of emotional or physical stamina to celebrate. But this year, I was determined to celebrate the holidays, no matter what!

I hadn't had much time to watch TV that year because I was trying to unpack. Those rare times when I did watch TV it was uncomfortable with my knees scrunched up to my chest due to the boxes piled up everywhere. However, I caught an advertisement on Facebook that heralded the upcoming 2018 Hallmark Christmas movie schedule, the first film scheduled for October 27. I've always loved Hallmark's Christmas movies; they have a

way of warming my heart and enticing me to bake holiday cookies and listen to Christmas music. On October 27, I was glued
to the dinky TV in my cramped, crowded bedroom, watching a
holiday movie that opened my heart to the upcoming Christmas
season. I watched over forty holiday movies that year and enjoyed
everyone. Sometimes, I recorded and watched two or three in
one evening. I guess I made up for the dismal Christmas we had
the year before.

Christmas has always been my favorite holiday. Not sure
what I love more, the brightly colored Christmas decorations,
mouth-watering aromas of baking cookies, or the excitement of
shopping for the ones I love. It's fun to wrap gifts in colorful
paper with beautiful bows and ribbons while listening to my
favorite Christmas songs as I sing along at the top of my lungs.
I enjoy Christmas novels with hot chocolate or a glass of wine.
I feel loved with the arrival of each and every Christmas card
from family and friends. I cry at the Christmas Eve candle light
service while I somberly sing *Silent Night*, my face upraised to
heaven. And I love Christmas movies! In the past, I was too busy
to enjoy the season because I was always juggling a multitude of
holiday chores while working a full-time job.

This year, I didn't have a job to keep me away from the house
forty plus hours each week. I purchased a new Christmas tree
and had it up and decorated by November 5. I worked for weeks
decorating the rest of the house. I even found locations for the
Christmas village, tucked in little places here and there, under the
tree, and on a credenza in the dining nook. I strung twinkling,
bright lights above the living room curtains—red, green, and
white. I even set up a white Christmas tree in my bedroom. I
was determined! We were going to celebrate Christmas this year!

I hoped the lights, decorations, and Christmas music would
trigger something in Phyllis' hidden memory bank, but instead,
her eyes stared blankly without recognition. On those rare occasions when my uncle wasn't ensconced in front of the TV, I played
Christmas music for my mom, songs I knew she'd be familiar
with, "Jingle Bells," "Silent Night," and "Away in a Manger." Did

she know why the house looked so different? Did she know we'd be celebrating the birth of baby Jesus soon? I doubted it. By now, Phyllis' condition was visibly deteriorating.

I was determined to make Christmas as magical, spiritual, and beautiful as I could make it. It was difficult to Christmas shop for my parents; neither one needed anything. But what was Christmas if there wasn't a gayly wrapped gift under the tree Christmas morning with your name on it? I wracked my brain to come up with perfect gifts for everyone. It finally dawned on me, Paul and Phyllis have no recollection of previous Christmases. Once I changed my mindset, shopping for them became so much easier. With that realization, I tackled Christmas shopping in an entirely new way. Phyllis enjoyed the large Build-A-Bible Activity books I'd previously purchased for her at Dollar Tree. So, I bought another one in the series and wrapped it in eye-catching holiday paper adorned with a big, beautiful, red bow. I made her another sewing board. No matter how much her mind had deteriorated, she still made the necessary motions with the makeshift needle I created using cardboard and tape to string the yarn in and out of the large, round holes. I searched the toy aisles at our local stores and found a toy cash register that makes noise when the keys are pushed. The staff at the Key Center said Phyllis often spent hours looking at an RV magazine, so I found a magazine for RV enthusiasts and wrapped that in bright, festive paper. In the past, Paul and Phyllis had a travel trailer and spent many enjoyable winters traveling the United States, especially Florida, reveling in the scenery and making new friends along the way. For Paul, a tub of popcorn was always a Paul pleaser along with aftershave and a basketball game I thought he'd enjoy.

My mom, back when she was functioning, always went overboard Christmas shopping. Our Christmas tree was surrounded by piles of gifts wrapped in beautiful paper, tied with coordinating, shiny ribbons and bows. Christmas morning took us hours to unwrap everything. Afterward, we marveled at all the new treasures we received.

When Matthew and I were first marred, he was taken aback by the extravagance he saw that first Christmas in 1996. For many years, I didn't understand this over indulgence myself until one day, I overheard my mom talking to a friend and it all made sense to me. As she explained, "When Paul was a child, there was no money to buy each of the eleven children a gift for Christmas. Instead, every Christmas they anxiously looked forward to receiving a gift box from their aunt, who managed a small general store. When we got married, I wanted to make-up to Paul for all the Christmases he never had as a child growing up." Several years after I heard my mom talking to her friend, my dad provided me with some additional insight into his childhood Christmases on the farm. It helped me appreciate and understand my mom's Christmas generosity and the depth of her love for my dad, "... it was my job to look for the box my Aunt Lena sent Mom each year. I looked around the hayloft, the sauna, the milk shed, in the basement, under the front porch, and in the attic. Once I found it, I told my brothers the box arrived, and then we were so excited we couldn't sleep at night. That box always contained the old, melted candies left over from the front window of Aunt Lena's store. We didn't mind; that box was the only Christmas present we ever received each year; it meant the world to us."

Every year, Mom did everything she could to make our holidays as cheerful, special, and as memorable as she could. For that reason, I wanted to make this Christmas as special for her as I could. I remember mentioning to a friend, "I wouldn't be surprised if next year is Phyllis' year to leave us." I felt sad to say that, but the subtle changes in her physical and cognitive condition gave me the gut instinct I couldn't ignore. As a result, I wanted Thanksgiving and Christmas 2018 to be the best holidays I could make for my parents, just in case these were Mom's last earthly ones.

We had a beautiful Christmas. Paul and Phyllis each received Christmas gifts from Senior Services of Citrus County. They had fun digging through the gift bags, packages, and tearing off and playing with the wrapping paper. Each unexpected gift was appreciated and helped make their Christmas extra special. I felt like a parent watching her children opening their gifts on Christmas morning. Sometimes, Phyllis got off course and distracted by the wrapping paper or bow, and I had to redirect her attention to the task at hand. We had a great day followed by a delicious Christmas dinner at the clubhouse with our neighbors.

We enjoyed the day, and I was thankful we had one more Christmas together, even though my parents wouldn't remember what we shared on this blessed of all holidays. I accepted that it was up to me to keep these memories alive and to treasure this time we have together as a true blessing from God. It was similar to the blessing God gave me in January 2017, when Matthew and I were both sick, and we had six weeks together. Those six weeks were the last time Matthew and I had any length of time together without the stress and demands of my job and before the drastic decline of his health. I viewed those six weeks as one of God's most wonderous of gifts. I thanked God for the Christmas of 2018, for His beautiful gift to me—another shared Christmas with my mom and dad. I didn't know what the next year would hold for us, but at that moment, we were together making memories I knew I'd be the only one to remember and cherish, but that was alright. We were together, and my parents had fun. I treasured the moment. What more could I ask for?

PART III

Acceptance, Moving Forward

CHAPTER 30

Let the New Year Begin!

January 2019

At the stroke of midnight, I heard my neighbors across the street at the clubhouse robustly heralding in the new year while my charges were home safely tucked into their beds, totally oblivious to the fact that a new year was beginning. With a glass of champagne, I curled up in bed toasting the arrival of 2019, hoping this new year would be better than the past two years. I was reading two books, my usual habit. On this night, I picked up *About My Mother*, a delightful first written by Peggy Rowe. Peggy's book was the perfect choice to read on such a sentimental night as New Year's Eve. It was written in a nostalgic and humorous manner. Peggy knew how to capture her reader's attention as she took you on a journey back to the 1930s-1960s, an era I heard my parents reminiscent about and one that interested me.

Outside my opened bedroom window, I heard the rapturous shouts of "Happy New Year!" emanating from the opened doors of the clubhouse. Neighbors joyously celebrated the dawn of a new year while in the distance, I heard fireworks peppering the midnight black sky, waking the pups from their slumber, arousing anxious and afraid body language. As I coaxed the pups onto my bed to appease their frightened souls, I gently petted their soft fur. I leaned back against the pillows and closed my eyes. After a few seconds, floating images of Matthew danced in my mind. I could have sworn I heard his voice softly, just barely, humming one of his favorite Irish songs, "The Parting Glass." Images of times past played before my closed eyes like old sixteen mm black and white celluloid. Was my mind playing tricks on me? I couldn't be happier. Straining my ears, I could have sworn I heard Matthew whispering to me, "Happy New Year, My Wicki Woo." In the background from the clubhouse, I heard a faint strain of "Auld Lang Syne" with its nostalgic lyrics, so synonymous with the new year that always brings tears to my eyes. While my neighbors were partying just fifty feet away, I began a private party of my own, thinking of loved ones.

My guests were the ghosts of cherished loved ones—Matthew, family and friends, people who meant the world to me. I dug out my photo albums and slowly turned the pages, reminiscing as I looked at photographs from past birthdays, anniversaries, and special times we shared and treasured. I was surprised at the number of loved ones, frozen mute images starring back at me who are now cherished fragments of my life, a lifetime that seemed so long ago. I couldn't help but wonder who I'd be saying good-bye to this year.

I hoped we'd ease into the new year gently, but January had a totally different plan for us. Within an eleven-day period, I experienced two GERD attacks. Since September 2017, I'd been averaging one GERD attack every five to six weeks. As the months progressed, the frequency drastically escalated. The first 2019 attack occurred on January 10 within minutes of eating lunch at a local seafood restaurant with a friend. I knew shrimp scampi was a forbidden fruit but when I ordered, thoughts of Matthew flashed into my mind. He loved shrimp scampi so much. The next thing I knew, I had ordered shrimp scampi. I enjoyed those tantalizing, tasty seafaring wonders. They looked so appetizing in their bath of garlicky butter, a buttery blend that sent explosions of flavor, igniting my taste buds while the slippery, slimy, gooey sauce dribbled down my chin, smeared my fingers, and left odd-shaped grease stains randomly scattered on the front of my blouse. I knew there was a chance I'd pay for it later, though it was sooner than I had expected. Before I left the restaurant, I felt the first tell-tale signs of a GERD attack before I got up from the table.

The second GERD attack started during the early hours of January 21. The culprit this time, I'm assuming, was the forbidden snack I nibbled on when I watched a movie. I didn't eat much popcorn, just a few kernels, but it was always so hard for me to resist watching a movie without some mouthwatering, buttery popcorn. Both attacks were ferocious and frightening. Both attacks were generated by foods I knew I shouldn't be eating but on those two occasions, I had little resistance. Maybe I was a glutton for punishment, or perhaps I had started to adopt an attitude because I was tired of being a prisoner of my own health. Medication provided no relief. The attacks were now lasting eighteen to twenty-four hours, and I started vomiting profusely with the last three to four attacks. Each attack made it more difficult to care for Paul and Phyllis. Playing an ignorant fool was no longer an option. I had a health problem, and it was time to seek medical intervention. And since I was *finally* trying to be intelligent about this, I anticipated that when I entered the sacred portals of the ER, I probably wouldn't be coming home any time soon.

The 21st was a Monday, and Phyllis' aide, Leroy, was his ever-punctual self. As he tended to her needs, I made arrangements for caregiving help for Paul and Phyllis in case I found myself an unwilling guest at the local medical center. My friend Dianne Terry stepped up to the plate in a true all-star manner, coordinating a caregiving schedule. I'm not sure what I would have done without Dianne's assistance. At 1:00 p.m., as Leroy left at the end of his shift, Dianne arrived and put her schedule into motion, catering to Paul and Phyllis' needs. I headed to the ER, dropped the pups off at the kennel, and knew I'd probably be hospitalized for a few days. It was a tremendous relief off my mind not to worry about Paul and Phyllis during those days, thanks to my friend Dianne. And if not for my support group, I'd never have met Dianne. What a wonderous, fortuitous Godsend my support group has been!

Less than a year earlier, in May 2018, I was in a similar situation shortly after returning from Cedar Key with the pups. On that occasion, I picked Paul and Phyllis up from the assisted living facility, where they spent a week in respite. My first night home I experienced a GERD attack. The next day, I went to my physician, hoping for a change in medication. Instead, he insisted that I go to the ER. I remember calling the marketing director at the assisted living facility, where I had just picked up Paul and Phyllis the day before. On the verge of tears, I panicked about this sudden turn of events, totally vexed about what do to with Phyllis during my stay at the hospital. The marketing director, who months earlier had become a Facebook friend, offered to readmit Phyllis to her facility. My friend Dianne agreed to check on Paul and Ron as did my neighbors, Shirley and Nancy.

When I arrived at the ER, even before any tests were run, they said I'd probably need gallbladder surgery. I was skeptical that they could come up with a diagnosis without running any bloodwork or tests. I also didn't like their condescending attitude, projecting guesstimates without conclusive evidence. Turns out the tests were inconclusive, but they still wanted to do surgery. I declined because I didn't see the need at the time. But most importantly, I didn't know anyone who could help with Phyllis for an entire month. Recuperation would curtail me from doing any heavy lifting for a month, and Phyllis needed help getting on and off the toilet. Plus, like with the time when I couldn't attend Matthew's Philadelphia funeral, there were no short-term respite care facilities in our area. I couldn't afford the added high cost of putting Phyllis back into an assisted living facility for a month. I had two trips planned for later that year and had to be frugal with finances.

In the meantime, between these two ER visits, May 2018 and January 2019, I experienced twenty-one GERD attacks. Each attack was slightly more intense than the one before and lasted longer, eighteen to twenty-four hours. Caregiving and being sick does not make for good bed fellows. If only there had been a short-term respite facility in my area, I could have had surgery back in 2018 and saved myself the pain, anxiety, and frustration I experienced all those months leading up to January 2019.

During the 2019 ER visit, they ran tests *before* the mention of surgery, and within twenty-four hours, I learned I had a badly infected gallbladder and could no longer put off surgery. I contacted Dianne to let her know my status and called Audry, our Citrus County case manager, to see what she could provide for additional assistance. My concerns were for *after* surgery when I'd be home recuperating. I voiced my concerns to Audry, begging for help. After a few hours, Audry called me back. She couldn't find another aide to help, and Leroy didn't have additional hours in his schedule. I felt frustrated and lamented to Audry, "What am I going to do? I won't be able to lift Phyllis for a month. I always have to lift her off the toilet. There are times when it takes everything I've got."

"I could place her temporarily in a facility."

"You can do that! That's great. It actually works better than having Phyllis at home. I was concerned if she fell, I wouldn't be able to get her up. Audry, thank you. You have no idea what this means to me."

What a difference a year can make! Last year when I faced this same challenge, I had no one to help and no choice but to decline surgery. I spent the past eight months a prisoner of my declining health, carefully watching what I ate, taking medication, and not drinking or eating anything after 6:00 p.m. I slept with my head and upper torso propped up with multiple pillows, hoping the precautions would circumvent another GERD attack, which they didn't. If anything, my condition kept getting worse. This year, God blessed me with the help I needed, and I was extremely thankful.

I've met caregivers who haven't been so fortunate. Their health took a back seat to the caregiving needs of their loved one, like my health took a back seat to caring for my parents. That's one very important reason why short-term respite houses are important. They provide a safe and nurturing place for our Alzheimer's and dementia loved ones to receive care while their caregivers recharge their batteries, tend to their health needs, or enjoy visits with family or friends such as family events like weddings or graduations. Several times during the previous two years, I declined attendance at important family events while caregiving for my parents, including the Philadelphia funeral of my husband Matthew in May 2017 and my granddaughter Melissa's funeral in December 2018.

Thanks to our case manager, Audry, and my dear friends, Leroy, Mary Ann, and Dianne, I was able to focus on the issue at hand, my surgery and recuperation. Dianne took care of Paul and Phyllis when I was in the hospital, and she dressed Phyllis for transport to the assisted living facility where Phyllis stayed for a month while I recuperated.

It was a cool, January morning. Phyllis was bundled in a sweater and tan knit hat squished down over her head. She had a large matching scarf wrapped around her head and throat. Her big, blue eyes and the base of her nose were visible when Phyllis boarded the bus for transport to respite care. Dianne and I stood side-by-side as the bus slowly pulled away from the curb with Phyllis safely ensconced inside. I waved, feeling melancholy and morose. *"So, this is what it feels like when a parent ships their kid off to camp?"* A part of me was relieved that I wouldn't have to care for Phyllis for the next month. She was going to be in competent hands, or so I believed. This facility was in the business of taking care of the elderly. They were experts at this, so I had nothing to worry about. But at the same time, another part of me already missed her, even though the bus wasn't five feet away from the house.

Although I don't have biological children, the emotions I sometimes felt stymied me. There was the time when Paul was at his ophthalmologist for an eye exam and treatment for macular degeneration. During the eye exams, there were times when the tech had to enlarge the letters because Paul couldn't see them. Sometimes, what Paul saw didn't jive with what I saw projected on the wall in front of us. I sat quietly, totally horrified at the state of his vision, too stunned to cry on the inside and too ashamed to do anything but sit in total, stoic pose, without showing concern or emotion. How do parents live through situations like this? I couldn't help but think to myself, *I can't believe his vision has declined so much in just a few short weeks.* On those occasions, Alzheimer's was a blessing since it saved my dad from the reality of how bad his vision was. Paul seemed to treat these visits as a game. He enjoyed his conversations with his doctor. He was still able to comprehend verbal instructions and followed through to some extent. Thankfully, he didn't comprehend what his physician was explaining to me. Whereas if this had been Phyllis, she wouldn't have had the ability to identify the letters or provide meaningful feedback so her physician could provide a diagnosis.

Communicating pain or illness is a true stumbling block when caring for Alzheimer's patients. They can't understand what you ask them, and you as their caregiver can only react to what you observe that indicates something is wrong. For this reason, caregivers need to be proactive 24/7 in regard to their loved one's bodily functions. You as the caregiver need to be clued into your loved one's *norm,* and you need to acquaint yourself with your loved one's current and overall medical history. The more you know about your loved one's health will make it easier, in case of an emergency, for medical staff to diagnose and treat your loved one. Also, please be aware that anesthesia can often affect the cognitive abilities of your loved one. I saw this happen with friends, especially my Aunt Lou, following hip replacement surgery. Lou experienced a reaction to the anesthesia, and the last two years of her life were a cognitive downhill spiral peppered with advancing dementia that she didn't have before the surgery.

Even though I had a month off while I recuperated, I still had Paul and Ron to care for. My month off from Phyllis caregiving didn't mean I could lounge around, read books, and take endless naps. What it meant was I still had to feed Paul and Ron, clean their bathroom, do their laundry, and change their sheets. I had to give Paul his meds and eye drops, entertain him, coordinate his clothes, and help with Paul's sundowning. And I still had to pay bills. It seemed like a picnic compared to when Phyllis was home. It's amazing having one less person to care for can change the dynamics. Things seemed more relaxed, less stressful. I even found time to take afternoon naps with the pretense that it was a requirement for recuperating. I felt like I had a month's vacation despite the household and caregiving chores!

Paul didn't seem to notice that Phyllis was missing during the month. He only asked about her twice. Once, around the second week after she was gone, he asked me, "Where's Phyllis?" and I replied, "She's taking a vacation. She'll be back in two weeks." He never asked where, why, or how come he didn't go with her. The second time Paul asked we were in the car; it was the third week. I had cabin fever and asked Paul if he wanted to take a short drive to get us out of the house. He agreed. We had a delightful fifteen-minute drive to nowhere in particular, and when we got home, Paul turned his head toward the back seat and asked, "Didn't Phyllis come with us?" Other than those two occasions, Paul never seemed to notice that Phyllis wasn't home, even when he sat in his recliner that sits right next to Phyllis's lift chair. A characteristic of Alzheimer's is our loved ones have difficulty connecting the dots when someone is missing from their everyday world. It's as if they have blinders on and can't see beyond their limited sphere of life.

While I was recuperating, Paul celebrated his 98th birthday on February 23. The day before, I drove him to Tallahassee to visit his sister, Phyllis, and brother-in-law, Bob Rogers. Paul and Bob shared the same birthday, and the two couples, Paul and

Phyllis and sister Phyllis and her husband Bob, celebrated their birthdays together for many years, creating happy memories which made this particular birthday bittersweet. This was the first time one of these four was missing. It was a tangible feeling. Despite the laughter, love, and storytelling, a void was evident. Phyllis wasn't there, and even if she had been, she wouldn't have had any idea who these people were. The days of this merry, fun-loving, adventuresome foursome was now a thing of the past.

Paul and I enjoyed our trip to Tallahassee, though he appeared a bit remote at times, as if he was delving into a bottomless void. Once in a while, he popped up to the surface, smiled, shook his head in agreement, then resumed a blank look as he'd stare off into space above the heads of those present. Paul seemed to recognize his nephew, Jim, but appeared a little unsure regarding his niece, Lori. He'd developed a knack of covering himself whenever he was around people who indicated they knew him, yet *he* had no clue who they were. Watching from the sidelines, I became adept in recognizing his recovery mechanism.

Paul had a special place in his heart for his nephew, Jim. There was a story Paul loved to tell about Jim, dating to when Jim was in 6th or 7th grade. It was fall and football season, and Paul and Phyllis were visiting Bob and Phyllis. I believe they were living in Ohio at the time. Jim, being the natural athlete that he was plus a member of his school's football team, asked his aunt and uncle if they'd like to attend his football game. Jim was playing, and he was one of the stars on the team. Uncle Paul jumped at the chance! He always took great pride in his nieces and nephews and felt honored whenever he had the opportunity to be a witness to their lives.

As Paul used to tell it, I've heard this story so often I could tell it in my sleep, "It was about half way through the game. We were sitting in the bleachers, and my butt was getting sore. So, I got up and walked down to the sidelines to stretch my legs and to get a better view of the game. Jim was having a great game, and I wanted to have a closer look. After a couple of minutes, I saw this kid running close to the side of the field, running right toward me clutching the football. As he got closer, he turned his head to look at me and yelled, 'Uncle Paul, I got the ball!' Jim ran that ball all the way for a touchdown. I was so proud of him!" It was always at the part where Jim turned and yelled at his uncle that Paul would strike a football pose with an imaginary football securely held in the crook of his left arm. His right arm extended upward above his head with his left leg bent up at the knee, just like he'd seen Jim do as he ran past him on his way to scoring a touchdown. While striking that football pose, Paul's eyes always twinkled, a big, broad smile beamed on his face, and he'd start to laugh, a big, loving belly laugh. Paul never got tired of telling that story, and I always enjoyed hearing it, especially the part when Paul would strike that distinctive Jim football pose.

Two days after our trip to Tallahassee, Phyllis came home. I had recovered, felt refreshed, and ready to resume our daily routine. Especially important, we were all back together again under the same roof. Even though it had only been a month, it felt much longer.

Several times when Phyllis was at the facility, I received phone calls to inform me of mini-emergencies. The first call informed me Phyllis's hair was pulled; strands were yanked out by the roots. Another patient walked up to her and started pulling her hair while she sat in the TV room. Another time, I received a call that Phyllis' ankles and legs were swollen. I was dumfounded by this, since Phyllis never had this problem at home. I contacted her physician, who prescribed medication. A week later, on Phyllis' first night home, as she sat on the toilet I noticed she didn't have socks on that were hers, and I couldn't get the socks off her feet. I yanked. I tugged. It was like those socks were painted on. I had to cut those darn socks off her feet; the socks were several sizes too small. No wonder they called me the week before about swollen feet and legs—they hadn't put Phyllis' own socks on her despite my having packed five pairs.

When I unpacked Phyllis' suitcase earlier that day, I noticed half the clothes weren't hers. When she was initially transported to the facility, I secured a letter to her suitcase asking the facility to call me when she had dirty laundry, and I'd do her laundry myself. They never called regarding laundry pick up. Also, when I packed her suitcase in preparation for the facility, I took photographs of all her clothes and toys. Most of Phyllis' clothes also had her name written in them. When I unpacked Phyllis' suitcase when she came home, I not only found clothes missing, but there were clothes they packed that didn't belong to her. Some of these clothes even had other people' names written inside the garment.

I bagged all the clothes that weren't Phyllis' and brought them back to the facility. I talked to both a nurse and an administrator and heard a song and dance about a broken washing machine. I showed photos of the missing clothes. It took days and repeated phone calls before we eventually regained about 73% of Phyllis' missing clothes. It's instances like this that I thank Matthew for helping me develop a backbone. There have been occasions, like this particular one, when I had to firmly stand my ground to bring about a right to a wrong. Otherwise, others would have walked all over me and thought nothing of it. I was fortunate the county was able to assist me in securing temporary short-term respite care for Phyllis on such short notice. I will forever be thankful to Audry and Citrus County. However, this proved again how important short-term respite care is for caregivers, especially those who are responsible for loved ones 24/7 with no help.

Phyllis appeared to be happy to be back home. It was almost as if she knew instinctively that she was safe and secure in the loving arms of someone who cared about her. Had there been other instances when she was at this facility when a problem developed, and she wasn't able to communicate for help? I can only imagine what must have been going through her mind when she was there. I know what emotions I grappled with while she was gone, and what I learned after the fact only compounded the sense of remorse I felt. It proved again that the care I provided for my parents was better than the care they would have received if they were full time at a facility. There was no doubt in my mind that the decision I made in the fall of 2017 was the right one to make. I never looked back or regretted it.

I never questioned my decision about quitting my job and caring for Paul and Phyllis 24/7. My times of hesitation and doubt have been those occasions when I was trying to find short-term respite care, juggling finances, and attempting to analyze the decline in both my parents' conditions and wondering what more I should be doing that I wasn't. I could tell very soon I'd be treading unknown territory. Phyllis was definitely transitioning into the final stage of Alzheimer's, and I had no idea what to expect. When I was recuperating, I read everything I could about the last stage of Alzheimer's. But until you face that part of the journey, no matter how well you *think* you're prepared, you actually aren't. Usually, your experience is much different than what you expected. That's one of those things about God; you can have a thought in your mind, but He has a way of surprising you. The gut feeling I'd been having since before Christmas wasn't going away. I could feel it in the marrow of my bones; a change was coming. I just didn't know when or what.

Caregiving Tips from the Heart

Caregiving Tip #31:

At some point, your loved one will balk at taking a shower. There are several non-rinse shower and shampoo products, such as body wash and body wipes, which take the anxiety out of personal hygiene for your Alzheimer's or dementia loved one.

Caregiving Tip #32:

If your loved one is prone to falling, you may consider mobility devices like a cane, walker, or wheelchair. To safeguard your loved one from falling out of bed and hurting themselves, consider attaching a bed rail to their bed.

Caregiving Tip #33:

Don't force your loved one to eat if they aren't hungry. Perhaps instead of three meals a day, feed them more frequently, but in smaller portions.

The elderly are susceptible to dehydration; they often refuse to drink water. To hydrate them, I'd recommend vitamin-packed drinks like Ensure or Boost. Clear fruit juices such as apple, grape, or cranberry juices are good, too. Gatorade is another beverage elderly will drink. Try to avoid sugary beverages like soda or high caffeine, high octane drinks.

CHAPTER 31

Back to Normal

February 2019

For two people with Alzheimer's, Paul and Phyllis' had a very busy, structured weekly schedule, especially when you consider one had extremely limited mobility and used a walker. At the same time, the other teetered around as he cautiously attempted to navigate within his small world. Monday mornings, Leroy came for three hours. That afternoon, Paul and Phyllis attended Memory Lane for two hours while I attended my caregiver's support meeting. Memory Lane provided Paul and Phyllis the opportunity to partake in games, sing-a-longs, and valuable social interaction with others. Leroy joyfully took care of Phyllis Tuesday and Wednesday afternoons, which provided me uninterrupted hours to run errands, do laundry, and take the pups for walks. Leroy was good for Phyllis. He was a quiet, generous person who learned very quickly how to anticipate her needs and actions.

Paul and Phyllis attended the Key Center of Lecanto on Thursday and Friday for seven hours each day. Saturdays, we'd all try to sleep in, and I did chores in the afternoon. Sundays, we attended church in Spring Hill and enjoyed the rest of the day at home. Paul and Phyllis had a structured week with variety and social interaction thanks to a multitude of nurturing individuals. Their life in Citrus County with services provided by the county, a support group, and friends we've made since living in Homosassa was so much richer and more stimulating *for them* than if we had stayed in Spring Hill. When I worked, the only person they saw for years was each other and Matthew. When Mary Ann entered our lives for a year, Phyllis and Paul had three hours each day of socialization. The physical move and quitting my job contributed to what I believe helped make my parents last years on earth a little happier, more enjoyable, and abundant with love. Fortunately, it was not only my love for them but also the love of others who interacted with them on a weekly basis—Ron, Leroy, Dianne, Mary, Karen, the ladies from Key Center of Lecanto, the volunteers at Memory Lane, and our neighbors.

The first eight months Paul attended the Key Center and he recognized where we were after I turned into the parking lot he'd grumble. Every time he'd ask, "Why are we here?" In his mind, he didn't need to be there because he didn't recognize he had dementia. I always quipped back, "We're here for Phyllis. Her doctor ordered it. She needs to be around more people, and you can keep an eye on her for me." It wasn't until Halloween when Paul finally started to enjoy going there. He no longer bellyached when I turned into the parking lot, and he'd enthusiastically get out of the car anticipating the bevy of ladies who would welcome him at the door with big, warm smiles and loving hugs. I will forever be thankful to the compassionate and kind-hearted ladies of the Key Center for being so accepting, compassionate, and warmhearted. They became my friends as well, always observant on those rare mornings when I dropped Paul and Phyllis off, noticing if I was having an emotional moment. Many times, they provided a shoulder for me to cry on and a loving hug to help wipe away my tears of what I could anticipate was yet to come. I will forever be grateful for the loving and compassionate friendship of Leah and her caring crew.

Paul continued to sundown every night with his up and down pattern of going to the bathroom, then his zombie walk into the kitchen where he grabbed big mittfuls of animal crackers from the pink, plastic bowl placed especially for him on the kitchen counter each night. He'd toss a few crackers on the floor for Kipper, who inevitably became glued to Grandpa's side, waiting expectantly for his next nocturnal sojourn and a free, generous handout of more animal crackers. Then, Paul zombie walked back into his bedroom and climbed into bed. He repeated this pattern all night long. Sometimes, fifteen or thirty minutes went by before Paul got up and patterned once again. I even noticed him popping back up after five minutes on several occasions. I couldn't predict or decipher a pattern with the exception of full moons. During a full moon, Paul's sundowning was worse, as was Phyllis'. Plus, Paul's restless legs were worse as well. One time, during a full moon, I counted Paul getting up seven times within a fifty-minute period. No wonder he was so tired during the day! Once the full moon passed, Paul and Phyllis' sundowning was a little less stressful and problematic, but his nightly routine remained the same every night—up down, up down, up down, up down—like clockwork! I'm surprised there wasn't a path worn into the floor as a result.

Throughout the night, in answer to Paul's nocturnal sojourns, I did a nightly toilet inspection and always found a superabundance of toilet paper in the toilet. The paper was rarely soiled. He never flushed the toilet, and I learned to always check the toilet before flushing. Otherwise, the toilet would plug up, and I'd have a mess to clean up. I'd don latex gloves and pull mounds of toilet paper out of the toilet, flush what I could, and throw the rest into the garbage.

I even tried to limit the amount of toilet paper accessible to Paul at night. I took the roll of toilet paper out of the bathroom and hid it. Instead, I left strips of toilet paper hanging over the toilet paper dispenser or neatly folded in rows on the counter. That worked to some extent, but on those occasions when he was up more frequently throughout the night, I often heard him banging cabinet doors or going into the laundry room looking for toilet paper. On those occasions, I got up for more toilet paper. Since I slept each night with one ear always fine-tuned, in case there were any problems. I never had a restful, deep sleep.

Paul was always consistent when it came to his nightly sundowning. How many times he made that journey each night was always the million-dollar question. The next morning, I found the floors littered with animal cracker crumbs. Thanks to Kipper's keen sense of smell, I often found him hunkered under Grandpa's bed with just his doggy butt and stubby tail visible trying to reach the crackers that fell and rolled to the furthest corners under the bed during the night. Oftentimes, Paul's bed was littered in cracker crumbs just like the floor. I found crackers piled on his dresser, and I learned to check the pockets of his pajama tops for stray bits of cracker, too.

I learned from one of Paul's stuffed toilet escapades to always lock the refrigerator at night. After cleaning the excess toilet paper from the toilet one night, it was almost overflowing with what appeared to be clean toilet paper, I found mixed in with the toilet paper apple cores, plastic wrappers from cheese, even banana peels. Every time Paul used the bathroom, he raided the kitchen. Not being in the habit of washing his hands, he opened the refrigerator and dug around looking for something to nibble on. Once he found something to eat, he walked back into the bathroom and tossed his refuse into the toilet. In his mind, when he sundowned at night, Paul was back on the farm where he grew up. They had an outhouse, and they thought nothing as kids to occasionally put household garbage into the hole of the outhouse. I learned quick, as a result, to lock the fridge and remove all food items from the counters at night. I even hid the cookie jar. It's amazing how much you can stuff inside a microwave to get food items off the counters—bread, bananas, the cookie jar, banana bread, English muffins, boxes of Girl Scout cookies, bags of candy, apples, and sometimes, cupcakes. If something inadvertently got left out on the counter at night, chances were Paul would find it and refuse would find its way into the toilet that night. Thank goodness for latex gloves. They made toilet duty so much easier and *less gross!*

After his birthday, I noticed subtle changes in Paul. He started staying in bed a little later in the mornings, sometimes as late as 10:00 a.m. or 11:00 a.m., which was very unusual for the country boy who had been an early riser all his life. Even though Paul had retired in 1980, up until now, he continued to start his day no later than 7:00 a.m.–8:00 a.m. He seldom, if ever, got up later, even when he was on vacation. Now, getting up later was a new norm for him. Plus, he took multiple naps throughout the day. He also stopped shaving every day shortly before this time as well. His bedtime for the last year had been at 6:30 p.m. Now, there were times when he wanted to go to bed at 5:00 p.m. I tried to convince him to stay up a few minutes longer, "I haven't seen much of you today. Why don't you stay up a little longer?" He'd grudgingly stay up a few more minutes to appease me, but it didn't take long before I'd see him slink off to bed.

When you take care of someone with Alzheimer's, at some point, modesty becomes a thing of the past. For several years, I assisted Phyllis when she needed to use the bathroom or to give her a shower. When we lived in our previous house, Phyllis could often be seen pushing her Tilly at a breakneck speed from the family room through the breakfast room, down the hallway, and into the bathroom before an accident occurred. Tell-tale signs that she hadn't made it in time could be seen on the seat of her pants, on her socks and shoes, and dribbles of brown on the cream-colored carpeting. I cleaned her up following these accidents, which seemed to happen very frequently.

When we moved to Homosassa, Paul got into the routine of not closing the bathroom door when he was using it. It didn't matter if it was in the middle of the day or at night. The door was wide open. He stood there trying to pee, holding his penis, often times with little or no success. He didn't seem self-conscious when I walked by. My relationship to him was obviously changing.

March 2019

March got off to a good start for us. Two of my cousins visited; it was beneficial for Paul and Phyllis to have company. Most of the time, they didn't know who was visiting, but the social interaction helped them. It meant a lot that family took the time to visit, and it was good for me as well. The first weekend of March, my cousin, John McFall, and his son, Max, flew in from Detroit. John is Uncle Ron's step-son. They hadn't seen each other for over four years. When I left for the airport to pick them up, I didn't tell Ron who was coming. I said, "A cousin of mine is coming for the weekend. I'm going to the airport to pick them up." When we got back from the airport, I walked into the house first and positioned myself behind Ron so when John and Max walked into the living room, I could move to the side and record Ron's reaction. For someone of few words and a normally apathetic expression, Ron's reaction was priceless. I'm glad I talked John into coming; he needed that visit as much as Ron did. Phyllis had no idea who they were, whereas Paul played his recovery mechanism game. If it helped him avoid an awkward moment, who was I to voice otherwise? The main thing, Paul and Phyllis enjoyed John and Max's visit, too.

The last week of March, cousin Dave Heltunen and his son, Landen, stopped by for a few days. They lived in the Upper Peninsula of Michigan. Dave purchased the Heltunen farm from our Aunt Verna. Thanks to Dave, the Heltunen farm is still in family hands, a rarity these days when it comes to multigenerational family homesteads.

Dave and I are only children, born to our respective parents later in their lives. Despite all my efforts at trying to be both a daughter and a son to my dad, it was Dave who Paul viewed as the son he never had. I'm thankful Paul and Dave had such a close, loving relationship. When Paul contracted Lyme disease in the early 1990s, it was Dave who gently coaxed his Uncle Paul from his pity chair to come out to Pointe Abbaye to supervise Dave's work as he constructed a cabin. Dave strategically placed a chair so his uncle could sit quietly and view Dave's progress. It must have been so difficult for Paul to sit passively since his nature was to want to help on projects like this, sitting and not doing must have been torture for him. Years later, I saw Paul looking through family albums, and I pointed to various family. Sometimes Paul recognized them and sometimes he didn't, but he always knew Dave. Every time Dave called, the usually silent and somber Paul perked up with a big smile, and all of a sudden mute Paul became a chatter box.

One night around 10:30 p.m., just days before Dave's visit, I heard Paul yell out from his bed, "Help!" I was reading in bed and responded immediately.

"Paul, what's wrong?" I asked him. At first, he didn't say anything, so I asked him again, "Do you hurt somewhere?"

"Yes."

"Where? Show me." He pointed to the lower left quadrant of his belly.

"Do you think you're going to get sick? Can I help you to the bathroom?"

"No," but he started to get out of bed anyway. Paul was unsteady of his feet, so I helped him into the bathroom. He appeared unsure of himself, disoriented. He stood in front of the toilet for a minute. After no success, Paul moved over to the sink. Within seconds, he vomited. After rinsing his mouth with water, I helped him into the living room where he sat down in his recliner. I felt his forehead, but it didn't feel warm. His breathing didn't appear labored, and he wasn't sweating. I sat down in the other recliner. We sat side by side for about fifteen minutes until he fell asleep. Paul woke up about two hours later, pain free without memory of pain the night before. I limited the foods he'd been eating for about the last two months. Sometimes, in the middle of the night, I woke up and heard him heaving in the bathroom. One morning, I found a trail of vomit on the hallway floor. I knew from the looks of it that it wasn't the pups, and when I questioned Paul the next morning, he didn't remember being sick the night before. As a result, I'd been monitoring what Paul was eating, eliminating foods high in acid like spaghetti and tomato basil soup which he loved, and taking notes whenever he got sick.

Paul had a similar attack the next night, which started about 11:30 p.m. and lasted a little longer. The next morning, he had no recollection of being sick the night before and was feeling alright. Cousins Dave and Landen arrived on Monday and left Wednesday morning. Paul felt fine during those nights, no reoccurrence. Wednesday night, though, Paul woke up again with pain in his lower left quadrant, and this time, he asked to go to the ER. Having been through this twice already, I agreed with Paul it was time to go to the hospital. I woke Ron and explained the situation to him.

By the time Paul got to the ER, his pain was practically gone. Hospital staff checked Paul's vitals, did an x-ray, and sent him home. No diagnosis and no: "If you experience this pain again, come back." No: "If he has pain again this is what I'd suggest he takes." When Paul was discharged, I asked his ER physician, "Are you a resident?" He stated, "No." I thought to myself, *You could have fooled me.* He spoke so fast when he first walked into Paul's ER cubicle that I never caught his name. His body language and lack of concern for Paul's pain made me think of a medical student, unsure of himself with a lack of interest in his patient. I had to ask the nurse as we were leaving if Paul experiences this pain again, what should I do. The nurse gave me more information than the physician did. As I drove home, I couldn't help but compare this ER visit with those I encountered with Matthew just nineteen months earlier. My thought was, *This was a waste of our time and money.* Once we got home, the first thing Paul asked, "Where's my bed?" I responded back, "Look for the Santa on the door."

Thursday was uneventful but Friday night Paul woke up with the same pain. I got him into the living room, sitting up seemed to alleviate his pain a bit. I gave him a pain pill, a medication he normally took for his back pain. An hour later, he seemed to feel a little better. He even dozed in his recliner. Paul woke up a couple hours later, complaining again of pain in the same location.

I gave him another pain pill. After an hour, it wasn't kicking in like it had earlier. By mid-morning, I contacted a friend to ask if she could watch Phyllis.

By 1:00 p.m., Paul was back at the ER. This time, he had a different ER physician, one I was familiar with and respected. After running several tests, Paul was diagnosed with a backlog of urine in his bladder, accounting for why he wasn't able to void urine. In other words, he had an enlarged prostate. The treatment plan was to insert a Foley catheter into his penis so the urine could drain out. I mentioned to his nurse, "You're going to have to monitor him 24/7. With his Alzheimer's, he's going to want to pull it out." Since Paul was going to be admitted for observation, and since my friend Dianne, who was watching Phyllis, had a previous engagement, I said good-bye to Paul, let the nurse know I was leaving and walked out of the hospital as fast as my two feet could carry me. To be honest, I didn't want to be anywhere close when they inserted that catheter into Paul's penis. Something told me we were embarking on a new chapter in our lives, and I didn't think Paul was going to like it.

CHAPTER 32

Who Is This Person? I Don't Recognize Him!

Paul was in the hospital for several days. Most of the time he was doped up, sleeping. That was the hospital's way of supervising him so he wouldn't try to get out of bed or pull his catheter out. I learned shortly after they inserted the Foley catheter, when Paul was in the ER, that he pulled it out, and they had to reinsert it. A Foley catheter has an inflated balloon that keeps the catheter inside the bladder. I had surgery once and woke up with a Foley catheter. I remember distinctly how unpleasant it felt. That sucker couldn't deflate fast enough and be removed. A Foley catheter is extremely uncomfortable for a man, and if he tries to pull it out without deflating the balloon, the pain is similar to giving birth through his penis. Just the thought, I'll leave it at that....

I received a call on April 3 that Paul was scheduled to be discharged later that day. I appreciated that the nurse listened to me the day before when we had a heated discussion. I was trying to make my point that I needed information, especially about his discharge *in advance* since I'd have to make arrangements for someone to sit with Phyllis when I picked Paul up from the hospital. I was also concerned about his prognosis and what I'd need to do to care for him once he was discharged home. I only spoke to two physicians, and that was within the first 24 hours he was in the hospital. No one called to relay information, and I couldn't sit at his bedside all day waiting for a physician to make rounds. When you care for two people who both have health problems, and one can't be left by herself, it's not possible to sit around a hospital all day waiting for a physician to round. I'd never cared for someone with a catheter before, and I'll be truthful, I was a little apprehensive about what to do and what was expected of me.

When I walked into Paul's hospital room to bring him home, the first thing I noticed was his right hand and arm. Paul's entire right forearm and hand were a deep, purplish black and blue. His arm didn't look like that the day before when I visited him. About eight minutes later his nurse walked into his room. I asked her about his arm, and she gave me a catatonic, blank stare, and said, "I don't know." She didn't appear concerned. She didn't walk up to check his arm, and she didn't provide any possible explanation. It was as if she either didn't care, she knew what had happened but was acting dumb, or she was just plain stupid. I couldn't figure out which it was, but I was glad I was getting Paul out of there ASAP!

Paul was happy to be home, adjusting to a catheter attached to his body took a little getting used to for him and for me. A long plastic tube was inserted into his penis and from this tube, his urine flowed into a large, clear plastic catheter bag. The bag could be propped up on the floor where he sat or attached to a pole so it would hang free from his body. Everywhere Paul went, the catheter bag went, too. It was awkward and cumbersome, and it made getting pants and underpants on him very difficult. In Paul's mind, he wasn't dressed unless he had on underpants, t-shirt, shirt, and pants with a belt. The only way I could clothe him was to eliminate the underpants and have the catheter tube sticking out from his pants zipper. He was very self-conscious, and I believe this was a contributing factor to his rapidly declining cognitive abilities from that date on.

Paul was discharged with a diagnosis of BPH, benign prostatic hyperplasia or, in layman's language, enlarged prostate. He was prescribed two medications, both to be taken in the morning. The doctor did not prescribe anything to help with his sundowning, which I anticipated would be worse now that he had a catheter. I found this hard to digest since the hospital constantly medicated him so they didn't need to monitor him 24/7. Did they seriously believe Paul would miraculously improve once he got home? That he wouldn't be tempted to pull out his catheter in the privacy of his own home? I explained to the nurse, who I had a heated discussion with two days before, that I also had a mom at home with Alzheimer's who was in much worse shape than Paul. I needed to be kept informed, but I couldn't be at the hospital constantly. Didn't she pass this information onto Paul's physicians? Medical staff are often quick to judge if no one visits a patient, but they don't seem to comprehend information you voluntarily provide so they can better understand why you aren't there all day at the hospital. It's not that I didn't care. I didn't have assistance at home to be at the hospital as frequently as I would have liked.

When Paul was discharged, I had to beg the nurse to contact the hospitalist to prescribe something for his sundowning. I ended up driving from the hospital to Paul's primary care physician to request something be prescribed. Half way to his primary care physician, my phone rang. It was the hospitalist responding to my request. He misunderstood what the nurse told him. Now, I found myself driving all over Spring Hill trying to get medications to help Paul with what I was anticipating would be a tough night.

Paul's first night home I dubbed "Hell Night." It was the only way to describe what Paul and I experienced that night. Once he got home, I immediately noticed a change in Paul's cognitive behavior and demeaner. I gave him a dose of Lorazepam, which his primary care prescribed. After three hours, it still hadn't kicked in. He was restless and couldn't settle in one place for more than a minute or two. Having a large catheter bag tagging along every time he wanted to get up just added to the tension we were both feeling.

When I'd see Paul try to get up I'd ask him, "Where you going?"

"Have to go to the bathroom."

"Paul, you have a catheter. You don't have to go to the bathroom."

"I have to pee."

"No, you don't. See this tube? It's taking the pee out of your body."

"I have to pee!"

"Paul, no, you don't."

"I have to pee!"

"Paul, you can go into the bathroom but nothing is going to dribble into the toilet."

"I have to go to the bathroom. I have to pee!"

Throughout the night we had many conversations like this. I tried to keep my temper in check, but it wasn't easy. And I knew I was breaking the golden rule of Alzheimer's, don't argue. Paul couldn't understand what that thing was sticking out of his penis, and he couldn't fathom why I was trying so desperately to keep him from going into the bathroom to pee. Dubbing that night *hell night* didn't come close to what he and I experienced. Every once in a while, I got him up to walk around a bit, hoping this would distract him and tire him out so he could finally fall asleep. We'd gingerly walk around the island in the kitchen. We did this two times before we headed back to the living room and his chair. That would placate him for a few minutes; it was easy to tell each time it taxed his stamina. He sat in his chair staring off into space. After a while, his fingers quietly searched for *peter*, which is what Paul referred to as his penis. This was a change I hadn't expected; it caught me totally off guard. When he wasn't trying to get up to go into the bathroom, he was fiddling with the catheter, not comprehending why he had a tube dangling out of his *peter*.

Even during those rare minutes when he actually fell asleep, I could see his fingers moving under the blanket. I saw hesitant little movements as his hands searched. I pulled back the blanket to see his fingers move like a stealthy snake. I moved his fingers away, rearranged the blanket, and waited until the next episode and repeated the same steps all over again. This went on over, and over, and over again all night. If he wasn't trying to get up to go to the bathroom, then he was trying to pull the catheter out. This was worse than his usual nightly sundowning. At least on those occasions, I could get snippets of sleep. Now, sleep wasn't even possible. I was on catheter patrol every single second.

After a couple of hours, Paul decided he wanted to sleep in his bed, so we waddled down the hallway together. I got him settled in bed and brought a chair over next to his bed so I could monitor him as he tried to fall asleep. After a couple of minutes of trying to get comfortable, Paul decided his bed wasn't going to work so we repeated the same procedure we went through minutes before, tottering Paul back down the hallway on unsteady feet into the living room. He chose a different chair to sit in. I propped the catheter bag on the floor against the base of the chair, covered him up with a blanket, and made sure his hands were resting *on top* of the blanket.

The little stinker tricked me a couple of times. Paul said he had to go to the bathroom. I gave him my usual response, and once in a while he indicated he had to go poo. I helped him up, and we walked into the bathroom and instead of sitting down on the commode, like I expected, he locked his legs and knees in place and reached for his penis like he was going to pee. Numskull me, after the second time he pulled this trick on me, I finally got wise!

The nightly routine that plagued Paul for years was now replaced by another. A nightly routine that I could see would be even more toxic than his previous one had been. Whereas before, Paul was the one who followed a regime that kept him up most of the night. At least I didn't have to be up with him constantly in those days. I had one ear always at attention, listening for any sounds or problems during the quiet of the night. A couple of times, I checked the toilet and discarded any abundance of toilet paper I saw. Now, I was on guard duty 24/7, and there was no opportunity to catch a five-minute nap. Too much could happen during that short period of time, and there was too much at stake if I caught a few winks. I figured I could handle one or two nights. I'm made of tough stuff. I'm Finnish, and I can handle anything, or so I thought. Whenever it got really difficult and I was ready to toss in the towel, I heard the voice of my Aunt Verna whispering to me, "Just hold out a little longer. This isn't forever. Remember, you have SISU flowing through your blood."

After the third day of being up more than seventy-two hours, I couldn't wait until Paul had his urologist's appointment. When I called to schedule the appointment as a follow-up to his hospitalization, they said the catheter would be removed at that time. When I heard those magic words, it was like manna from heaven. That day couldn't come soon enough!

In the meantime, I was not only keeping my eyes locked on Paul to circumvent his getting up unassisted or pulling the catheter out, but I also still needed to take care of Phyllis. Just trying to find an odd minute to use the bathroom myself was difficult or next to impossible. And squeezing in time for a shower, to wash my hair, brush my teeth, or change my clothes was totally impossible. It was especially difficult to find time to take the pups out for potty breaks. If it hadn't been for Leroy's scheduled times Monday through Wednesday, I'm not sure what I would have done. I couldn't take Phyllis to the Key Center on Thursdays and Fridays because Paul was too weak to get into the car, and I couldn't leave him unattended. And I knew Paul wouldn't listen to Ron if I left the two guys together. I was the only one Paul listened to. Before Paul got sick, Phyllis had been my problem child. Now, their roles were reversed. Paul was my problem child, and Phyllis was my good bambino.

I was a platoon of one, full speed ahead! I'm not sure how I survived until Friday, April 12, the date Paul's catheter was removed. I learned to catch short naps when Leroy was scheduled, which was also when I took a shower, shampooed, and changed my clothes. I doubt if Leroy's scheduled hours were ever more appreciated!

Paul was a real trooper at the urologist. It was hard for me to witness the painful procedure when the nurse removed the catheter and equally difficult when the urologist performed an even more painful test on him. Just months ago, I would have cringed and felt embarrassed to have a front row seat with my dad's penis in full view, inches from my nose. Now, it was a happenstance I was used to. As a caregiver to someone with Alzheimer's, it becomes a nonissue to be embarrassed of a loved one's naked body.

I assumed once Paul came home after having the catheter removed, our days and nights would get easier; boy, was I mistaken! The very night after the catheter was removed, on April 12, was another night from hell! His calming meds had no effect. Since his appetite had been declining, Paul was very unsteady on his feet. I continued to monitor his movements. I couldn't take the chance that he'd try to get up, walk around, and fall.

Paul's previous behavior of trying to pull out the catheter was replaced with belligerent and combative behavior. I thought the catheter patrol was bad. The new behavior was even worse. We were still trying to sleep in recliners in the living room as Paul seemed more comfortable there than in his bed. When he got restless, we switched chairs, which would appease him for a few minutes, and then we switched chairs again. It started to feel like musical chairs. All we were missing was the music! One night, I fell asleep from exhaustion and within a few short minutes, something woke me. Paul was leaning over me, inches from my face. I had to arm wrestle him because he was getting violent with me. It took all my strength to keep him upright so he wouldn't fall on top of me. After I got him back into his chair, I noticed he scraped the skin on the arm that was black and blue from his most recent hospitalization. I bandaged his arm, careful not to get any sticky adhesive on his delicate, tissue-thin skin.

Every few minutes, he wanted to get up to pee, and I helped him down the hall to the bathroom. It helped that he didn't have a catheter bag to drag around with him anymore. We stood there, side by side. I held him upright, and he stood there in front of the commode trying to pee, sometimes with success, sometimes not.

Paul had a great night on Sunday, April 14. His meds finally started to work, and both he and I actually got some much-needed sleep that night, even if it was only for a few hours. Early in the morning on Monday, April 15, Paul woke up complaining about pain in his lower left quadrant again. He had been voiding urine since the catheter was removed, but I wasn't about to take any chances. Phyllis was still asleep. Thank goodness for the guard rail on her bed. I woke Ron and told him I was taking Paul back to the ER.

Paul was treated by the same ER physician he had the second time he was in the ER, thank goodness. Shortly after the nurse took Paul's vitals, the physician informed me Paul had an irregular heartbeat. Paul was admitted as an observation patient, and a cardiologist was assigned to his case. I was a bit perplexed. The reason for bringing Paul to the ER was totally ignored. After a few days in the hospital, Paul was discharged to rehabilitation at a facility in Brooksville. The plan of care was to get Paul steadier on his feet. At the same time, it would provide me a week or two of much-needed rest.

I picked Paul up from the hospital on April 17 and drove him directly to a respected and highly recommended rehabilitation facility in Brooksville. I packed a suitcase for him, took photographs of all his clothes, and brought a walker, too, anticipating he'd be using a walker as part of his rehab. It felt strange leaving Paul at rehab although he seemed okay with it. He had a roommate who didn't talk much and was glued to his TV. I left Paul stretched out on his bed, staring up at the ceiling like he was contemplating all the problems of the world, deep in thought.

Paul was in rehab for ten nights. When I visited him, he was often disoriented, confused, and very unhappy. I asked his nurse the status of his physical therapy, which was why he was there, and I never got an answer. I heard the physical therapist was busy, and she'd stop by later. My later was short-lived because I couldn't be away from home for very long. I could only visit after Phyllis went to bed at night or during Leroy's scheduled days. As a result, I never got to talk to a therapist, and the nurses never provided me with any feedback regarding Paul's condition. I started to wonder, was he even having physical therapy?

There was an incident one day that stuck in my mind. I arrived in the afternoon to visit Paul, and as I walked up to the nurse's station to inquire about his progress like I normally did, a commotion to my left caught my attention. Three staff members congregated around a set of glass doors that led outside to an atrium. Their attitude struck me as strange. My inner voice compelled me to check it out, so I walked over to see what was going on. I looked from the staff members to the doors to see what was causing this disorderly conduct. What I saw surprised me! On the other side, Paul was partially standing, partially leaning on his wheelchair blocking the doors. I looked at the staff members who were standing there. They didn't appear to be trying to do anything to help the situation, and they looked totally perplexed. I shook my head in disgust, yanked a door open, and walked outside. In my sternest voice, I said a few choice words to Paul, like I was chastising a child who should know better but was caught red-handed just the same. I opened a door and ordered him back inside, helping him maneuver his wheelchair through the doors and down the hall to his room. How could three trained staff members have no control over one 98-year-old man in a wheelchair? And why was he using a wheelchair all the fricking time when he was there for physical therapy? Why wasn't he using the walker I brought for him? Wouldn't using a walker help to exercise and strengthen his legs so he could come home sooner?

When Paul was in rehab, they called me several times. The first call was to inform me that Paul had been caught trying to exit the building; this happened shortly after he got there. They put a monitor on him that would buzz if he tried to exit a door. Since wandering wasn't in his normal makeup, I was surprised by this turn of events and attributed this to his unhappiness being there. Just days after the glass door episode, I received three more phone calls. Each call was more distressing than the previous one, and all three phone calls foreshadowed behavior to come. The first call was the night after the glass door incident. Paul had blocked the doorway into his room and wouldn't let anyone in or out. They had to move him to a private room across the hall because his behavior was disturbing his roommate and making it difficult for his roommate to enter or exit their shared room.

The very next morning, I received another distressing call that Paul was going to be discharged in two days. When he was admitted for rehab, the administrator led me to believe Paul would be there in all likelihood for twenty-two days since Medicare would only pay for that amount of time. I was skeptical at the time and didn't think he'd need that long, but I was trying to keep an open mind. And since he was always sitting in a wheelchair every time I visited him, I had no true assessment on what type of progress Paul was really making. I must admit, I was in a quandary. I saw no evidence to support that rehab was actually helping Paul, yet our home was quiet, and I was getting some much-needed rest at night. I was selfish; I was getting used to the peace and quiet at home. The prospect of Paul coming home before the twenty-two days were up was a bit disappointing to me from a strictly selfish point of view. I received a third call from rehab the same day as the second call but in the evening. Paul had tried to stand up and fell, scraped his arm, and the aide bandaged it.

Every time I visited Paul in rehab, he was despondent, frightened, and scared. As the aides walked down the hallway, he turned to me and said, "I'm in prison. See how they watch me? This is prison." His Alzheimer's corroded mind couldn't fathom that the aides were doing their job, keeping an eye on him so he wouldn't get hurt, stay safe, wander outside, or get lost. I could see the aides had their hands full taking care of Paul, yet if anyone could relate to what they were going through I could since I lived this same chaos every day.

The last time I visited Paul before he was discharged, I told him, "I'll pick you up on Saturday and bring you home."

He looked at me with the saddest, most dejected expression, "You will?"

"Yes, I promise."

"When's that?"

"Today is Thursday. You have all day tomorrow, and I'll pick you up the next day. How's that?"

"I'm in prison, and they won't let me out."

"I promise. I'll spring you on Saturday. Do you trust me?"

After a minute, he looked up at me with a woebegone expression and whispered, "Yes, I trust you. I'm counting on you."

Saturday dawned a beautiful, bright sunny Florida day. A friend came to stay with Phyllis while I traveled thirty minutes to spring Paul from his prison. As I was packing his suitcase, I noticed a small, white tissue on the table. I picked it up to toss it in the trash when I noticed what appeared to be some writing on it. Printed in black pen were the following words, "PAUL HELTUNEN PLEASE HELP ME SOME ONE." My poor dad was reaching out in pain and confusion; I seemed to be the only person who cared or understood what he needed. I signed the discharge paperwork as quick as I could, finished packing his suitcase, and found his glasses which were not on his face but on the windowsill. I located his never-used walker, which was behind the door, and we hightailed it out of there as fast as we could like I was springing a convict from a high-security prison. We never looked back! As we sailed westward on Highway 98 for home, I was thankful Paul's ordeal was finally over. I prayed these ten days didn't scar his psyche and further derail his behavior. I was relieved and thankful Paul was coming home.

I wasn't sure what loomed ahead of us, but I was thankful we would all be back together again under the same roof. I didn't

know what type of behavior was coming next, but I knew anything was now possible. I was thankful I had a mini-break when
Paul was in rehab. It helped to recharge my battery. In the days
to come, I came to curse that rehab time, yet at the same time,
it was a blessing in disguise. If it wasn't for Paul's ten days in
rehab, I'm not sure I would have been strong enough, physically
or emotionally, to handle what came next.

CHAPTER 33

"You Need Help!"

I don't know who was happier to be home, Paul because he was no longer in his imaginary prison or me because we were now one big happy family. As long as we were together, I felt I had more control protecting everyone, keeping Paul and Phyllis safe and happy. Paul's first night home was uneventful with no strange behavior. He voided urine at 11:30 p.m., and we settled into recliners side by side in the living room. He finally fell asleep shortly before midnight and had a relatively restful night. The next day, he was quiet, reserved, and spent hours looking at family photo albums. He took a long nap stretched out on the loveseat on the screened porch. In other words, Paul had a very good day. I was naively thinking to myself that those days of crazy behavior were finally behind us, and we could now get back to some semblance of normal.

Sunday mid-afternoon, Paul walked into the bathroom to urinate. I hovered in the hallway, making sure he wasn't having any problems, wanting to be close by in case his legs started to give out. He stood there in front of the commode trying his darndest to pee without success. After a couple of minutes, I suggested he try again later on. An hour later, Paul shuffled back into the bathroom to urinate. He stood there giving it his best and once again, no success. A second time I mentioned to him to try again in an hour. At 5:20 p.m., he still couldn't pee. I called a Patient Hotline and explained the situation. The nurse asked several questions, and I answered. Her recommendation was what I expected—take him to the ER. I put Phyllis to bed early, asked Ron to keep an ear open for her, and bundled Paul off to the ER. This was going to be his fifth trip to a medical center in a little over a month. At the ER, they asked why we were there, and I told them. Within a couple of hours, they recatetered Paul and sent him home. We were now back where we started just a month ago. It seemed like we took a step forward, then two steps back, followed shortly by another step back.

Sunday night after we got home from the hospital, I was expecting the worst but was pleasantly surprised with a fairly good night. Paul's meds kicked in early, and he rested comfortably for most of the night. He wasn't attempting to pull out the catheter, and his fingers never even searched for it. I was naive and couldn't help but think, *Maybe he's getting used to it.*

Monday dawned. I was optimistic we'd have another good day like we had the night before. As the day wore on, I started to notice subtle changes to Paul's persona. He sat in a chair or on the couch with his head hanging down, feet slightly apart, and his arms rested on his knees. He had a hanged dog look, like he was despondent and dejected. He looked friendless and wouldn't talk; there was no life to him. Once in a while, he tried to pull the catheter out, and he tried to get up to use the bathroom. He wouldn't eat and wasn't interested in a cup of coffee. When a Finlander doesn't drink a cup of coffee, you know something is wrong. We had an appointment the next day with his primary care physician as follow-up to his rehab. Looking at Paul, all I could see was a once vibrant man who was slowly deteriorating before my eyes. Something told me it was time to do some serious soul searching.

Tuesday morning, April 30, I took Paul to see Dr. Abskhroun. The night before, as Paul fitfully slept, I tossed and turned, knowing I had to make a decision. My mind told me one thing while my heart conveyed something totally different. When Dr. Abskhroun walked into the exam room, he looked me in the eye, and the first thing I said was, "I think it's time for hospice." Dr. Abskhroun studied Paul carefully, checked his vitals, and agreed with my decision. It was a decision I wasn't ready for but one that was warranted at this time. When I looked at the shell of the person who used to be so full of life, known for his quick wit and bright smile, what I saw instead was in stark contrast to the person who was now sitting meekly, unresponsive, and silent before us.

Twenty-five years ago when I moved to Florida, I moved with the belief this day might come. Twenty-five years later, I was no more ready for this day than I was then. Emotionally and psychologically, I had to carry on and be the decision maker once again. I didn't want to. I wanted to do a Paul thing and bury my head in the sand and hope everything bad would go away. When I married Mathew, I assumed he'd be here as my anchor for when this day came. He'd be there to steady me and keep me grounded. Matthew should have been there to help me! *I can't do this without you Matthew! Why did you desert me? I need you so much! Why aren't you here to help me? You weren't supposed to die before my parents! I need your strength so much right now. Where are you?* I felt a preponderance of tears wanting to flood my eyes, yet Paul was right there in front of me. I believed he needed me to stay calm so I wouldn't upset him. Not knowing what he was able to comprehend at this point, I needed to keep a level head. I gave the performance of a lifetime. I should have won an Oscar!

Wednesday, May 1, a hospice evaluator arrived. Hospice approval was dependent on the recommendation and approval of several individuals. First, you need a physician to make a hospice referral. Next, a hospice evaluator evaluates the patient, and based on that person's assessment, a hospice physician will either conduct their assessment or acquiesce to the evaluator's assessment. Based on their evaluations, the patient is either approved or denied hospice services. Paul was accepted, and the evaluator ordered a hospital bed delivered to our home. Between listening to my tales of woe for the past month and observing for herself the situation I was in caring for both my parents with Alzheimer's, the evaluator stated, "You need help!" I'm not sure why but based on our conversation, I believed the hospice nurse would come the next day and could make arrangements for help.

The hospice nurse came the next day and did an assessment of Paul. She was friendly, helpful, and agreed with the evaluator, "You need help!" I learned she wasn't the one who could provide help. I was led to believe the social worker could assist with that, and she'd be around within a day. A hospice chaplain came who was very nice, recited a prayer, and said, "You need help!" The social worker came and explained her job, but it turned out she's not the person who could provide help, either. I struck out on all fronts, but she, too, stated those same three words I heard before from three other hospice employees, "You need help!" Four people all said the same thing, and not one could provide me with the assistance I so desperately needed to get some rest, take a shower, or even to use the bathroom. The person I learned who could help was the volunteer coordinator, who only worked Monday through Friday. I was told she'd call me. By early Friday afternoon, I hadn't heard from the volunteer coordinator. So, thanks to the backbone I acquired from Matthew, I called her. She asked what my zip code was. I told her, and she said, "I have no volunteers in your area, and if I did, I could only provide you with three hours of respite care a week." Although four hospice employees told me what I already knew, I found myself back at square one. I didn't have help except for Leroy, but his hours weren't enough. There were still four days in the week when he didn't come.

Paul lost all desire to eat or drink. I made him foods he used to enjoy but he no longer had the appetite or the desire to eat them. He wasn't even interested in ice cream, and in the past, he never turned down ice cream. I started giving him fluids in an eyedropper because he couldn't drink any longer from a cup; I even tried a child's sippy cup. I squirted small drops of water, juice, or Gatorade into his mouth with an eyedropper, which was far easier on him and a lot less messy as well.

The hospital bed was more comfortable for Paul than sitting and sleeping in a recliner, like he'd been doing on and off for the past five weeks when he was home. It was set up in the living room directly in front of the TV with Phyllis' lift chair to its left.

These were challenging days. Paul's demeanor changed daily, and I couldn't take my eyes off him. Most times, he struggled to get out of bed, yanking on his catheter to try to pull it out, or he was argumentative and combatant. I was amazed at how strong a 98-year-old man can be who hasn't eaten anything for several days. One night, he clamped his fist over my hand when I was trying to move his hands off the catheter. His grip was like steel; there was no resistance. I couldn't get his hold to release. I never experienced anything like it before. Just the year before, when I was assembling some new furniture for the screened porch, Paul tried to tighten the bolts, and he couldn't. Now, his fists were like a death grip that wouldn't let go. It was frightening. The most logical thing to do would have been to take a swipe at the him hoping that would release his hold on me but I couldn't do that; I didn't want to hurt him. Luckily, I thought of a ploy I'd recently started using with Phyllis. I wasn't sure if it would work, but I was desperate. I looked Paul in the eye, and with the sternest voice I could muster and a strong, menacing conviction in my eyes, I said, "Let go, Paul, your mother wants you to let go!" This trick helped with Phyllis. In the past, whenever Phyllis got difficult to handle, I called for Paul, and he walked into the room, talked to her, and she acquiesced. With Paul in and out of the hospital and rehab for over a month, I started to reference Phyllis' mom on those occasions when Phyllis got argumentative. It worked every time. In this instance, it worked, too, thank goodness.

Under hospice, Paul's meds were doubled. As the days passed, it got more difficult to give him his meds. At first, Paul could still swallow pills. After a couple of days, I noticed him chewing the pills, then when my back was turned, I found him spitting the pills out. Little pieces of pill littered his sheets, clothes, and even the floor. Thank goodness for eyes in the back of my head, fine-tuned from my years teaching school. I couldn't have him do that. I have two dogs who would be tempted to eat anything they found on the floor, but more important, Paul needed those pills for his safety. I began crushing his pills and gave him the medication in a spoon of chocolate pudding. This worked for a couple of days until it, too, started to get problematic. Even when I could get the pills in him, I never knew how long they would take to kick in. Sometimes, he calmed down after two hours. Sometimes it took as long as ten hours. In the meantime, my normally sweet, dear, quiet, unassuming dad became a monster, his behavior mercurial! I felt like I was riding the Manta rollercoaster at SeaWorld, totally unprepared for what I was experiencing and even more so for what was soon to come.

During this hospice time, I was awake 24/7. The minute my back was turned, Paul had his legs over the side of the bed trying to get out of bed, or he was trying to remove the catheter. Hospital beds provided by hospice do not have guard rails to assist keeping someone in bed. And every chance he could find, Paul attempted to get out of bed. I tried putting extra pillows on both sides of the bed near his legs to serve as a guard rail. That didn't help; he kicked the pillows away or lifted his legs over the pillows. It was a constant battle to keep him in bed.

On several occasions, Paul tried to lift my shirt up. I battled with him and yanked my shirt back down. I didn't recognize my dad these days. The person in that hospital bed and the person I grew up hero-worshipping were two totally, distinctly different people. It felt like I was taking care of Dr. Jekyll and Mr. Hyde, never knowing which of these characters would make an appearance. I was always on my guard, never at rest, and ever vigilant for whatever ugly monster might raise its frightening head.

Paul's eyes were closed most of the time now, so it was difficult to determine if he was awake or sleeping. Therefore, it got more difficult to time when to get Phyllis up in the morning or put her to bed at night, take the pups out for a quick potty break, or allow myself a brief bathroom break. Timing was either my best friend or my worst enemy. I said a lot of silent prayers, hoping while my back was turned Paul wouldn't wake up and try to get out of bed. As I was learning, Paul could now be a sneaky, willy coyote. I couldn't take my eyes off of him for a minute without tempting fate. The stress I was under created so much tension, compounded by lack of sleep, that physical and psychological ramifications heightened my temperament, gripped my digestive system, and tightened my nervous anxiety. I never knew what to expect. I was dragging my butt, losing energy and stamina, and was argumentative with anyone who said two words to me. I doubted myself.

I kept meticulous notes during this time; it was the only way I could remember when I last gave Paul his meds, what his urine output had been for a specific timeframe, and how much fluids he'd ingested as well. I showed my notes to the hospice nurse during her weekly visits, hoping they'd provide information to assist in providing Paul with a more peaceful transition to the hereafter.

I learned from the hospice nurse that the odd behaviors Paul was experiencing was terminal restlessness, a behavior some people experience as they transition to death. It could last days or even weeks. It was characterized by clutching or pulling at clothes or bedsheets, anxious behavior, hallucinations, delirium, inattentiveness, lethargy, hostile behavior, uncomfortability, and restlessness. They were all behaviors Paul had been experiencing since he was first hospitalized the end of March.

Paul was hallucinating. I remember one occasion when he motioned with his hands. From his mumbling, it appeared he was getting ready to go deer hunting, gathering his hunting paraphernalia. Deer hunting was a pastime Paul enjoyed throughout his life, treasuring the male comradery of deer camp more than the notion of bagging a trophy buck. I played along with him, "Paul, do you have your hunting jacket?" His hands reached out like he was grabbing his red, plaid hunting jacket from a closet.

"Paul, did you get your license?" He'd appear flustered, like he was looking for his hunting license in a drawer. "Paul, I have your license right here. I'll pack it for you. "Paul, do you want a thermos of hot coffee? It can get pretty cold out there, traipsing in the woods."

When I was a child, Dad always abandoned Mom and me for two weeks in mid-November, starting November 15, the opening day of firearm deer hunting season. We didn't mind because it was the norm in our family. We knew how much Paul looked forward to deer hunting each year, camping in the boonies on Pointe Abbaye hunting with his brothers Herman, John, Arnold, and Ralph. Anyone living in Michigan is familiar with this mid-November past time. Even though I've always been adamantly opposed to deer hunting, I felt blessed on this occasion to be a part of Paul's final deer hunting trip, even if it was only in his hallucinating mind.

As usual, finances continued to worry me. I couldn't afford to pay someone to sit with Phyllis or Paul on a regular basis during this time. Since Paul was dying, I knew our finances would soon take a drastic hit. I had to conserve every dime possible, not knowing what loomed in the near future. The few true friends I have, as compared to my abundance of acquaintances, weren't in the position to help, or they had recently experienced the death of a loved one and were not in the emotional state to experience death again so soon. I posted in Facebook, hoping someone would step up to the plate and volunteer. I heard from a cousin in Minnesota who offered to jump on the first plane to Florida to help, but I declined her offer. Although I greatly appreciated her offer to help, I knew she had a family, job, and a new business demanding a lot of her time. Instead, I was hoping my church or hospice would finally come through with assistance rather than put my cousin through the expense of a plane ride to hell.

I knew in my heart I was doing the best I could for Paul. I also came to realize that my efforts were starting to take a physical toll on me. Paul moved so much in bed. Every couple of hours I had to reposition him, otherwise his legs got tangled up at the end of the bed, scrunched up against the footboard. When someone isn't available to help you move your loved one in bed, and your loved one can't help you, it's very hard to move and reposition that person singlehandedly, especially when you haven't received any formal training. A week before, the hospice nurse placed a sheet under Paul to make repositioning him a little easier, but every time Paul moved, the sheet moved with him. It got twisted under and about him, gradually inching its way down the bed until a few inches remained under his body. I tried to grab hold of and yank the sheet up toward the head of the bed, but with Paul's body lying on top of it, it was back-breaking, difficult work. With every pull on the sheet, I felt my back, neck, and arm muscles strain. I had to do this grab, pull, strain routine several times throughout the day, and each time it didn't get any easier. It actually got worse.

May 9 was a typical day in what I'd been thinking of as *Paul hell*; he did appear to catch brief moments of rest now and then. By that evening, after doubling up his meds, Paul finally fell asleep around 8:30 p.m., a relief considering the day we had. He was scheduled to have another dose within an hour, but I didn't want to wake him just to medicate him, especially since his earlier meds took so long to work. I was hedging my bet and hoping I'd win. I remember sitting down on the couch around 11:35 p.m. I used the time once he fell asleep to catch up on some chores around the house and take the pups out. I was hesitant at first to sit on the couch. It looked too tempting, so comfy, but I was exhausted. Actually, I was beyond exhausted. Paul appeared to be sleeping, so I sat down just for a minute, figuring I could still monitor him from where I sat.

I don't know what happened, but the next thing I knew, I suddenly woke up by a loud noise. I looked around, startled, my heart pounding like a drum played erratically by Ringo Starr. I instantly saw the time, shortly after midnight. Despite the partially darkened room, I noticed that Paul wasn't in his bed. *Dammit, what happened?* was my first thought coupled with, *Where is he? I bet he tried to go to the bathroom.* With these thoughts crashing through my mind, the house seemed eerily quiet. I jumped up and started to run toward the hall. I didn't get far. As I rounded the foot of the bed, I heard a faint, barely audible moaning sound. My eyes instantly darted downward, and that's when I saw Paul, laying in a prone position on the floor. I turned a light on and saw blood on the right side of his face. He started to moan louder. I couldn't help but think of another similar occasion when Paul was injured. That accident happened five years before.

It was mid-June and Paul, Phyllis, and I drove to Aura, Michigan to celebrate Aura's 100th anniversary. Paul was born and raised in Aura where Phyllis had family as well. Mom and Dad spent eleven years of retirement in Aura before moving to Florida. With a weekend of festivities planned, Paul was determined to go. Family from out of state were coming. Even Phyllis' two siblings were going to be in attendance. It would be the first time in eighteen years they'd be together. The day was typical for the U.P., or as many refer to it, God's Country. The day was a little cool, with a hint of rain hovering in the air, and a slight breeze which kept the U.P.'s ever-present air force in check, mosquitos. It was shaping up to be a great weekend. That Saturday also happened to be Phyllis's 86th birthday.

After Saturday's speeches, luncheon, cake cutting, and opportunities to visit with neighbors and friends, both my Heltunen relatives and the Miller siblings converged onto the Heltunen farm to continue the party and celebrate Phyllis' birthday. We had a great time with lots of laughs, birthday cake, and ice cream, and catching up with each other as we compared notes on who we reconnected with earlier in the day. After everyone left, I was putting leftovers away in the pantry, and Paul and Phyllis were getting ready for bed. All of a sudden, I heard a loud noise, punctuated a few seconds later by soft moaning, "Help me!" I followed the sounds and noticed an opened door. I looked down and saw Paul laying at the bottom of the basement stairs. In all probability, he opened the door thinking it was the bathroom, and when he went to step over the threshold, instead of putting his foot on what he anticipated was the solid floor, his foot stepped, instead into nothingness, which began a downward motion he had no control over, falling into space, crashing down a flight of basement stairs.

Now, this night in 2019 felt like déjà vu all over again. I was praying Paul would be as fortunate this time as he was then. Before, he walked away with only badly scraped arms, a dislocated shoulder, and a small broken bone in his right hand. At least this time, his flight to the floor didn't include an eleven foot drop down wooden stairs landing on a cement floor.

I called Ron for help. We tried to get Paul up, but with Ron's diminished energy due to his Parkinson's and my lack of sleep for almost two weeks, we couldn't budge Paul from the floor. I debated what to do, call EMS or hospice. Since he was under hospice care, I called hospice. Hospice called EMS, and paramedics arrived shortly. As I watched the paramedics lift Paul up from the floor, I remember thinking, *They made it look so easy.* With Paul sitting up, we could see where the blood was coming from. Paul had a gash on his forehead above his right eye. The paramedic informed me, "He'll need stitches." Once again, Paul found himself back at the ER, his sixth trip to a medical facility in seven weeks.

Paul was a real trooper. The injury above his eye took five stitches. I, on the other hand, was squeamish, squirming in my seat trying to find a place where I could safely divert my eyes and pretend I was anywhere but where I was. Yet at the same time, I was mesmerized by how well Paul was taking it. The ER doc was one of their better ones. He kept me informed and listened when I asked questions or had concerns. He told me Paul was going to be discharged and transportation was arranged to bring him home. When the transporters arrived, I warned them that Paul was starting to get a little combative. As we were waiting in the ER cubicle, I had started to see tell-tale signs that Paul's behavior was changing. He was frequently reaching up to his forehead, verbally trying to pick a fight, and wanting to get out of bed. I gave the transporters directions to our home, told them I'd wait for them at the gate since the gate would be closed at this time in the morning, and left.

It took me twenty-two minutes to get home. I waited at the gate; it was pitch dark. I could hear tree frogs croaking messages to each other in the distance. My eyes had a hard time adjusting to the darkness. I checked my watch; thirty minutes had gone by and no ambulance. I looked in my purse and couldn't find my phone. I must have left it at the house in my rush to get to the hospital. I had been charging it earlier. At least I knew where it was. Ten minutes went by, and I started getting a strange feeling that something was wrong. I debated, do I go through the gate, go home, and get my phone, with the off chance the transporters might arrive during this time, or do I stay at the gate and wait? I took the chance, opened the gate, went home, got my phone, and immediately checked for messages. The hospital's number was listed as having called an hour ago, but there was no message. I called the hospital and asked for the ER. Turns out, after I left, Paul's behavior got worse. The ambulance crew I met at the hospital decided Paul would need restraints, and they didn't have any, so another ambulance crew was called. That delayed Paul's departure for home. Shortly after I spoke with the ER, I saw the ambulance turn off Highway 19 heading toward me. I met them at the gate and opened it. As I provided directions to the driver, he didn't look very happy. When Paul's gurney was lifted out of the ambulance, I noticed a mask over his mouth. I asked the female transporter about the mask. She looked me in the eye with an angry, pissed off expression that shot daggers at me. "He was spitting! He was spitting all over the ambulance!" I was mortified. I couldn't believe my normally, mild-mannered Dad had been spitting in the ambulance. How do you tell someone, "That's not what he's normally like!" They'd never believe me, and what disheartened me most is this was one of the last impressions my dad would leave to mankind, impressions that contradict the type of person he'd been for the majority of his life.

After the transporters got Paul settled into bed, they seemed to race out of the house as fast as their feet would carry them, and from what they told me, I couldn't blame them. It was 6:05 a.m., Thursday, May 9. I called hospice to report Paul was back home. I spoke to a very sympathetic person who listened to my lament, while at the time I chastised myself that Paul had fallen. Yet despite my monologue of despair and anguish, the volunteer listened with rapt, sympathetic attention. He recommended sage words of advice I should follow, "Keep calling hospice, and don't give up. If you have to call every hour, do so. Call until someone listens to you and provides you with the help you need." Finally, someone was listening, but it took a fall to do it.

Four hours later, there was a knock on the door. With the pups barking a friendly welcome, a woman identified herself as a nurse from hospice. She was there to get Paul ready for transport to Hospice House, and she needed to do an assessment first. This was news to me because no one contacted me about this change in plans. A transport team was scheduled for 2:00 p.m. Those were the best words I'd heard in a very long time. I was angry at myself for falling asleep, which resulted in Paul getting hurt. But I was thankful someone had listened and sent help; it was like a two-edged sword. I thanked God for this miracle. Maybe the help we were finally receiving was a little late in coming, but nevertheless, I was appreciative that someone was finally understanding our situation and responding with much needed help. Thank you, hospice!

After the ambulance team transported Paul to Hospice House, our home suddenly took on a somber, melancholy persona. Time seemed to stand still; it was deathly quiet. I couldn't even hear the customary traffic on Highway 19 or birds singing in the trees outside. The house felt this same way after Phyllis was picked up for respite care following my surgery. The only thought running through my mind, *Paul will never again be in this house. He'll never sit in his chair and watch TV. He won't look at photograph albums daydreaming of memories of Aura. I won't see him stretched out on the loveseat in the screened porch taking a nap.*

As I wandered through the house, room by room, I remembered those days immediately after Matthew died when the void of his presence loomed like a cloud over the whole house. Paul wasn't dead, but it felt like he was. I started to think of those things which had become part of my everyday life, things I did especially for Paul like record Michigan State basketball games or Tiger baseball games so he could watch them whenever he got restless and bored. I always had ice cream on hand because he loved it so much. I'd no longer give him his meds and put in his eye drops each night. I no longer needed to lock the doors of the refrigerator and hide the counter foods in the microwave. I didn't have to do so many common, everyday occurrences that Paul was the center of. It brought the enormity of this situation to the forefront of my consciousness. The next morning, when I opened the kitchen cabinet to pour a bowl of cereal for Phyllis, I saw the opened bag of animal crackers, and it brought tears to my eyes. My life was changing like it did two years before, and I wasn't any more prepared for this change than I was when Matthew died.

I visited Paul Friday night after I put Phyllis to bed. He was sleeping and had no idea I was there. It was good to finally see him sleeping so peacefully, such a sharp contrast to what he and I had gone through the past month. Why couldn't he have been at peace like this at home? Hospice House didn't rely on giving meds orally, which helped. When Paul was home, I kept detailed notes and communicated my findings to the hospice nurse hoping that someone would realize Paul was not transitioning in a peaceful manner like he was now. It seemed like all my careful note-taking fell on deaf ears, and my poor dad had been suffering the consequences as a result. It was frustrating. I was thankful, though, Paul was finally comfortable and at peace, which was the most important thing at that moment. Months later, when I think about what that poor man went through, I can't help but shake my head and wish I had been more proactive and a bigger pain in the ass to hospice in communicating what my dad needed.

That Friday night, as I watched Paul sleeping peacefully in bed, each breath shallow but not labored, it reminded me of when I visited my Aunt Lou when she was at Hospice House eighteen months earlier. I visited her every day. She slept, totally oblivious to my being there, just like Paul was now. It was a waiting game, a slow, painful waiting game.

Did a stream of Paul memories come flooding into my mind? No. Was I reminded of what he and I recently went through at the house? Yes, but I tried to push those fresh memories to the furthest reaches of my mind. Did I have regrets that were tormenting me? No. I knew I had done everything I could for Paul. It was at this time when I finally ripped off my caregiver cloak and once again became his daughter, and he became my dad. I needed to relinquish my caregiving duties, so I could grieve and prepare my heart for what was soon to come. I couldn't do that while I was caring for him at home because I was too busy and consumed with taking care of both Paul and Phyllis. I learned to steel myself from the pain of seeing my parents disintegrate before my eyes. I needed to build and fortify a wall around my emotions. That kept my feelings at bay and allowed me to put blinders on. The blinders narrowed my world to caregiving and nothing else. That's how I handled caregiving; it doesn't mean others handle this task in this manner. I didn't know any other way to handle it, and perhaps, because Matthew died shortly before I started this journey, I believed deep down in my heart that the grieving and sorrow I felt for my husband hardened my heart, and most importantly, my mind. It was like all my emotions had dried up. These emotions weren't accessible to me at this time. I felt like I was a conscientious observer, watching from the sidelines, trying to be mindful and respectful of a devasting event that was soon to come.

The next day, Saturday, May 11, the sun was shining, birds were singing, "Get up, embrace this wonderful day!" I was going to visit Paul after Phyllis went to bed that night, but a little voice told me to go earlier in the afternoon. Since I believe that was God's way of talking to me, I contacted my friend Dianne to see if she was available to Phyllis sit, and she was. Dianne came after lunch. I signed the log book at Hospice House around 1:45 p.m. I talked to his nurse, Keith, who provided me with a Dad update. While I was visiting with Dad, the hospice physician, Dr. McCartney, stopped by to check on him. I knew Dr. McCartney from my days working at a local hospital, and we'd been Facebook buddies for a year. After his evaluation, I asked Dr. McCartney, "Will Paul be around for May 21, their 70th wedding anniversary?"

"What's today's date?"

"The eleventh."

After a short pause, he quietly said, "No."

"What's the prognosis?"

"One to three days."

That short conversation took my breath away. Mom and Dad were so close to celebrating their 70th wedding anniversary. It was hard to believe this monumental anniversary wouldn't happen. In that brief instant, my mind started to calculate what I needed to do. I had to run a few errands so there would be provisions at home for Phyllis and Ron for the next few days, make arrangements for Phyllis sitters, and make a mental list of people and places to contact once he died. I stood there looking at my dad, thankful he was at Hospice House where I was finally able to be his daughter. As I touched his arm and smoothed the hair off his forehead, I whispered in his ear, "I love you, Dad. I'll take good care of Mom for you. When you see Matthew, tell him I love him and miss him." There was no indication he heard me, no slight squeeze of my hand, no fluttering of eyelids, nothing. I turned away and walked to the nurses' station, which was next to my dad's room, to let Keith know I had errands to run and arrangements to make. I'd be back shortly, and call me if there was any change. I signed out of Hospice House at 2:30 p.m.

Fifteen minutes later, as I was driving around the parking lot at Walmart looking for a parking space, my phone range. "Vicki, it's Keith. Can you come back? Your dad's breathing has changed."

"I'm at Walmart. I'll be there in six minutes. Thanks for calling."

I hightailed it back onto Cortez Boulevard, thankful the traffic wasn't any worse than it was, especially for a Saturday afternoon. Minutes later, I was at Hospice House, ran for the door, and pressed the button. As soon as I walked through the door, I noticed my dad's bedroom door was closed, and Keith standing solemnly in front of it. I had a sinking feeling I knew what that meant. My dad already gained his wings.

Keith said, "He passed away minutes ago. I'm sorry. His aide is with him." I knew who Keith was referring to, Mary Ann. I had contacted her the night before, letting her know Paul was at Hospice House. She had indicated she'd stop by the next day. I walked into the room; Dad was peacefully lying in bed like he was taking an afternoon nap. I couldn't believe my dad was gone. It wasn't possible, now both of the men in my life were gone. First, Matthew, now, Dad. Mary Ann and I embraced, both caught up in our grief, sorrow, and those random memories that all of a sudden crash into our thoughts.

"If only I hadn't stopped for gas, I would have been here when he died, and he wouldn't have been alone," Mary Ann said.

"I was just here, left less than twenty minutes ago. It wouldn't have mattered, Mary Ann. He didn't want anyone here. You stopped for gas because you were meant to."

We both kept looking at Paul, lost in our thoughts as my minister, Pastor Robin, walked in. The three of us comforted each other. A few minutes later, a priest from St. Frances Cabrini stopped by to say a prayer. I viewed the visit by the Cabrini priest as a sign from Matthew. We were married at St. Frances Cabrini on May 17, twenty-three years before. I believed Matthew sent this man of God into Dad's room at this time to provide me with solace and to ease my pain. This man of God was an earthly substitute for Matthew since he couldn't be there himself. As the priest recited a prayer, I could feel Matthew's arms embracing me, letting me know my dad was at peace and that I'd be okay as well.

Mary Ann started talking about how much she had learned from Paul. Mary Ann was like a sponge, absorbing and retaining every Paul story or bits and pieces of information Paul relayed to her. Hearing Mary Ann recite these stories, which I had heard frequently throughout my life, reminded me of things I had inadvertently forgotten. Did that make me a bad daughter? I'd like to believe not. When we are so close to a relationship, parent-child or spouse-spouse, it's easy to listen with half an ear sometimes when you've already heard the same stories countless times before. Now, I wish I could relive one of those times when I could sit back and listen to my dad tell about the mornings when he had to milk the cows before going to school. I remembered the time when he ate in a restaurant for the very first time, in Marquette, just before a varsity basketball game. As he reached out to help the waitress with the hot plates in her hands, his fingertips got burned in the process, and he had to play the whole game with badly burned fingers. Now, I kicked myself that I didn't listen a little more carefully, if only...

So, once again, I had another funeral to plan. I was torn between what was ahead and trying to come to terms with what the last seven weeks of my dad's life had been like. It had been a living hell for me, combating his terminal restlessness. I hoped and prayed it hadn't been as hard on him. My dad was finally at peace, and I was thankful for that.

CHAPTER 34

Does She Know?

I debated about telling Phyllis that her beloved Paul had passed away. Late last year, I had anticipated that she'd be the first to die since she was transitioning into the final stage of Alzheimer's. I never imagined that it would be my dad who would go first. How could I tell my mom? I was scared and wasn't sure how she'd react. She didn't seem to know who he was for the last six months to a year and tended to blend the two Pauls in her mind—her dad Paul, and her husband, Paul. I was also afraid that if I told her, she might pass away of a broken heart, something in the farthest reaches of her ravaged mind might resurrect a fragmented memory of her husband Paul. They were always so close, but even more so after his AAA rupture in 1998. Since then, Phyllis clung to her Paul like a drowning man grasps a life preserver, in a white-knuckle death-gripe.

Monday, May 13, after I got home from making funeral arrangements, I was emotionally drained. All I wanted to do was sit down and empty my mind. However, that wasn't possible. My friend Dianne relieved Leroy after his Monday morning shift ended, and she anxiously whispered to me "Phyllis asked Leroy,

'Where's my husband?' Leroy was caught off guard and told her, 'He's napping.' She asked me the same question when I got here. Thought you'd like to know."

Did Phyllis have a brief moment of lucidity? Did she actually understand more than she lets on? It's so hard to know what's going on inside her mind. I posted to two private Alzheimer's/Dementia Facebook groups I belong to asking for advice, "Should I tell my mom my dad passed? They both had Alzheimer's." Every response I received was the same, an emphatic, "No!" I followed my gut instincts, and I never told her. Any references I made in front of Phyllis regarding my dad were kept to a minimum.

The funeral was on Friday. I took Phyllis to the Key Center of Lecanto and informed the ladies of what was going on so they would be on the lookout for any unusual behavior and to provide comfort and love for Phyllis. A Phyllis who, in all respects, had no idea her husband had died. But somewhere in the destroyed reaches of her mind she had a gut instinct, perhaps a message from God or from Paul himself helping her to understand that her Paul was no longer. I'll never know, but in my heart, I believed she knew.

Also, around this time, Phyllis developed a rash on her back, upper torso, arms, and legs. She scratched herself so bad a week later, the Key Center called me after I dropped Phyllis off one morning to inform me they believed she had scabies. I picked her up and took Phyllis to a Quick Care. The physician ruled out scabies and agreed with me, Phyllis was having an emotional reaction to her husband's death. Whatever she comprehended within the inner reaches of her mind was manifesting itself in a psychosomatic rash. Ointments helped, but every once in a while, the rash came back to a lesser degree. I've been amazed with this disease called Alzheimer's. When you think you understand it, something happens, and you find yourself scratching your head, wondering, *How did she remember that?*

Now that our immediate family had dwindled in number, I dedicated myself to keeping Phyllis' world as quiet, tranquil, and peaceful as possible. At least Alzheimer's was useful for something.

It spared Mom the heartache and sorrow I've been experiencing since the day Matthew died. Mom and I were now both widows, something new we had in common. Miraculously, Phyllis was spared the sorrow and grief associated with widowhood, learning how to adjust, adapt, and live without the person she loved with all her heart. I didn't know what to expect. I feared I had an inkling but how soon would it come; I had no idea.

After the funeral, I kept busy dealing with paperwork regarding my dad's estate and establishing a new norm for Phyllis. Why does death create so much paperwork? Once you complete and fax forms as requested, it takes weeks to get a response back. Or, you don't hear anything, so you call in desperation and learn you need to fill out one more form. Insurance companies follow their time frames without considering the impact their lack of action places on the family, a family that might have dire need of the insurance money following a funeral.

After what transpired with Paul during the last couple of weeks of his life, I was surprised that Phyllis' demeanor had improved. Normally, her disposition and temperament resembled a sweet and endearing small child who erupted into tantrums during potty or hygiene times. Now, she never gave me any problems going into the bathroom or going to bed at night. It felt strange not hearing her customary, "Bullshit," every time she sat on the toilet. I'd hover in the cramped bathroom, trying unsuccessfully most of the time to encourage her to go potty, "Go pee. Pee Phyllis," or "Try to poo poo." Now, Phyllis had no idea what those instructions meant, let alone the words themselves. Last year, I made up farcical lyrics to the tune of Old Mac Donald, needing something to refocus her attention to the business at hand, namely to go potty. Singing helped to keep Phyllis focused on what she needed to do. Otherwise, she got easily distracted by the artwork on the walls, the towels on the towel rack, or her shoes on the floor. Singing drew her attention to me, and while I was singing, I pantomimed the bodily actions I'd seen her do many times when she had a bowel movement. I'd sing, often off-key,

"I see a bullshit here, a bullshit there, everywhere a bullshit shit, shit. Phyllis sits on the toidy, bullshit, shit, shit, shit."

It was difficult, at first, to have to take such an active part in my mother's most personal daily ministrations, but with Alzheimer's, you have no choice if you want to keep your loved one healthy and clean. I was fortunate. Most of the time Phyllis never gave me problems about this. I have friends whose parents have Alzheimer's who still guard this most personal of bodily functions like they were guarding the queen's jewels. This though, can lead to health issues since our loved ones, in all likelihood, won't remember the last time they had a bowel movement. It's important that your loved one avoid an impacted bowel, if at all possible, because any health issues have the capacity of increasing the advancement of your loved one's dementia.

Another new change in Phyllis' demeanor was she ceased to give me any problems when I washed her hair. Up until a month ago, when I washed her hair with a liquid, rinse-free shampoo, she hooped and hollered. You'd think I was trying to kill her. I'd drape a towel around her neck, squirted a little shampoo into my hands and some on her head. That was when she'd scream and yell like a banshee, whimpering as I'd work the shampoo into her scalp and along her hair follicles. By the time I towel dried and combed her hair, I'd put the mirror in front of her saying, "See, Fi Fi's hair, all clean! Doesn't she look pretty?" Phyllis had totally forgotten the hissy fit she just threw.

It's difficult to train yourself as a caregiver to treat your loved one like a child. I had to keep reminding myself Phyllis was now a child, at least in her mind she was. Phyllis's make-believe environment was that of a child, even though she lived inside an aging, decaying body. Such a discrepancy, the inabilities of her mind versus the outer, bodily requiem housing her soul.

Along with this change in Phyllis, I found myself frequently comparing this new, temporary Phyllis version to what she had been like a few short years before, as late as 2017 when Matthew was ill. It was such a stark contrast two years can make and heartbreaking how fast her decline had spearheaded downward into a quickly approaching death spiral. I now spent nights sitting on the screened porch, wine in hand, reflecting on those times when Phyllis was a real handful, thinking about how much I've learned through the years. I thought about information I've gained but wished I had back then, information that would have made our lives so much easier and more pleasant back when Phyllis was in the beginning of the middle stage of Alzheimer's.

Phyllis loved showers, at least at the beginning of our caregiving journey. Since she used a walker, being unsteady on her feet, I started, as early as 2012, helping her into the shower, watched over her to safeguard her from falling. Phyllis sat on a plastic chair I moved into the shower for those occasions. Every time I turned the handheld shower head on, she was shocked at first by the spray of the water, but after a couple of seconds, she loved the feel of it. As I talked to her, I shampooed and rinsed her hair. During those early years, she could follow simple directions like, *cup your hands.* I squirted some shampoo into her outstretched hands and directed her to put her hands up and scrub her hair. She seemed to enjoy this, moving her hands around, feeling the foamy squishiness of the shampoo between her fingers like a child loves to play with wet sand at the beach. Next, I handed her a washcloth, squirted some liquid soap onto the cloth, and instructed her to wash her body. She instinctively remembered to start with her face, scrubbing her forehead, cheeks, neck, and nose. Then, she proceeded to her upper torso, arms, belly, and legs. I took the washcloth from her and scrubbed her back. Phyllis loved a good back massage coupled with an all over, warm rinse. Her bath was complete after I helped her stand up so she could wash her tushy and butt. I helped her to sit back down, rinsed out the washcloth, instructed her to hold the cloth over her face, and I used the handheld shower head to rinse her hair and body. She loved the feel of the warm water softly cascading, dripping down her body; it always radiated an ecstatic smile on her face!

At the beginning, Phyllis showers were a good time. Phyllis got clean. She wasn't a problem, and life was copasetic. After two blissful shower years, she started to balk. That little balk gradually turned into little hissy fits, but like before, once she got into the shower and felt that warm, pulsing water all over her body, Phyllis' demeanor changed, and she once again reveled in the experience. Then, before I knew it, Phyllis' attitude about showers changed once again. Her hissy fits turned into full-blown tornados. She got downright nasty with me and belligerent. She even tried to bite me sometimes.

I came to dread Phyllis shower times, and I hate to admit it. I even tried to postpone these showering excursions as much as was humanly possible. When Phyllis decided she didn't want to do something in those days, nothing I did could convince her otherwise. She got so bad she wouldn't let me help her take off her clothes. I'd sometimes have to resort to calling in the troops, namely General Paul to the rescue. Paul would come into the bathroom and talk to her in a stern, yet quiet voice, "Phyllis, let Vicki help you take a shower. You need a bath." It never took long for Phyllis to quiet down when the general came into the bathroom. Those few words by her Paul always did the trick, and she'd slowly lose her muster and let me help her. I used to thank God that Paul still had that effect on her. And I silently prayed that when the time came, Phyllis would pass away before Paul since he always had such a calming effect on her. Most of the time, she listened to me, but on shower days, she no longer saw me as her alpha. Instead, I was her beta. In the meantime, as Paul attempted to rein in Phyllis, I tried to calm my boiling blood pressure in response to and in frustration to the hurricane that had erupted. I hated those witches' brews. Then again, that was during my ignorant years, when I reacted to Phyllis' tempests not from knowledgeable experience but by gut instinct, uneducated ignorance. I wish I knew then what I gained in knowledge since.

It wasn't until we moved to Citrus County that I had an epiphany. A random thought popped into my pea brain one day. Hospitals give sponge baths to their patients. The liquid soap they use is rinse-free. I checked the phone book for medical supply stores near me. I found one and called and learned they had rinse free products. That store, I'm sorry to say, ceases to exist, but they opened a whole new world for me. Not only did they have liquid rinse-free shampoo and body wash, but also bathing wipes. It now became possible to wash Phyllis without problems trying to get her into the shower. Add to that the stress of constant worry that she might slip and fall going into or coming out of the shower. This all made a big difference in caring for Phyllis. As her legs slowly started to fail her, falling became a dreaded norm rather than a rare occurrence. It was also around this time when I learned daily bathing wasn't necessary for older people since the risk of falls was so great, and they spend much of their time sequestered in a chair. I cleaned Phyllis's lower extremities with rinse-free wipes every time her diaper was changed. Rinse-free bathing products are a true blessing for caregivers of Alzheimer's patients. I wish I had learned of these products sooner!

During the ensuing months after my dad died, Phyllis seldom experienced sundowning. It was a welcome reprieve from years past, when sundowning had been a normal staple of her day. Both Mom and Dad's sundowning were always worse leading up to and during a full moon. Dad's restless leg syndrome would be worse during a full moon, as well. Looking back, with my dad gone, I realized those little things which used to bother me were now never more. There were no more restless legs for my dad to contend with. They often acted up when we were at church, in the car running errands, or at night keeping him awake. When his legs would start a-twitchin', I'd grab the Hyland's Restless Leg pills, ask him to pop a couple under his tongue, and after mere seconds, he usually felt relief. Then, there were those times when no matter what I did to help his restless legs, nothing worked including his daily medication, tonic water, Hyland's Restless Leg pills, foot massages, or Epsom salt foot baths. So many times I agonized right along with him, praying something would relieve the pain and itching sensations he was feeling.

There was no more sundowning to keep both Dad and I awake at night. I used to joke I was surprised he hadn't worn a path in the floor with his nocturnal trips to the bathroom and kitchen every night. I reluctantly removed the plastic tie loops from the refrigerator doors and stored the lock in a drawer. I also came to realize I wasn't buying as much toilet paper any more, since Paul wasn't putting tons of toilet paper in the toilet each night. Two months after he died, I was cleaning out a kitchen cabinet and saw an unopened bag of animal crackers and cried. I haven't bought a package of Oreos—his favorite cookies and mine—since Dad died. I just can't seem to put Oreo's in the grocery cart these days. I no longer find strings of dental floss laying on the floor. I kept his DNR on the refrigerator for months, just like his scent kit was above the refrigerator. I reached for both items periodically to put them in the trash. Then, at the last second, I pulled my arm away, not sure why. Maybe I was reluctant to get rid of another sign that Dad ever existed. Now, with Dad gone, these have become memories I tucked away in a memory drawer, buried amongst the remnants of a life that are now fragments in my mind.

Phyllis was now napping more often and had a diminished appetite. Her incontinence was getting worse. She still chattered but not as much. She was staring off into space more. It was getting harder for her to move her legs, harder to lift her leg into the car or to walk down the hall. She was grinding her teeth constantly and was storing her food in her cheeks like a little chipmunk.

However, despite these changes, I felt a sense of peace surrounding Phyllis. When Phyllis smiled, her smile looked so angelic like she was an innocent lamb protected by God. My heart melted every time I saw her smile. My mind wanted to believe that Phyllis and I now have two guardian angels watching over us, Matthew and Paul. Maybe that's why it felt like we'd been graced by God. I didn't feel sad. Instead, I knew my dad was at peace and was no longer suffering. In all probability, he and Phyllis would be reunited sometime soon.

I still called my mom by her first name, Phyllis, because she didn't know who I was. She couldn't put a name to my presence but she knew that I was familiar to her. I was like those old, broken-in house slippers that looked crappy but felt so soft and comfortable on your feet. On the mornings when possible, I let her sleep until noon or 1:00 p.m. She seemed to need more sleep these days. Usually, when I looked in on her, she was curled up on her side, clutching her stuffed doggy, sound asleep. On Mondays, when Leroy came early, I reluctantly got her up. Sometimes, when I heard her awake, I tiptoed down the hall and looked in on her. She'd be playing in her bed similar to a baby, her eyes open, looking out the window next to her bed, scrunching up the blinds. When she wanted to get up, she'd whistle for attention.

These days, my years of caregiving finally paid off. I knew how important it was to be prepared before getting Phyllis up. Before going into her bedroom to wake her, I'd have all the supplies ready in the bathroom: clean diaper, plastic bag, wet wipes, shoes, socks, clean clothes, and a headband. Then I'd go into her bedroom, turn the overhead light on and say, "Good Morning, Fi Fi, I love you!" I'd then clarify my words with "And it's a beautiful day," with the biggest smile I could plaster on my face. At first, it was hard for me to say those words. I couldn't help but think of Matthew since those precious five words were our secret greeting to each other, reserved for us. At first, I felt like a traitor. I started adding the second statement to my greeting, which seemed to appease my inner turmoil. After a couple of weeks, those precious five words started to sooth my heart. Each time I greeted my mom in the morning with those simple words of endearment, my heart seemed to heal a little more. Gradually, I no longer felt like a traitor to Matthew but a daughter to my mom.

Each day we muddled through, my focus now entirely on Phyllis. I could feel in my bones it was getting time to shed my caregiver cloak and put my daughter cloak on one last time, like I did before my dad died. I never thought my dad would go first. I always assumed Mom would. Now, Mom is the only one I had left, besides the pups. In my gut, those feelings that haunted me since that last Christmas, that 2019 would be Mom's last year, vibrated loud and clear, like Native American tom toms sending communications to neighboring tribes. Each day, the vibe got louder and stronger. Time felt like it was ebbing through an hourglass, so close to losing its last minuscule fragments of precious, time measuring sand.

Caregiving Tips from the Heart

Caregiving Tip #34:

As your loved one transitions into the final stage of Alzheimer's, their eating habits will change. Softer foods like applesauce, mashed potatoes with gravy, puddings, and even baby food will be helpful. Try to encourage your loved one to drink more. If they balk at water, try clear juices, Gatorade, and nutritious beverages packed with vitamins and minerals, like Boost and Ensure.

Caregiving Tip #35:

In the final stage, your loved one won't have the appetite they used to have. Their bodies are preparing for death; their body knows what it needs. Don't force them to eat or drink, but gently coax them with what they are willing to eat or drink. I used an eyedropper to administer sips of water and juices. It helped to quench a dry mouth while providing some nourishment. Plus, it wasn't messy.

Caregiving Tip #36:

Use an absorbent, disposable bed pad on your loved one's bed. These can be purchased at stores, usually 36" x 30" in size. Compare the different brands carefully since some are stronger and more absorbent than others. These pads will help reduce your laundry, saving you time and frustration.

CHAPTER 35

And Then There Was One

Phyllis's last day at the Key Center of Lecanto was Thursday, July 18. That morning, I had a difficult time getting her legs to support her as she lifted her left leg up into the car. Her overall physical condition had weakened as well. At the Key Center I talked to the staff, letting them know her condition had declined since the week before and in all probability that day would be Phyllis's last day at the Key Center. I was concerned not only about the risk of Phyllis falling and getting hurt but also anxious about the risk factor if Phyllis were to fall while at the Key Center. It was a bitter sweet day. I had come to think of the ladies at the Key Center as good friends. We'd shared lots of laughs. They've provided a shoulder for me to cry on, and they were always genuinely concerned about Paul and Phyllis. After my dad died, the ladies at the Key Center gave me a framed photograph taken months before of Paul and Phyllis napping, side-by-side. Paul's head is leaning back, his mouth partially open, a WWII veteran's cap firmly sits on his head. Phyllis's head rests on her beloved's shoulder. And they are holding hands. I treasure that photograph. It symbolizes to me not only their love for each other but also how their love could transcend even the brokenness of Alzheimer's riddled minds. So often, Phyllis didn't know who Paul was, but there were times when it appeared that an ember still smoldered even when the initial memories had long been forgotten. It was going to be difficult to say good-bye to these wonderful, kind-hearted ladies, Leah, Jessica, Debbie, Rita, and Nasue. When I picked Phyllis up at the end of the day, the ladies mentioned that Phyllis slept most of the day, which was so unlike her.

I now lost two days to run errands or to have time for myself. The only time I now had for errands was either after Phyllis went to bed at night or on Leroy's scheduled hours on Monday morning or Tuesday and Wednesday afternoons. I made the most of Leroy's time, not knowing when that unforeseen, unpredictable moment would come when Phyllis would no longer be mobile.

Activities that used to capture Phyllis's attention were slowly fading from her interest. There were times when she even slept through most of Leroy's visits. In the past, he had the knack of being able to keep her engaged, now she was a shadow of herself. Each day seemed to foreshadow an upcoming, scheduled event I was reluctant to attend, having attended this same event twice already.

Phyllis' appetite was quickly declining now as well. Her normal bowl of cereal in the morning was reduced in half, and she didn't even eat most of that. For months, she'd been squirreling food in her cheeks like a little chipmunk. This continued to be an even more noticeable problem now. I bought a blender and made her nutritious ice cream shakes, with the hope that this sweet nectar would heighten her appetite. It did at first. I'd whip up ice cream, liquid vitamins, strawberries, and blueberries. She enjoyed these afternoon treats, spoonful after yummy spoonful. But one day, she turned her head away. I also noticed that she was taking forever to chew her food. I started feeding her softer foods, like mashed potatoes, mashed cooked carrots, broths from soups and stews, knowing it wouldn't be too much longer before I started feeding her baby food, instead.

Phyllis tried her best to smile, but even her smile was starting to fade. Watching her, it was like looking at a candle on a birthday cake that flickers when someone tries to blow it out but the flame barely comes back. It was agony to watch. I was still reeling from the unexpected death of my dad. There was no doubt in my mind Phyllis wouldn't be around to celebrate another Christmas, let alone another Labor Day. There was nothing I could do to delay the inevitable. It was a waiting game with only two players, Phyllis and myself, with little doubt who the loser will be and who will live to see another day. It was only a question of time when the losing hand will be placed on the table, face down.

Saturday, July 20 was a pivotal day. That morning was like any other. Phyllis was sitting on the toilet. Her diaper and nightgown were off. I turned my head to pick up a rinse-free wipe from the counter when all of a sudden, I heard a thud. I turned my head and instead of seeing Phyllis sitting on the toilet where I left her a second ago, she was now laying on her right side on the floor, in a heap. It appeared she must have fallen like a sack of potatoes; it's the only way I could imagine what had happened during that split second when my eyes were turned away from her. I tried to get her to sit up, but the confining space of the bathroom made this difficult. Within a minute, she emptied her bladder. Urine was flowing, creating a lake of urine slowly spreading outward. As I grabbed some paper towels to mop up the urine, her bowels let loose, and before I knew it, she was now lying in a pool of urine and smelly, liquidy feces. I felt so sorry for her. The fall seemed to have knocked some sense of lucidity into her. Phyllis appeared to understand the predicament she was in, and she seemed to know that I was trying everything in my power to get her up, off the floor, and cleaned. There have been other times in the past when Phyllis's legs went out from under her like a deck of cards. On those occasions, I was able to talk her into helping me. Now, due to the angle of her body and her diminished strength, she was no longer able to help. I'm not sure how I got her up that morning. I know I prayed, similar to how I prayed when I had to move Matthew from the chair to the bed when he was home under hospice care. That time with the grace of God, I was able to find the inner strength to move him. This time, I found that same inner strength to get Mom up and off the floor and back on the toilet. The only way I can explain it is God must have been helping me. There's no other way to account for it.

Each day was becoming more precious than the day before. I tried to anticipate her needs, her wants, and I did everything I could to help her. No matter what I did, I couldn't stop or slow down this progressively fast decline.

On the night of Monday, August 5, Phyllis and I were in the bathroom. I was getting her ready for bed. After putting a clean diaper and nightie on her, I started to help her up off the toilet when she uttered, "My legs," a very lucid comment for her. The fact that she could use the correct word to identify her legs, and she understood she was experiencing problems with her legs was in itself a miracle. I knew I needed to get her into bed as fast as I could. I didn't want to experience the same thing we did on July 20, fearing if she went down this time, I wouldn't be able to get her up or into bed. The only thing I could think of was to do everything in my power to keep her moving and pray for a miracle. We were so close, just across the hall, approximately seven feet from her bed.

As we progressed out of the bathroom and across the hall, it was a slow process. Her feet no longer moved by putting one foot in front of the other. It was more like one foot would barely slide across the floor, mere inches, and then after a minute or two, the same process repeated itself with the other foot sliding to meet it. It was an arduous, grueling process that took forever to traverse. On a normal day, the walk from the bathroom across the hall into her bedroom normally took less than a minute. Now, it was taking painstaking, labored minutes to travel an extremely short distance. It was becoming obvious any second her legs would be totally giving out on her.

I was playing Russian Roulette as each slow, tedious, agonizing slide across the floor took place. It was torture to watch. I was praying we'd complete our journey against time before she lost the race. I whispered words of encouragement and love, hoping with all my might I'd be able to get her into bed before the final last breaths of her energy expired. Hold on to her. Keep her upright. I said words of endearment as she did a slight foot slide. I kept holding on, kept her upright, saying my words of love tenderly in her ear. Her foot barely dragged across the floor. This process kept repeating itself, and each cycle was snail-paced, over and over. The longer it took, the more effort I had to exert to keep her upright. I wasn't sure which would happen first; her legs would go out, or my energy and strength to help her would diminish. It felt like hours to cross three feet of hallway. We finally made it into her bedroom. We were so close now. Her bed was visible; just a few more steps until the safety of her bed. As we continued to mount our efforts, I kept praying that we'd make it. I thought we had a slim chance. Miraculously, we got this far. How can a few feet seem so close yet feel like the Grand Canyon?

This space she's maneuvered so many times in the past now felt like we were trying to scale Mt. Everest. I could see the summit, but it seemed like such a drastic distance away. Each agonizing foot slide brought us half an inch closer to our destination. It was touch and go. We were now right next to her bed. I just needed a final sprint of energy from her *and me* to get Phyllis into her bed when all of a sudden, with no warning, she started to crumble like a balloon that's popped, as all its air starts to slowly spew out. In a slow-motion descent, her legs collapsed, and Phyllis slid to the floor sideways. I felt devastated, helpless in circumventing this from happening. I couldn't believe we'd gotten so close. My first reaction was to break down and cry. My eyes burned from tears I was desperately trying not to shed. There was a lump in my throat that made talking difficult. Any emotional reaction from me wouldn't help Phyllis. I needed to be strong for her.

That moment of lucidity I briefly saw in the bathroom seemed to have followed us into the bedroom. As she laid on the floor,

Phyllis seemed to know she needed to get into bed but she appeared resigned she'd be spending the night on the floor. Her legs were now totally useless. I tried, like before, to get her up by myself, but this time, I wasn't able to. I must have expended so much of my strength getting her this far from the bathroom that I had nothing left to give. No matter what I did, I couldn't budge her up, and she wasn't able to help me. Phyllis was total dead weight. I didn't know what to do. I stood there despondent for a minute or two trying to develop a game plan when that little voice in my head called out to me, *Get Ron to help!* Despite his frail, emaciated self, under one hundred pounds and unsteady on his feet, between the two of us, we were able to find the strength to get Phyllis up and into bed. It was a struggle, but I believe God was again helping us, uniting us as a team to get Phyllis safely into bed. I couldn't get her moved lengthwise, so she slept crosswise, scrunched up in a fetal position. Phyllis didn't appear to be in any pain, and I left her in that position. I raised the bed rail; thankful it would keep her from falling out of bed during the night.

I had a fitful night, tossing and turning, thinking about the phone call I needed to make the next day. A call to Phyllis's physician requesting a referral for hospice care. When I checked Phyllis throughout the night, she didn't appear to have moved, and she was in the same fetal position in the morning. When I checked Phyllis' diaper, I noticed her bed and clothes were soiled. She'd had a bowel movement during the night, and she and the bed were a mess. I tried to clean her up, but every time I attempted to move her legs to remove her diaper, she cried out in pain. I contemplated what to do, and God pointed me in the right direction—call my friend Mary Ann. I'm not sure how I sounded to Mary Ann when I called her, probably a pinch of frustration, a dab of panic, and a cup of anxiety. Nevertheless, Mary Ann, the trooper that she was, came to my rescue.

Within a half hour Mary Ann bounded into our house in her usual cheerful manner, assessed the situation, and took charge. She didn't get flustered but talked softly in a soothing, quiet whisper, explaining to Phyllis what she was going to do. Phyllis responded with a smile on her face. Mary Ann always had that effect on Phyllis. She's definitely been our guardian angel. After Mary Ann and I got Phyllis changed and cleaned, Mary Ann sat with Phyllis as I geared myself in making the phone call I was dreading. Her physician had seen her recently and knew this day would be coming soon. I had been down this road less than three months earlier with my dad. Now I was traveling it again. I didn't want to. My inner demon balked while my heart knew it was time; it was the right thing to do, but I didn't want to do it. Making arrangements for hospice is one of the most difficult things I've had to do, right up there with visiting a funeral parlor to make funeral arrangements and calling family and friends to report the death of a loved one.

When I got off the phone with Phyllis's physician, I checked with Mary Ann to see how Phyllis was doing. "Vicki," Mary Ann stepped away from Phyllis's bed and whispered to me, "I was sitting talking with Phyllis, and she asked me to get her a box. I didn't know what she meant, so I asked her to explain, and she said a rectangular box, a coffin. It took me by surprise, she knows Vicki, she knows." When I heard that, I immediately thought about her sense of lucidity the night before, just before her legs started to give out on her. At that moment, Phyllis seemed to know her world was changing, like her conversation with Mary Ann now indicated as well. Phyllis was telling us she knew her time was nearing. That thought should have made me feel better, but instead, my heart broke. I guess you're never ready to say good bye to someone you love. I lost my husband two years before, my dad three months ago, and now, my mom. I wanted to cry, but I had too much to take care of. Crying would be a luxury I didn't have time for.

Phyllis officially entered hospice care late Tuesday, August 6, her sister Peggy's 75th birthday. The hospice evaluator ordered a hospital bed and a portable wheelchair so I could move Phyllis from her bedroom into the hospital bed, which would be set up in the living room. I wasn't sure how I was supposed to move

Phyllis from her current bed into the wheelchair and from the wheelchair into the hospital bed. Phyllis was in no shape to sit up in bed, swing her legs over, stand up, and walk to the wheelchair. With the shape Phyllis was now in, lifting and moving her was going to be entirely on me, and I knew I didn't have the strength to move her. When I asked the evaluator how I was supposed to move Phyllis using the wheelchair, she turned her head to glance at Leroy, who was there at the time, and said, "Leroy can help you, if he's here when the bed comes." I wanted to say to her, "That's presumptuous of you. What if he isn't?" but I kept my mouth shut. I've learned from my prior two experiences with hospice, a lot falls on you to do, and they can only do so much to help. I told the evaluator what happened with my dad. She was surprised, and as I was thumbing through the hospice binder she gave me, I pointed to the chapter on caregiving and asked her, "It says right here caregivers are encouraged to take time for themselves. How is that possible if hospice can't provide help? Three months ago, I heard there were no volunteers in my zip code, so this section should be removed from these binders because it doesn't apply everywhere." The hospice evaluator didn't know how to respond.

Due to the lateness of the day, the hospital bed wasn't scheduled for delivery until the next day. Phyllis would be spending one last night in her bed. I kept an eye on her during the night. She called out around 9:40 p.m. I checked on her. She was agitated, and I calmed her down. I tried to give her some applesauce since she hadn't eaten much throughout the day, but she declined and drifted off to sleep. Around 6:07 a.m., I heard her call out for help. I checked her diaper, which was loaded and her hands were dirty. Obviously, Phyllis had been digging into her dirty diaper. I tried calling Mary Ann for help, but she didn't pick up. I gathered materials and a clean diaper, focused on what Mary Ann had done the day before. *Mind over matter. You can do this, Vicki. Mind over matter.*

What makes it difficult to change a diaper on an adult when they are lying in bed and can't help you is the size and weight of their body. With a baby, it doesn't take much to lift the baby's legs in the air with one hand as their little butt lifts off the bed. Then, use your free hand to whip the dirty diaper out as you place the clean diaper under their cute, dinky tushy. It doesn't quite work that way with an adult. An adult's legs are longer and heavier. Their bodies are larger and weigh a *lot* more. Add to that every time I tried to move Phyllis's legs or her body, she cried out in pain. Psychologically, it's very difficult to move someone when you hear them crying in pain. Hearing Phyllis's cries automatically stopped me in my tracks. I had to talk myself into ignoring her cries. I tried to lift her legs and place them on my shoulders, talk about awkward and heavy. The extra weight on my shoulders was giving me a neckache and a backache. This wasn't working; it was both awkward and extremely painful for Phyllis and me. I tugged at the dirty diaper, and it came out from under her in pieces. I rolled her from side to side, cleaning her up the best I could.

I had started using bed protectors on Phyllis' bed earlier in the year, and those helped so the mess in Phyllis' bed wasn't worse than it could have been. I finally got Phyllis cleaned and moved her torso over to the side as far as I could. I slipped her clean diaper under her as far as I could. I rolled her body toward me as far as I could so I could then reach the diaper under her and get it straightened out. Then, I moved her butt so it was resting evenly on the diaper and secured the tabs. As I was doing this, it was thundering a downpour outside. After getting Phyllis tucked into bed with a clean diaper, I put the thunder vests on the pups to appease their frightened souls. We crawled back into bed, and I turned the light out. What a way to start the day!

The hospital bed was miraculously delivered during Leroy's shift. I was thankful Leroy was there when the time came to move Phyllis. Leroy lifted Phyllis into his strong, caring arms. He made it look so easy; I couldn't help but think about the struggle Ron and I had just two nights before. Leroy gently placed Phyllis in the wheelchair and wheeled her down the hallway into the living room where he repeated the same process, in reverse. He lifted her up and carefully positioned her in the hospital bed. I'm not sure what I would have done if Leroy hadn't been there at the time.

Now, there was another hospital bed sitting in the living room, in the exact same location as Paul's bed had been just three months earlier. I was bombarded with déjà vu memories nonstop. I did not want to relive the Paul nightmare all over again. Once was enough. I wasn't sure what to expect this time. I prayed it would be a little less stressful than the time before.

For the first couple of days, Phyllis spent most of her time either sleeping, cradling her baby doll, talking to her stuffed dog, or swallowing spoonfuls of soft foods or sips of fluids. Each day, her appetite continued to decline. I started to feed her baby food.

Phyllis received her baby doll the year before from Karen Kline at Memory Lane. Every time Phyllis attended Memory Lane, they gave her a doll, and she spent most of the two hours talking and playing with it. One Monday afternoon after our meetings, Karen handed me a baby doll and said, "Let Phyllis keep it. She enjoys playing with it." I was reluctant at first, but it was a nice gesture on Karen's part, and I didn't want to offend her, and if Phyllis was enjoying it, then so be it.

Phyllis spent endless hours cradling, talking to, kissing, and taking the clothes off that poor baby doll. Whenever Phyllis got restless, I handed her the doll, and she quieted down and her inbred mothering instinct took over. Now, she was doing the same thing, lifting the doll in the air, just in front of her face, smiling as she whispered to it, "I love you," and showering it with little, mommy kisses. The love shimmering from her eyes for her imaginary baby was the epitome of motherly love. It provided me a glimpse of the mothering she must have bestowed upon me when I was a small baby. It was like watching a movie of my babyhood played before my eyes, bittersweet and mesmerizing all at the same time.

Too bad once we become adults, we no longer remember our mother's loving embraces when we were innocent babes in arms. Perhaps, if we could, the world might be a better, more loving and compassionate place. I couldn't help but view this as

350

another gift from God, these final moments in my mom's life like seeing her life being flashed before my eyes. It was at this time when the caregiver cloak fell away being replaced by my daughter's role. I realized it was time, I had learned my lesson well from when my dad was in his final hours of life. I needed this to happen so I could start to grieve for my mom, to mourn her as her daughter, to experience this final time together. I couldn't help but lament what Alzheimer's had robbed us of while at the same time, Alzheimer's provided a veil over Mom's eyes. It spared her the agonizing heartache of her Paul's passing, a mourning of grief and sorrow I had an up close and intimate knowledge of. I believed, in some strange way, Mom knew her Paul was gone. I also believed, like I've thought for years, that if Paul died first, Mom would die shortly thereafter. My gut instinct was proving correct.

I didn't get much sleep during this time, maybe snatches here and there, but not much. The only times I was away from Mom's side was when Leroy or Mary Ann were there. Then, I'd run errands, take a shower, walk the pups, or catch a few z's. Each day, there was a visible decline in Mom's status. Two of the hardest aspects of caring for her at this time was changing her diaper and accepting the visible clues to her impending death.

The nights, though, were the hardest. By the fourth night, it seemed she was about to pass, and by early morning, she rallied—alive, just barely. I was amazed at the tenacious thread of life that was keeping Mom firmly ensconced in this earthly life. One night, she closed her eyes, and the most beautiful smile graced her face. She reached out her hands like she was reaching out to someone. I thought she was dying that time, but she didn't. I remember looking from her face to where she was looking, with a glowing, radiant smile on her face, wondering, *Who is she smiling at? Is she seeing her husband? Her parents? Is she seeing God?* Being so close to what was going on yet not being able to see what Mom was seeing, I felt like someone who receives an invitation to a party, but when you walk up to the door and knock, no one answers, yet you can hear the party going on in full swing on the other side of the door. I felt excluded, disappointed, and lonely since I wasn't privy to this private party taking place right in front of me.

Mom's terminal restlessness wasn't as bad as Dad's. She'd scrunch up the edge of the sheet but thank goodness she never attempted to get out of bed. At night, she was more restless, often appearing scared and frightened. It was almost like she knew she was dying and was petrified. The hospice chaplain made an appointment to see Mom. The day of the appointment, he never showed. It wasn't until the following day when he called and apologized for missing his scheduled appointment. A relative passed away, and he was on the other side of the state. I couldn't figure out why his calendar wasn't accessible to others and why he didn't ask someone at the hospice office to call and cancel our appointment. One of those things that shouldn't be ignored that left a bitter taste in my mouth and didn't do much to improve my overall opinion of hospice—at least hospice in my area of the country.

As I kept my vigil, I pulled out photo albums and started looking for photographs for Mom's funeral cards and for the storyboard I'd be creating for her funeral. Mom spent a lot of time creating her photograph albums and took great pride in them. Each album was identified regarding the time period or which family it represented. She made albums for each of my dad's siblings and their families, albums for the early years, my babyhood, their numerous vacations, their many homes, and even an album for their years living in Florida. I once counted how many photograph albums Mom created, and I stopped counting after nineteen. Those were the albums Dad loved to pour over, spending hours reminiscing before he got sick and died. These same albums provided those treasured photographs I included in the two Heltunen Family Directories I created for family reunions. And they were the same albums I was looking at now. I viewed those photographs in a different way, like I was seeing them for the very first time. I saw photos of Mom as a young baby, during her high school years, in 1946 when she met her Paul, their wedding photographs, and the years since. I've looked at those photographs many times in the past, but never really looked at them as closely as I was now. Those photographs never meant so much to me as they did at that moment. Those photographs triggered tears. My heart ached, and I grieved even before my mom died.

I hadn't realized how much I missed my mom until I viewed those photographs. As her Alzheimer's advanced through the years, I replaced my love for her with a sense of feeling jaded, like I had buried her years before even though she was still alive. It didn't feel like she was alive because the person I was seeing every day didn't act like my mom. She couldn't converse like my mom. She wasn't that fun-loving person my mom used to be. In those middle Alzheimer' years my mom, I'm ashamed to admit, felt more like an albatross around my neck. I had a hard time even associating that shell of a person as the once vibrant, loving person I knew my mom to be. What stared back at me each day was someone I didn't know, understand, or want to admit knowing. Whatever happened to my mom had been replaced by a thing that sounded like her, looked vaguely like her, but wasn't my mom. After you live with this for many years, your heart becomes like a pillar of salt. It doesn't feel anything but contempt. That's what I had been living with for so long—contempt for my mom because she had Alzheimer's. And for years, I kept my guilt and shame bottled up. I didn't admit this to myself or anyone else. I came to realize this the year before when I was driving home from the November concert and asked God for forgiveness. I couldn't ask my mom for forgiveness because Mom wouldn't have any idea what I was asking forgiveness for. And perhaps the hardest thing of all was looking myself in the mirror and asking forgiveness of the person staring back at me. Now, all I could do was be there for her, stroke her forehead, gently care for her, and whisper to her over and over again, "I love you."

We human beings make so many mistakes, mistakes we often don't even realize we are making. And many times, the blinders we wear that we hide behind cheat us of life's experiences, of love, and of knowing other people because we are too afraid to reach out and express what's really in our hearts. Why is it we gain such valuable insight when it's either to late or almost too late to correct a wrong, to make up for transgressions, and make peace with our souls?

As each nightly vigil unfolded, the nights started to blend into each other with no delineating feature to distinguish one night from the other, other than Mom was still alive. Mom's condition continued to spiral downward. I found myself glued to her bedside trying to ease her pain, whisper words of endearment and courage, hoping that her death scene would soon be played out to its climax. And with the dawn of each new day, I was amazed that Mom was once again still alive. And with each new, wonderous morning, I couldn't help but think, *How much longer will this game continue to play out before it reaches its scheduled outcome?*

Late in the morning of Wednesday, August 14, I tried to entice Mom with her stuffed doggy, a toy she'd been sleeping with every night even during her death watch, and for the first time, she showed no interest in it. I moved it next to her pillow. She reached out to her baby doll, held it briefly, tried to whisper to it, kissed it, then put it down on her bed. I could tell by looking into her eyes she no longer had any interest in her beloved baby doll. When her eyes closed, I moved the doll off the bed, along with her dog. She never again kissed her beloved baby doll or slept cuddling her stuffed dog.

I had often heard that when someone is dying their hearing is the last sense to go. And I had also heard people say that sometimes you have to tell your loved one it's okay for them to die. By the fourth night, I started whispering into Mom's ear, "I love you. It's okay. I'll be alright, and Paul is waiting for you. Your parents are waiting for you. God will take care of me, so you don't have to worry about me. I'll be fine." It became my nightly chant, my new mantra, just like "It is what it is" had become my mantra the year before. By now, her eyes weren't open much. When they were, she either wasn't seeing me or she was seeing something I couldn't see. As each night passed, the sense of spirituality in the room was more heightened than the night before. With each breath I took, I knew it represented one less breath my mom would soon be taking.

On the few times I stepped away from Mom's bedside and returned, I noticed her breathing had slowed. Her breathing was hardly noticeable, just the slightest movement of her chest. Yet when I'd talk to her, Mom's breathing always quickened. It was as if she had a sixth sense when I was within hearing distance of her. I started to sit behind her head and watched her. When I was sitting behind her, her breathing visibly slowed down. It sometimes seemed as if she wasn't breathing at all. On those occasions when I was sitting next to her, I whispered to her, and Mom's breathing always quickened. You could visibly see her blanket moving up and down. That's when I came to realize Mom was holding on for me, something in her subconscious didn't want to leave her baby girl. Despite her cognitive decline, those last ten days of her life God seemed to have granted Mom a slight reprieve from Alzheimer's. I believe she consciously knew every time I sat next to her, and her strong will to live was for my benefit. Mom was making God's job a little harder all because of me.

Wednesday afternoon, August 14, Mom's breathing started to become labored, and by the next day, you could hear what's referred to as a death rattle. A death rattle is a sound a person nearing death makes when they no longer are able to clear their throat of saliva. It reminded me of hearing an air conditioner constantly running without turning off. You can hear it, and after a while it becomes annoying. You're waiting for the air conditioner to finally turn off. Hearing her death rattle was like that. I knew the end was now near. That night, like with all the previous nights, she reminded me of a dying ember, slowly fading but kept hanging in there by a whisper of a thread. I sat quietly, listening, never knowing if the next breath would be her last. There were several times when I thought she had died, but when I moved away her blanket, I saw the barest movement as her heart continued to beat. Mom had such a strong, inner will to live, a true testimony of her love for me. Once I realized this, I felt so guilty keeping my beloved Mom's soul away from everlasting peace.

Friday morning, August 16, promised to be another, hot, sultry, scorching summer day in the Sunshine State. No sleep for me during the night. Mom's death rattle was still audible. Around 10:00 a.m., her brother, Ron, got up. He was reading the newspaper in a chair next to her bed. I remembered I had bills that needed to be paid. I'd been putting off doing anything constructive because my thoughts and emotions were consumed with Mom. About 10:30 a.m., I stood up to get my checkbook and the invoices I needed to pay. I was sitting in the rust-colored chair near the window that my dad liked to sit in to look through the family photograph albums, the chair I used to sit in behind Mom's bed. I became immersed in my bill paying when after a few minutes, it suddenly dawned on me the room was quiet. I couldn't hear anything, especially Mom's rattled breathing. I popped up from my chair, ran to the side of her bed, and looked at her. I couldn't hear or see any breathing. There was no subtle movement of her chest. I lifted her blanket. As I stood there in utter sadness, I told Ron, "Phyllis has passed."

Mom's Alzheimer's journey was finally over, and she was reunited with her husband, my ever-faithful Dad. I couldn't be sad, or at least that's what I told anyone who asked. How could I be grieving when my parents were now healthy and together? They belonged together. How could I be selfish and cry when they were now so happy? As the tears flowed on the inside, I smiled on the outside knowing I had done the right thing in caring for my parents when they needed me most. And if I had to do it over again, I wouldn't have changed a damn thing, except be more understanding, knowledgeable, compassionate, and loving to my parents, especially earlier in Mom's Alzheimer's journey.

Christmas Letter 2019

Merry Christmas Family and Friends,

I thought 2017 was a bad year, this year has been just as disheartening. As some of you know, my dad, Paul, passed away on May 11. Dad was 98, he passed away ten days shy of my parent's 70th wedding anniversary. Three months later my mom, Phyllis, died at 91 on August 16, three days before the second heavenly anniversary of Matthew's death. I know my parents are now happy, healthy, and together, I couldn't ask for more! I've been my parents' caregiver for over thirteen years, the last two years I was with them 24/7. As a result, life now seems strange, it's taking a little getting used to. I feel blessed, though, we had the last two years together, it makes this new chapter in my life a little easier to accept and to deal with.

Emotionally, I've been plugging along, keeping busy, using this time to focus on reconnecting with friends, loving the pups, examining my life, enjoying hobbies, and trying to learn who this new me is. I plan on continuing my advocacy for Alzheimer's, caregiving, and widowhood. I believe the journey I've just traveled was God's plan for my future, to help others who find themselves traveling the same path I just traveled. It would be a waste of knowledge and experience to turn my back on those in need, disregard what I've learned and not help others. Something in my soul just won't let me do that! So once again I find myself embracing a new chapter in my life, looking forward to making new friends, exploring new places, and praying more short-term respite facilities are established to help caregivers.

I can feel it in my bones, 2020 will be a much better year, as will this new decade!
Wishing You and Yours a Christmas holiday filled with love and good cheer!
Peace, Prosperity, Health, Happiness & Love in 2020!

Vicki, Kipper & Katy

Final Thoughts

I'm a Better Person for the Journey I've Been On

When I was a freshman in college, I attended a psych lecture that dissected the five stages of grief as outlined by Elizbeth Kübler-Ross in her 1969 book *On Death and Dying*. In those days, I believed I had the world by its tail. Death had no relevance to me. The concept of dying was too abstract. I had no true perception of death or its sobering ramifications. Only old people died, and I wasn't old. Dammit, I was only eighteen! Never realizing once I graduated and entered the *real world*, reality would quickly smack me right in the face. The speed of sound transformed my super charged life and with it the rapid progression of my life.

In a blink of an eye I was in my thirties and bam! Before I knew it, I was fifty. What happened to my forties? I have no idea! I contend to this day—I never lived a 40s day in my life. I'm actually ten years younger than my birth certificate states. Space aliens must have abducted and dumped me headfirst back to earth on my fifth birthday. It's the only way I can explain it, because those darn years went by too damn fast to suit me.

I lived most of my life assuming I'd get up in the morning. My day would follow its normal breakneck speed, and the next day would fly by at the same unbelievable velocity. If I wasn't at work checking off items from an endless to-do list then I was home, cleaning, shopping, doing laundry. And when I was at work, I wondered about home and vice versa. I was pulled in a million different directions. This mad dash life I took for granted was normal, wasn't it? The older I got, the faster my world spun out of control. A vicious cycle, like a dog trying to chase its own tail, never quite catching it, or in this case, never quite getting everything accomplished.

Then, one day, August 19, 2017, my world came to a crashing, painful, sudden halt! My husband died. All of a sudden, my world stopped revolving at 200 mph. My world wasn't moving at all; it was standing still. Life without the constant juggling of a multitude of plates. It felt so unreal. Life had never seemed so quiet as it did then.

Becoming a widow was the hardest challenge I've had to face. Being a widow opened my eyes to the true meaning of life. My regret is Matthew wasn't alive when I learned this valuable lesson. It's hard to realize something so extremely important and have no one else to share it with.

Once Matthew passed away, my world of normal no longer existed. It was replaced by a new life that took a lot of getting used to. My parents needed full time care and being an only child with no children and no family who offered to help, I had no choice. It was the lesser of two evils, at least that's how I viewed it at the time.

I continue to mourn Matthew, and I anticipate a part of me always will. As the months and years went by, my mourning changes. Memories are slowly no longer my enemy but my friend. My tears don't flow as easily as they used to or for as long. Don't get me wrong, there are still times when I suddenly erupt into a thunderstorm, and when I wrote this book, I cried a torrent of tears as I relived every memory.

When I was married to Matthew, I never laughed as much as I did with him. Matthew unleashed the hidden extrovert in me. He helped me to laugh at life and at myself. This was a major accomplishment for someone who's been known for having a limited, warped sense of humor; a person known for not laughing at life's events. Laughing, I learned thanks to Matthew, helped to lighten my soul and allowed me to view life through a different set of lenses, with a new attitude, a greater sense of enjoyment. So, it's not surprising I've never cried as much as I've cried since the day he died. My endless well of tears is slowly cleansing my soul, helping me embrace a new purpose in my life.

It's the simple things I miss doing with Matthew, almost as much as I miss Matthew himself. Those everyday things I took for granted at the time. Yet, have you noticed those everyday occurrences comprise, in reality, a big chunk of our lives? Those every day, boring things you do day after day, and sometimes not even thinking about them because you've done them so often in the past. Like cleaning the kitchen after dinner, working together to fold laundry, driving to the grocery store, or going out on a date night. That's what's so hard about being a widow is you can't get those precious times back. The ordinary never seemed so important until they no longer exist.

Although my old life no longer exists, it's up to me to accept the hand fate has dealt me. I've learned no matter how much I cry; my tears will not bring Matthew back. Matthew satisfied his life's journey. God's plan for Matthew has been fulfilled. It's up to me to treasure my memories, hold on to precious keepsakes and photographs, and love his family. It's now my responsibility to accept God's plan. It doesn't mean I like it. I didn't get a vote, but neither did Matthew. I know in my heart if he could, he would have asked God for a couple more years. However, you don't bargain with God. Matthew would have loved to meet his great-grandson Michael and spend a little more time with MacKenzie, Reznor, and watch Elysia grow up into a beautiful, fulfilled, young woman. Life doesn't always work the way we want it.

I could wallow in self-pity, especially now that my parents are now both gone, too. It would be the easy way out. However, life is God's gift to us, and life is a precious commodity many do not have the luxury to enjoy. Do I take a chance on what's on the other side of the door, or do I resolve myself that life is over and resign myself to nothingness? Each person deals with death differently, but I must admit I'm getting curious about what's on the other side of that newly opened door.

If not for God's gift of Matthew into my life, I believe I'd probably be dead. A doctor's appointment I made before we were married saved my life. If not for Matthew, I wouldn't have made the appointment and a precancerous condition would have gone undetected until it was too late. In those days, I took my good health for granted and shied away from doctors. If not for Matthew coming into my life at that particular moment, I probably would have become a cancer statistic. And, as a result I'd hate to think what would have happened to my parents when they needed me most, and I wasn't there. Caregiving for my parents hasn't always been easy, but it has been rewarding. I have Matthew to thank that I was alive to care for my parents during the years they needed me most.

What hurts most is not realizing the depth of the love I felt for Matthew until it was too late to tell him. I let everyday life get in the way and rule my life. I took for granted tomorrow would come. As a result, I jeopardized not saying more frequently what was in my heart. When you no longer have tomorrows to look forward to is when you realize how precious life is. And how fast your life as you've known it can be taken away from you, just as quickly as the flutter of a hummingbird's wing.

I worry one day I may forget my Matthew memories. I can't help but be concerned since my Mom and Grandma both had Alzheimer's. Will I be the third generation to have her memories erased from her consciousness? I hope not. All I know is I don't want to forget my memories. They are all I have left of a life where I felt whole, felt loved, and felt like a normal person.

It took me a while to understand and accept God's plan for Matthew's passing. Since it was my destiny to care for my parents, it would have been very difficult for Matthew to witness how much time caring for my parents would take. Matthew guarded our time very closely. He didn't like anyone to infringe upon our time even if it was my parents. I believe in my heart God knew this about Matthew and in His wise judgment, He knew how divided my feelings and loyalties would have been if Matthew was still alive. This side of Matthew got easier to deal with once we moved into my parents' home in 2008. However, there were times, even then, when Matthew made me take sides. Those were challenging times for me. I hated being pitted between my husband and my parents. On those occasions, I'd go to bed at night knowing I let someone down, and it was usually my parents. My time caring for my parents provided me a chance to compensate for those times from the past when I sided with my husband. I'm human. I have my strengths and weaknesses like everyone else. When I'm strong, I'm determined like a dog with a bone. When I'm weak, my frailties are like a fresh baked cake, soft to the touch, and just as prone to breakage if the cake is lifted the wrong way.

I believe the hardest thing about taking care of my parents has been grieving for Matthew as I've trudged through each day. There were times when I yearned for the loving embrace of my mom's arms, her soft voice comforting me, her understanding motherly wisdom of what I was going through when my heart felt the despair and loneliness of widowhood. On those occasions, my mom couldn't comfort me. She didn't even know who I was let alone remember who I was mourning for. Even my dad, just once asked where Matthew was after we moved. It was as if all remembrance of Matthew had been erased from his mind. I had no one I could talk to about my husband. No one who I felt close enough to who knew Matthew or who I felt comfortable enough to confine in. After Matthew died hospice sent a letter about bereavement classes, but at the time I had no one to parent-sit. My church friend Gloria loaned me a four-volume set of books, *Journeying through Grief*, published by Stephens Ministry. These books helped me to understand and accept my emotions, emotions felt by millions since the beginning of time.

Grieving can do strange things to a person. Everyone handles death in a uniquely different way, and sometimes we react to death differently depending on how the person is related to us, and the impact they've had on our life. It took me days after Matthew died before I was able to cry for him. Since I started crying for Matthew, my well hasn't dried. The strange thing about my parents' deaths, I haven't cried much. I thought I would. Their deaths have left me devoid of immediate family. My three biggest supporters in my life are never more. I should be crying. Maybe I used up all my tears after Matthew died. In reality, I had months to prepare for Matthew's death, yet I was in denial. I kept holding out for hope, praying, hoping for a magic pill that would cure him. With my parents, I'd been living with their Alzheimer's for years. Alzheimer's had already steeled my heart of the eventual outcome to be expected. For years, my mom, especially, had already been dead to me. It was my dad's passing that hit me a little harder at the time since he was in better shape overall, and I wasn't expecting him to go first. And watching my mom slowly pass away, night after excruciating night, I regained my mom in my heart with each diminished breath she took.

With time, I learned to deal with my grief in the only way I could, to grab it by its collar and shake it. Shake it until the tears stopped flowing and memories no longer cloud my mind like an early morning fog. One night that first winter after Matthew died and my uncle moved in with us, I overheard the hockey announcer on TV say, "The Bolts score thanks to Matthew Joseph's pass!" I almost fainted! Ron's a huge Tampa Bay Lightning fan. He's glued to every televised Bolts games. I instantly stopped what I was doing, and thoughts of Matthew flooded my heart. I remember running to the TV trying to figure out who this hockey player was by the name of Matthew Joseph. When Matthew and I were married, and he was in Philadelphia visiting his family or our schedules were unbelievably hectic, I'd frequently whisper to myself, "Matthew Joseph, I hope you are okay," or "Matthew Joseph, I miss you." Now, I've come to accept there is a fleet-footed winger whose name sounds the same as my Matthew, spelled a little different. He is much younger, but both have February birthdays only six days apart. It took me a while not to cry every time I heard Mathieu Joseph's name mentioned by the hockey announcer. Though I must admit my ears still perk up, and I still stop what I'm doing, I reflect, and a soft smile now brightens my face. Yes, sometimes a few tears still coast down my face, but not as often as before. It's amazing how time gradually heals the soul, and with time you learn that no matter how long you stare at a photograph, you eventually come to realize you can't roll back the hands of time.

With Matthew's passing, I was able to concentrate on caregiving. Caregiving for my parents provided me the distraction to get through each day in just the same way the pups' love convinced me to get up each morning. Knowing my parents needed me gave me a reason for being. They, like the pups, needed me. The difference being my parents couldn't say those three little words I yearned to hear, *I love you*. Whereas the pups conveyed their love every time I looked at their tail wagging, wiggling little bodies as they welcomed me home.

There have been times when I'd shout, "I can't do this anymore. I can't live like this any longer!" It took time for my anger and frustrations to leave my heart, floating into oblivion, dissipating into the baby blue sky. I looked at my situation and reminded myself these were my parents. Even though I'd started calling them Paul and Phyllis the year before, they were still my parents. That's something I had conveniently forgotten in order to get through each day. If I thought of them as my parents, the anger became overwhelming. If I saw them as two people named Paul and Phyllis, then I could deal with it. They became two elderly people who needed someone to take care of them. It wasn't until Paul was dying at Hospice House when I was able to surrender my caregiver roll and become his daughter again. Calling my parents by their first names was how I was able to cope with my situation. Now it seems like I took the coward's way out. I finally grew up and was able to separate myself from my caregiving job and my duty as their daughter. At the same time, tears flowed for all the family times we'd shared through the years. Holidays and fun times will never be celebrated in the same way ever again. My memories keep these times alive, even though it's painful. And then I knock myself down from my pity pole and realize how thankful I should be. There are so many people in the world who haven't had the love of a spouse or parent and who don't have good memories to look back on and treasure.

I've forced myself to move forward, to move beyond my anger—painfully, reluctantly, anxiously. That's life. You have to keep going even when it knocks you down, whether you like it or not. I know if I had to live my life over again, I'd still marry Matthew. I'd still become a caregiver for my parents, and I'd still adopt our little fur babies. Everything else would be a crapshoot. As my mantra says, "I'm hanging in there; it is what it is."

Every Sunday at church, there's a Cares Choral response recited by the congregation, written by Kelly Willard, that's kept me grounded. It's kept me moving forward during those most trying of times. After Matthew died, I'd stare at the cross behind the altar, thinking to myself, *Help me, dear Lord. Help me. I don't know what to do; I feel so lost.* During the week, whenever I'd have a particularly tough day, I'd recite this choral response silently in my mind, hoping God would hear me. As the months flew by, like the first anniversary of Matthew's death, I found myself slowly regaining some semblance of peace. I felt God was listening. God was helping this poor sinner after all. I have learned to trust in the Lord. He does hear me. He guides me. He plants ideas in my mind, and He points me in the direction I should be going. His plan may not be the same plan as I imagine for myself, but I've learned, His plan is usually much better.

I feel as if my eyes have been opened. Guess I'm a slow learner. Or, as I'd like to think, God opened my eyes for the best that's yet to come. I don't know what the future holds. What I do know is I've learned from my past and now live each day as a true gift from God. My life was blessed with the best parents a girl could have. My parents supported me, loved me, were there for me when I needed them, and they let me make mistakes. I was loved by a man who loved me and saved my life. He did the best he could for me, and we grew into a family. Matthew learned love could also be conveyed by four-legged creatures. The pups, in all reality, were the glue that united us as a family, our little gifts from God.

My family and friends played integral parts in my life as Matthew and I melded into one. They witnessed our evolution, just as we witnessed theirs. Part of the evolution was the death of those closest to me—my husband, my dad, and lastly, my mom. One gone too soon. The other graced with longevity whose mind and body just finally wore out. And the other with such a strong will to live, she couldn't say good-bye.

I feel fortunate, I learned my purpose in life. For years, I had wondered. My destiny was to love Matthew, to keep his memory alive while caring for my parents in much the same way they cared for me when I was a child. I know Matthew and my parents are now in heaven, their respective illnesses wiped from their bodies. They are enjoying their new-found peace, and someday, they will be welcoming me into heaven with outstretched arms when my time comes.

In the meantime, I'm left on this earth. In just the position I always dreaded being in one day. It's one of the reasons I married Matthew, so I wouldn't be alone after my parents died. Coming from a loner like me, I know that sounds preposterous. As long as the three most important people in my life were alive, I knew I wasn't alone. Now, I am in the position I prayed I'd never be in, alone with no immediate family. However, I still have the pups, and my uncle still lives with me, too. Maybe it's not the life I had before, but life never stands still. It's always evolving, as I used to tell Matthew. Matthew's death opened my eyes and prepared me for this day. I have so much to be thankful for, and I have so much to look forward to. My evolution is still a work in progress, and thanks to Matthew, I've gained a sense of God that I never really felt before. I listen to the little voice in my head. I believe that's God talking to me, and he's never steered me wrong. God blessed me with wonderful parents, a loving husband, devoted pups, and cherished family and friends. So even though I'm now alone, I'm really not because as I whispered into my mom's ear when she was dying, "God will be with me. He will take care of me. I'll never be alone."

My journey has taught me so much, and I believe God used Matthew as the catalyst in my search about life. God brought Matthew into my life to assure I'd be alive to care for my parents in the same way God brought me into Matthew's life so he'd evolve into a person more compassionate toward others. If Matthew hadn't met me, I doubt this evolution would have manifested itself in Matthew's persona. This change made Matthew a better person. And this change wasn't due directly to me but to the love he gleaned from three four-legged balls of fur, Casey, Kipper and Katy. If not for me, though, Matthew would never have welcomed into his life such unconditional love. Life does come full circle.

I hope my story helps those who face the challenge of losing a loved one. Widowhood has been the hardest thing for me to endure. Life is daunting without a spouse. Our lives entwine with our spouse in so many different ways, more so than with any other relationship we have in life. My advice to you is take time to mourn and heal. Forgive yourself of those things you wished you could have done or said at the end of your spouses' life but didn't. Accept it's God's intention and plan for you to travel a new path. A path with challenges but also pleasant surprises. The hard part is relinquishing your old life and stepping through the door into a new chapter. It's scary, lonely, and intimidating, but you can do it. Life is a precious gift, don't squander it. Don't turn your back on your life. You may come to realize what you learn about yourself is a strength of character you never realized you had. It's the uncertainty and the reluctance to let go of the past and the fear of what you may be facing that makes it so hard to accept this new chapter of your life. I hate to be the bearer of bad news, but you don't have a choice. Your old life is no longer. Be brave, and take a chance on yourself. Reach out, and open the door. See what's on the other side. You just might be surprised!

Alzheimer's is a hell of a way to go. Aside from the obvious, robbing a person of their memories and the opportunity to enjoy time with their family and friends, it's the randomness of the disease that makes it so criminal. For some, this disease takes a slow progression to claim a life. For others just a few short years until the person is mercifully gone. Some victims of Alzheimer's recognize, at the beginning, something just isn't right with them. They ponder and question what's wrong, never able to put their finger on the problem. However, family and friends usually recognize the culprit much sooner than the poor victim. Add to the sorrow of this disease is that there still is no cure. Everyone who is diagnosed will eventually succumb to the same fate—death—whether it's in two years or twelve.

Caregivers must be applauded for their selfless efforts for caring for a loved one with Alzheimer's or dementia. They put their lives on hold in order to provide the daily ministrations required to care for their loved one. A caregiver's task can be daunting, challenging, stressful, nerve-wracking, nurturing, loving, funny, and frightening. Most are unpaid, accepting of a job they recognize needs doing.

If someone asked me what every caregiver needs—that's easy. Every caregiver needs short-term respite care. They need a safe place, specializing in caring for Alzheimer's and dementia patients so caregivers can take a much-needed break from caregiving. It shouldn't matter whether it's for a couple of days or a couple of weeks, as long as it's a place where caregivers can make a reservation for their loved one at a reasonable rate. Caregivers don't always have family or friends to rely on for help. A caregiver should never be expected to sacrifice their health or not attend the funeral of a loved one because they have no one to care for their afflicted loved one. If my book accomplishes anything, I pray it helps to establish short-term respite care facilities so caregivers can take a periodic break from caregiving.

Taking care of a loved one may not be the right thing for everyone, I accept that. If that's the case, I plead with you to at least develop and maintain a relationship with your Alzheimer's loved one whether they live with someone else, or they live in a memory care facility. Your loved one shouldn't be sequestered away, forgotten, or ignored. Social interaction is vital for anyone with Alzheimer's and dementia. They may not know who you are, but *you* know who they are. A gentle touch, listening to music together, singing a song, a loving embrace, just being there with your loved one are the everyday things which mean the most to them. Your loved one is still a person whose journey through life has taken a detour, a detour not of their own making, but of God's. A journey with only one conclusion, there's no hope for recovery. The ultimate outcome is death. Providing some semblance of quality of life will assure your loved one's last days, months, or years are lived in peace, safety, and love.

I am the person I am today thanks to my parents, my husband, family, and friends. My parents shaped my psyche, grounded me with respected values, and molded my perspective on life. Matthew taught me about love. He inadvertently instilled in me a backbone, to stand up for myself, a valued commodity that's been numerously tested. Family and friends helped me to stop having so many expectations and appreciate those who reached out to me versus those who were fair-weathered and untrue. Life events and what appear to be random occurrences are things I have come to realize are not as random as we are led to believe. I no longer believe in coincidence; things happen for a reason in much the same way as our lives comingle with others as we traverse this journey called life.

I did what I could for my parents when they needed me most. Yes, it disrupted my life, but my life was already in a state of chaos after Matthew died. Taking care of my parents gave me a new sense of purpose. Caring for my parents helped me to heal, gave me the opportunity to reexamine my life, take stock of where I'd been, where I was, and determine what I wanted for my future. And eventually, I was able to look myself in the mirror at night, smile, and remind myself *I'm an amazing caregiver.*

I need to move on. I still have a life to live; I owe it to myself. And as I told Matthew after Casey died when he wanted to wait before getting another pup, "After everything Casey did to win you over, it would be a travesty to not honor her love for us and not get another pup." In this same vein, I now have to apply my own words to myself, *After all that Matthew taught me about love and marriage, it would be a travesty to turn my back on life. Instead, I need to live life to its fullest as if I'm living it for both of us.*

It's humbling to bear witness to the slow, arduous death of a loved one. I witnessed three, each one slightly different, each one gut wrenching. Each one helped me better understand myself and the love I felt for that person. Death is a part of life, welcoming a person into heavenly paradise. I know in my heart I did the best I could taking care of my parents and believe they knew I was doing everything in my power to keep them safe, fed, nurtured, engaged, and loved. Would I do it over again? An unequivocal, *yes!* I know more about myself now than I ever did before. My strengths have become my best friends. My weaknesses, I recognize and strive to overcome. I'm not perfect, and I never will be, I'm human! I feel blessed for recognizing that in myself. We never know what's around the next corner, just take your blinders off. Find out, and embrace it!

I've had people tell me, "You're so strong; I can't believe what you've endured!" I didn't have a choice; what I experienced was my destiny. And on those occasions when I thought I couldn't face anything more, I'd think of a Bible verse that's been my shadow since I first read it on my confirmation certificate, Deuteronomy 31:6 (KJV), "Be strong and of a good courage, fear not, nor be afraid of them: for the Lord thy God, he it is that doth go with thee; he will not fail thee, nor forsake thee."[35] Whenever I needed inner strength, fortitude of courage, or unwavering faith, this verse has uplifted my spirit and kept my soul soaring like nothing else could. One simple Bible verse, randomly typed on a certificate when I was a teenager has helped sustain me throughout my life. The power of the Bible!

God was there with me every step of the way, pointing me in the right direction. I can't take all the credit for my rebirth, my renewed baptism. I was amazed, no matter how often I'd screwup as a caregiver, God didn't turn his back on me. If anything, He knew I had the best intentions for my parents despite those times when my humanness got in the way. I learned to place myself in my parents' shoes, coming to understand they had no control over their illness. I don't know if I, too, will become another victim of this damn disease. At least I know I'll just have to face that road if it looms its ugly head. In the meantime, I'm trying to conquer my fears, take time for myself, and enjoy each moment I have with my pups, my family and my friends. Life isn't what it was before Matthew died, but it's not so bad. I know Matthew's my guardian angel now, just as my parents are, too.

As I look in the mirror, I see a person who stares back at me, but I don't recognize her. On a closer look, she looks a little familiar. A little older, maybe a smidgen wiser. A bit heavier around the middle with a look of acceptance of where her journey has taken her, of where she's been, and a glimmer of hope that hints of an uncertain future. When I step closer, I see something in her eyes. A look betrays the road she just traveled—a weariness sprinkled with a touch of skepticism. The reflection appears resolved of a new journey awaiting her. She can't rest forever in a state of limbo, turning her back on her future while clinging to the past. She's a woman who's learned a lifetime of knowledge gained from each garment she's worn and discarded along the way. When I look deeper, into the farthest reaches of her heart, I see anguish of loss, pain of remembering, fear of the unknown, and a flicker of curiosity about what's to come. Reading between the lines that are softly etched within the confines of her face, I recognize resilience, strength of character, a sense of worth, and most importantly no regrets. This is a person who faced each challenge, stood her ground, and didn't turn a blind eye to those in need. Instead, she did what she could based on what her heart, conscious, and mind told her were the right things to do, even when those decisions robbed her of a legacy most people would have chosen instead. On those occasions, she chose the road of most resistance and learned more about herself in the process. She loved a husband until his dying day. She loved and cared for her parents until they too, left this earth. And she learned to love and like herself as well. She wouldn't have learned so much about herself and what she was capable of accomplishing, feeling, or doing for others if she hadn't taken the low, rutted road, a journey she just completed. How do I know so much about this person? Because that person who's staring back at me—is me.

All I Want to Do...

All I want to do is turn back the hands of time,
Erase the pain and heartache of losing the one I love.
If only I had known how short our present was destined to be,
I would have spent more time with the one I love.
I've shed an ocean of tears; I've prayed for just one more moment
with the one I love.

All I want to do is face the challenge of one less tear,
Reluctant mornings, longing for the one I love.
Loneliness of night, when memories agonizingly haunt me,
I wonder why this happened, to the one I love.
I've shed an ocean of tears; I've prayed for comfort, please ease
my heartache for the one I love.

All I want to do is shake this empty, daunting loneliness,
I feel lost, empty, without the one I love.
Days blur into night, nights stand silently still,
I reach out, longing to hold on to the one I love,

I've shed an ocean of tears; please, dear Lord, please give me the
courage to live without the one I love.

All I want to do is accept the changes I couldn't control,
Cherish my memories, remember the voice of the one I love.
I feel guilty, living as one is so much harder than I thought,
Something holds me back, I'm afraid I'll forget the one I love.
I've shed an ocean of tears; please dear Lord, please guide me as
I live without the one I love.

All I want to do is cherish each day with a smile in my heart,
Treasure my life, accept this detour without the one I love.
My love was my past, my future is my life,
I've been blessed having known the love of my life.
I've shed an ocean of tears; thank you, dear Lord, thank you for
the memories I treasure of the one I loved.
Thank you, dear Lord, thank you for the memories I treasure of
the one I loved.

Vicki Veasey
Dedicated in loving memory to Matthew J. Veasey, Jr.

If Only I Had Known...

If only I had known…your loving memories would be denied you,
I would have spent more time making memories with you.

If only I had known…your beautiful spirit would evaporate into
the night sky,
I would have treasured you more like a baby's lullaby.

If only I had known…your hard-earned achievements would be
lost to you,
I would have taken a front row seat more often to applaud you.

If only I had known…you'd eventually forget me,
I would have rejoiced more loudly, "I love you!" to the highest degree.

Vicki Veasey
Dedicated in loving memory to Paul and Phyllis Heltunen

Matthew with Kipper and Katy in Cedar Key, Florida,
January 2, 2016. Our last Cedar Key vacation as a family.

Our wedding day, May 17, 1996. Never dreamed twenty-one years could fly by so quickly!

Matthew and I standing in front of the hot pink crepe myrtle tree we planted two months after our wedding. We named her, Honey Do. After Matthew died, my parents and I moved to Citrus County. I planted a hot pink crepe myrtle tree at our new home and named her, Honey Do II, dedicated in memory of Matthew.

Matthew and Casey, summer 2005. Thanks to Casey, Matthew learned unconditional love of a pet.

Celebrating my birthday at our favorite restaurant, Nouvelle Cuisine. Spring Hill, FL, March 2016.

Our trip to Ireland, celebrating our 15th wedding anniversary, May 2011. Visible behind Matthew is Dublin's Ha'penny Bridge. During this trip, I fell deeper in love with my husband and became enamored of Ireland as well!

One of my favorite photos of Matthew, taken at Stage West's Hami's awards, c. 2009.

Matthew singing his signature song, Kelley Mooney's version of *Hallelujah*, accompanied by his golfing partner, Stage West buddy, and UCC choir director Wayne Raymond at the Spring Hill United Church of Christ, Spring Hill, FL.

Matthew as John Dickinson in *1776*.
Stage West Community Playhouse,
Spring Hill, FL, 2008.

Matthew won a Hami award
playing Toddy in *Victor/
Victoria*, Stage West, 2001.

Known as "Uncle Matt" to the young thespians he
worked with, here with Victoria Riggs, Nuncrackers,
2014.

Matthew twice appeared as oldest brother Reuben in Stage West's productions of *Joseph and the Amazing Technicolor Dreamcoat*. His musical number, *Those Canaan Days*, was always a crowd pleaser!

Mom and Dad's wedding photo, May 21, 1949.

Happier times before Alzheimer's was introduced into our lives. Celebrating Mom and Dad's 50th anniversary and our 3rd anniversary, May 1999.

Dad wearing his favorite cap, Michigan State University. He always wore this cap when watching his favorite basketball team, the MSU Spartans, coached by his fellow Yooper Tom Izzo.

At this time, Alzheimer's was a fixture in our lives. Dad and I were in denial, while Mom was asking questions repeatedly. The only one who seemed to understand the direction we were heading toward was Matthew, November 2009.

Mom and Dad's last trip to Michigan, June 2014. The iconic symbol of Michigan, the Mackinac Bridge, is visible directly behind them.

Dad and Mom, 2018. By this time, both had Alzheimer's. Soon, Mom would be transitioning into the final stage.

Dad, Mom, and her brother Ron, Christmas 2018. Dad and Mom's last Christmas.

Celebrating Dad's last birthday, February 2019, Tallahassee, FL. Bob Rogers, Dad, his sister Phyllis, and niece, Lori Demetrion. Dad and Bob shared the same birthday, and it became a family tradition for the two couples to celebrate together every February 23.

Dad with nephews Landen and Dave Heltunen, March 2019. Dad thought of Dave as the son he never had.

Dad with his nephew, Jim Rogers. One of Dad's favorite stories he loved to tell was about attending one of Jim's school football games and scoring a touchdown.

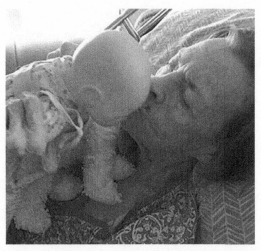

Mom loving and kissing her baby doll. Her mothering instinct was still very strong despite being in the final stage of Alzheimer's. This photo was taken just days before her death, August 2019.

Appendices

End Notes

1 Yan Liu et al. "Primary mucinous adenocarcinoma of the lung: A case report and review of the literature," *Oncology Letters*, Spandidos Publications, 20 July 2017, viewed 24 March 2019, https://www.ncbi.nlm.nih.gov/pmc/articles/PMC5587939/.

2 Ibid.

3 In 2011 the West African rhinoceros was declared extinct. Wikipedia, viewed 02 Jan 2020, https://en.wikipedia.org/wiki/Western_black_rhinoceros.

4 "More Irish Terms of Endearment." Claddagh Design, 7 May 2019, Ireland, https://www.claddaghdesign.com/ireland/more-irish-terms-of-endearment/.

5 Possibly the most recognized and recited Irish prayer, author unknown, often included at weddings, funerals, and commemorative events, public domain.

6 Caregivers Bill of Rights written by Jo Horne, author of *Caregiving: Helping an Aging Loved One*, published by American Association of Retired Persons, Washington, DC; Glenview IL, Scott, Foreman, Lifelong Learning Division,

1985. I originally obtained a copy of this document through my support group, Memory Lane. I conducted numerous searches trying to contact Ms. Horne for permission to use her Caregiver Bill of Rights within this book, with no success. Her Caregivers Bill of Rights appears on many Alzheimer's and caregivers websites, when I contacted those organizations for information on Ms. Horne these communications were unsuccessful as well. One website that provides Ms. Horne's Caregiver Bill of Rights is the Family Caregiver Alliance, viewed January 20, 2020, https://www.caregiver.org/caregiver's-bill-rights

[7] Alzheimer's Association, 2019 Alzheimer's Disease Facts and Figures, viewed 24 July 2019, https://www.alz.org/media/Documents/alzheimers-facts-and-figures-infographic-2019.pdf.

[8] Ibid.

[9] Alzheimer's News Today, "Alzheimer's Disease Statistics," Bionews Services, https://alzheimersnewstoday.com/alzheimers-disease-statistics/.

[10] Kerr, Mandi, "Famous People Who You Probably Didn't Know Had Dementia;" "Famous People Who Lived With Alzheimer's Disease;" Kennard, Christine, "Famous People With Alzheimer's Disease and Other Types of Dementia;" "50 Celebrities Who Have Had Alzheimer's Disease." https://www.cheatsheet.com/health-fitness/famous-people-who-you-probably-didnt-know-had-dementia.html/, https://www.thefamouspeople.com/alzheimers.php, https://www.verywellhealth.com/famous-people-with-alzheimers-98082?print.

[11] Alzheimer's Association, 2019 Alzheimer's Facts and Figures, Includes a Special Report on Alzheimer's Detection in the Primary Care Setting: Connecting Patients and Physicians, p. 43, 50, 52, https://www.alz.org/media/Documents/alzheimers-facts-and-figures-2019-r.pdf.

[12] Ibid, p. 43.

[13] Ibid., p. 48.

[14] Ibid., p. 43.

15   Ibid.
16   Alzheimer's Association, 2019 Alzheimer's Disease Facts and Figures
17   Alzheimer's Association, 2019 Alzheimer's Facts and Figures, Includes a Special Report on Alzheimer's Detection in the Primary Care Setting: Connecting Patients and Physicians, p. 31.
18   Ibid.
19   Ibid., p. 33.
20   Ibid., p. 31.
21   Ibid.
22   Ibid.
23   Ibid., p. 34.
24   Ingber, Ron. "Caregiver Stress Syndrome," Today's Caregiver, 18 Dec 2018, viewed 11 Nov 2019, https://caregiver.com/articles/caregiver-stress-syndrome/.
25   Ibid.
26   Alzheimer's Association, 2019 Alzheimer's Facts and Figures, Includes a Special Report on Alzheimer's Detection in the Primary Care Setting: Connecting Patients and Physicians, p. 35.
27   Small, Barbara. "Caregiver Syndrome," Family Caregivers' Network Society, https://www.familycaregiversbc.ca/wp-content/uploads/2016/03/Caregiver-Syndrome.pdf.
28   Brenoff, Ann. "This is everything That's Wrong With Caregiving In America Today, Public policy lags woefully behind today's reality." *Post 50*, Huff Post, viewed 22 September 2016, https://www.huffpost.com/entry/this-is-everything-thats-wrong-with-caregiving-in-america-today_n_57e2e78ce4b0e80b1b9fff6e.
29   Ingber.
30   "Lack of Sleep May be Linked to Risk Factor for Alzheimer's Disease." *National Institutes of Health... Turning Discovery Into Health, NIH Research Matters*, Office of Communications and Public Liaison in the NIH Office of the Director, 13 April 2018, https://www.nih.gov/news-events/lack-sleep-may-be-linked-risk-factor-alzheimers-disease.

31 Alzheimer's Association, 2019 Alzheimer's Facts and Figures, pg 34.

32 Barba, Christine. "What You Should Know Before Getting a Genetic Test for Alzheimer's." Being Patient. 6 Nov 2018, viewed 26 Dec 2019, https://www.beingpatient.com/genetic-test-for-alzheimers/.

33 Cook, John, compiled and arranged. *The Book of Positive Quotations*. 2nd ed. Minneapolis: Fairview Press, 1993, p. 123.

34 "My Love [Petula Clark song]," Wikipedia, 11 Nov 2019, viewed 4 Jan 2020, https://en.wikipedia.org/wiki/List_of_Billboard_Hot_100_number-one_singles_of_1966.

35 The Holy Bible, King James Version, Cleveland and New York: The World Publishing Company, no year, no copyright, public domain, Deuteronomy 31:6, p. 159.

Acknowledgment

First and foremost, I want to thank you, the reader. If you found this book helpful, I'm thankful! In order to help others in need of assistance I'd like to ask you to please write an online book review. Your review will help others as they seek information to assist them as they enter into widowhood or become a new caregiver. Whatever we can do to help each other unites us as friends. Again, many *Thanks* for becoming a new friend!

My heartfelt thank you to the following family and friends who supported me, especially during my caregiving years. You have no idea what your love, encouragement, and friendship means to me: Peggy and Jim Bailey, Phyllis and Bob Rogers, Ron Miller, Lori Demetrion, Anne Brewer, Grace Croke, Mary Ann Adams, Leroy Hill, Jr., Dianne Terry, Rev. Robin DeAngelis and my church family at the Spring Hill United Church of Christ, Wayne and Sherrie Raymond, Gail Mattox, John Laconca, Cynthia Haring, Katia Valdeos, Linda McKenna, Mariann Eckman, Keith Golka, Dr. Hany Abskhroun, Diane Cox, Diana Veasey, Debbie Veasey, Matthew Veasey III, Michael Veasey, Betty Phillips, Donnamarie Mooney, Dave Heltunen, Tricia Piernock, Estie Sturos, Sue Sturos,

GOOD MORNING I LOVE YOU

Rev. Daniel Horn, Vicky Carlson, Kris King, Jenny Van Pamel, Katy Bailey, Sandy Myers, Marietta Ferguson, Shannon Maxwell, Kathy Fate, Shirley Button, Shirley Hartsfield, Nancy Casey, Jean Edwards, Heather McCraw, Joyce Cotton, Cheral Riddick, my neighbors at WWS, Kim Bettineschi, Katherine Haghighi, Niccie Kliegl, and all my Igniting Souls on Fire tribe. I suspect there are others who I've been remise to mention, please forgive me. I appreciate you; it wasn't intentional.

The compassionate ladies of the Key Center of Lecanto deserve a special thank you. They cared for Mom and Dad with love, humor, and kindness. Their concern didn't stop with my parents, they adopted me as well. Leah and her girls, Jessica, Debbie, Rita, and Nasue, have an innate sense of knowing when I needed a shoulder to cry on and I will forever be grateful for their friendship. Their weekly calls of concern when Mom was dying were a balm for my grieving soul and meant so much. Thank you!

A special thank you to Karen Kline, RN, BSN Faith Community Nurse, First United Methodist Church, Homosassa. Karen recently retired as the coordinator of Memory Lane Respite and Support Group. Her gentle soul, understanding nature, and compassionate heart helped me embrace my caregiver responsibilities. I'm not sure if I would have evolved into the caregiver I became if not for Karen and my support group. To the members of Memory Lane Support Group, two words convey what's in my heart to each and every one of you, *Thank You!* And I don't want to forget Karen's volunteers who nurtured and cared for Mom and Dad every Monday afternoon, a resounding *Thank You!*

Thank you to Russel Trong, IT professional and owner of Personal Computer Services of Sugarmill Woods. Many times during the writing of this book I reached out to Russ with technical, PC problems. If not for Russ, this book might still be in the editing stage.

Two persons stand out during the production phase of this book. Debbie O'Byrne, who designed the cover. I had a vision, and Debbie's never ending patience helped my vision to become a reality, thank you! Felicity Fox, my editor, mere words can not

396

convey what's in my heart for my new friend. Felicity understood my story and believed in it. She knew what my "baby" meant to me and embraced it with the same conviction that I felt, thank you!

I'm indebted to my publisher, Author Academy Elite and my Igniting Souls Tribe, especially Kary Oberbrunner and David Branderhorst. Their vision enabled me to realize my lifelong dream, to write the book I knew I was destined to write. Their guidance opened my eyes to how I can help others who journey along a similar path.

Last, and I always save the best for last, I want to thank God for the journey I've just traveled. God graced me with the very best parents and husband. Thanks to God, He pointed me in the right direction. The story you read is totally different from my original intent; what you read speaks from my heart in a way my original story never would have. Through God's grace I've learned to keep an open mind, appreciate each day, and embrace the future.

Group Discussion Questions

1) If the author's situation happened to you, becoming either a widow/widower or a caregiver, what would you do?

2) How do you think you would change and react to such a drastic change in your life?

3) How did the author change as a result of becoming a widow?

4) How did the author change as a result of becoming a caregiver to her parents?

5) Which do you believe would be the biggest challenge, becoming a widow/widower or a caregiver 24/7? Why?

6) If your spouse or significant other passed away, what changes would you make in your life? Any dreams you'd try to pursue?

7) If your spouse or significant other passed away would you continue to live in the same home? Why or why not?

8) Where do you believe the author obtained her will to go on despite the challenges she faced?

9) What personal strengths would help you? What personal weaknesses would you need to overcome—either from the perspective of a widow/widower or caregiver?

10) How do you anticipate being a caregiver could change the dynamics of your family? How do you anticipate it could change your daily life?

11) If your spouse or significant other passed away is there a plan in place for settling the estate? Would you be prepared to live on the financial resources available to you? Could you survive each month financially? Would you have to make adjustments to your monthly budget?

12) How would you handle the challenges a caregiver contends with on a daily basis?

13) If your spouse or significant other passed away, what do you think would be your biggest hurdles to accepting and embracing the new chapter of your life?

14) Looking at your community, what services are you aware of could assist you as either a widow/widower or as a caregiver?

15) After your role as caregiver is over, how do you anticipate you would handle the change in your daily routine? Psychologically, how do you think you would feel?

16) How did the author change after the death of her husband? After the death of her parents?

17) As a widow/widower would you continue to celebrate birthdays, family events, and holidays? If not, why not? And if so, why?

18) In your opinion, what did the author learn about life, about herself?

19) Life is full of challenges, what do you believe was the author's biggest challenge? Why?

20) The author makes reference to her pups many times during the story, what role did they play in her life during this time?

21) Throughout the first part of the book, the author made numerous references, almost like hints of impending death, what were these references and why do you think the author made them?

22) If you had been in the author's shoes, how would you have reacted to those events in her life?

Bibliography

50 Celebrities who have had Alzheimer's Disease, MindCafe, viewed 14 Nov 2019, http://www.mindcafe.org/2009/05/1 2/50-celebrities-who-have-had-alzheimers-disease/.

"2020 Census Will Help Policymakers Prepare for the Incoming Wave of Aging Boomers," America Counts Staff, 19 Dec 2019, viewed 20 Jan 2020, https://www.census.gov/library/ stories/2019/12/by-2030-all-baby-boomers-will-be-age-65-or-older.html.

Administration for Community Living, ACL Awards Grant to Establish National Volunteer Care Corps, 19 Sept 2019, viewed 11 Nov 2019, https://acl.gov/news-and-events/announcements/ acl-awards-grant-establish-national-volunteer-care-corps.

Alzheimer's and Related Dementias, Basics on Alzheimer's Disease and Dementia, Alzheimer's Disease Fact Sheet, National Institute on Aging, US Department on Health and Human Services,

viewed 20 November 2019, https://www.nia.nih.gov/health/
alzheimers-disease-fact-sheet.

Alzheimer's Association, 2019 Alzheimer's Facts and
Figures, Includes a Special Report on Alzheimer's Detection
in the Primary Care Setting: Connecting Patients and
Physicians, viewed https://www.alz.org/media/Documents/
alzheimers-facts-and-figures-2019-r.pdf.

Alzheimer's Association, March 2019, Fact Sheet, Alzheimer's
Disease Caregivers, viewed 24 May 2019, https://act.alz.org/site/
DocServer/caregivers_fact_sheet.pdf?docID=3022.

Alzheimer's Association, March 2018, Fact Sheet, 2018 Alzheimer's
Disease Facts and Figures, viewed 24 May 2019, https://www.alz.
org/aaic/_downloads/aaic-facts-and-figures-fact-sheet-2018.pdf.

Alzheimer's Association, March 2017, Fact Sheet, 2017 Alzheimer's
Disease Facts and Figures, viewed 24 May 2019, https://www.alz.
org/email/alz-media-insider/downloads/2017-FF-Factsheet.pdf.

Alzheimer's Association. Genetic Testing, reviewed by Alzheimer's
Association Medical and Scientific Advisory Council June 2017,
viewed 26 Dec 2019, https://www.alz.org/media/Documents/
genetic-testing-statement.pdf.

Alzheimer's Association. Genetic Testing, TS-0044. Updated
Feb 2019, viewed 26 Dec 2019.https://www.alz.org/media/
Documents/alzheimers-dementia-genetic-testing-ts.pdf.

Alzheimer's Association, 2019, Fact Sheet, 2019 Alzheimer's
Disease Facts and Figures, viewed 20 November 2019,
https://www.alz.org/media/Documents/alzheimers-facts-and-
figures-infographic-2019.pdf.

Alzheimer's News Today, "Alzheimer's Disease Statistics," Bionews Services, https://alzheimersnewstoday.com/alzheimers-disease-statistics/

Alzheimer's Society. Genetics of dementia, Factsheet 405LP, May 2016, viewed 26 Dec 2019, https://www.alzheimers.org.uk/sites/default/files/pdf/factsheet_genetics_of_dementia.pdf.

Alzheimer's Society. Alzheimer's Society's view on genetic testing, information updated April 2015 by Laurence Thraves, viewed 26 Dec 2019, https://www.alzheimers.org.uk/about-us/policy-and-influencing/what-we-think/genetic-testing.

Anderson, Jeff. "22 Famous People with Alzheimer's," Seior Living Blog, 16 Oct 2015, viewed 1 Jan 2020, https://www.aplaceformom.com/blog/10-celebrities-with-alzheimers-disease/.

Barba, Christine. "What You Should Know Before Getting a Genetic Test for Alzheimer's." Being Patient. 6 Nov 2018, viewed 26 Dec 2019, https://www.beingpatient.com/genetic-test-for-alzheimers/.

Being Patient, Dec 28, 2018, Good Dogs: Dementia Service Dogs Provide Patients, Caregivers With Improved Quality of Life, viewed 18 Oct 2019, https://www.beingpatient.com/dementia-service-dogs/.

Beyer, Monica. "A Lack of Deep Sleep Could Indicate Alzheimer's Development." *Medical New Today.* Fact checked by Gianna D'Emilio, Healthline Media UK Ltd., 14 January 2019, https://www.medicalnewstoday.com/articles/324161.php#1.

Bolton, Kerra L. and Tausha Robertson. "Self-Care, Caregiving Is Killing Us: A Nation of Daughters in Crisis," Ms X Factor, 1 Oct 2018, viewed 20 Nov 2019, https://msxfactor.com/

caregiving-is-killing-us-a-nation-of-daughters-in-crisis/?fb_
comment_id=1994978420559723_1995895627134669.

Brenoff, Ann. "This is Everything That's Wrong With Caregiving
In America Today, Public policy lags woefully behind today's
reality." *Post 50*, Huff Post, viewed 22 September 2016, https://
www.huffpost.com/entry/this-is-everything-thats-wrong-wit
h-caregiving-in-america-today_n_57e2e78ce4b0e80b1b9fff6e.

Brenoff, Ann. "When Loved Ones Die At Home, Family
Caregivers Pay The Price." Huff Post, 1 June 2017 updated 7
June 2017, viewed 10 Oct 2019, https://www.huffpost.com/entry/
dying-at-home-family-caregivers_n_592738e6e4b0df34c35ab57f.

"Can a direct-to-consumer genetic test tell me whether I will
develop Alzheimer disease?" U.S. National Library of Medicine.
10 Dec 2019, viewed 26 Dec 2019, https://ghr.nlm.nih.gov/
primer/dtcgenetictesting/dtcalzheimer.

"Caregiver Burnout," AginginPlace.org, updated Nov 2019, viewed
2 Jan 2020, https://www.aginginplace.org/caregiver-burnout/.

"Caregiver Support and Resources." Caregiver.com, viewed 26
Dec 2019, https://www.caring.com/caregivers/caregiver-suppor
t/#10-organizations-caregivers-should-know.

"Caregiver Syndrome: How to Support Yourself While Caring for
a Sick Loved One," www.SixWise.com, 13 Aug 2008, viewed 11
Nov 2019, http://www.sixwise.com/Newsletters/2008/August/13/
Caregiver-Syndrome-Support-Yourself-Support-Others.htm.

"Chains." Wikipedia, viewed 13 Jan 2020, https://beatles.fandom.
com/wiki/Chains.

Charvat, Mylea, Ph.D. "Can Sleep Deprivation Cause
Alzheimer's, A growing body of research says yes." *Psychology*

Today, Sussex Publications, 15 July 2019, https://www.psy-chologytoday.com/us/blog/the-fifth-vital-sign/201907/can-sleep-deprivation-cause-alzheimer-s.

Cook, John, compiled and arranged. Edited by Steve Deger and Leslie Ann Gibson. *The Book of Positive Quotations*. 2nd ed. Minneapolis: Fairview Press, 1993.

"Famous People Who Lived With Alzheimer's Disease," The Famous People, viewed 10 Nov 2019, https://www.thefamous-people.com/alzheimers.php.

FDA. (2017, April 6). FDA allows marketing of first direct-to-consumer tests that provide genetic risk information for certain conditions [Press Release] retrieved from https://www.fda.gov/news-events/press-announcements/fda-allows-marketing-first-direct-consumer-tests-provide-genetic-risk-information-certain-conditions text: (FDA, 2017).

Graham, Judith. "Volunteer Group May Provide Care for an Aging America." *Tampa Bay Times* 136, Oct 14, 2019, 1A & 9A.

Griffin, Justine. "Caregiving is a Heavy Burden for Families." Tampa Bay Times 136, 17 Nov 2019, 1A & 6A.

Haugk, Kenneth C. *Journeying through Grief.* Four book series. St. Louis: Stephens Ministries, 2004.

"Help Me Understand Genetics Direct-to-Consumer Genetic Testing" Genetics Home Reference, Lister Hill National Center for Biomedical Communications, U.S. National Library of Medicine, National Institutes of Health, Dept of Health & Human Services, 10 Dec 2019, viewed 26 Dec 2019, reprinted from https://ghr.nlm.nih.gov/.

Horne, Jo. *Caregiving: Helping an Aging Loved One, (A Caregiver's Bill of Rights)*. Washington, D.C.: American Association of Retired Persons; Glenview, IL.: Scott, Foresman, Lifelong Learning Division, 1985.

Horsley, Gloria. "10 Places Grieving Widows Can Get Help." Huff Post, 26 Aug 2015, updated 26 Aug 2016, viewed 26 Dec 2019, https://www.huffpost.com/entry/ten-places-grieving-widow_b_8039916.

"How Sleep Clears the Brain." *National Institutes of Health… Turning Discovery Into Health, NIH Research Matters*, Office of Communications and Public Liaison in the NIH Office of the Director, 28 October 2013, https://www.nih.gov/news-events/nih-research-matters/how-sleep-clears-brain.

Ingber, Ron. "Caregiver Stress Syndrome," Today's Caregiver, 18 Dec 2018, viewed 11 Nov 2019, https://caregiver.com/articles/caregiver-stress-syndrome/.

Johnson, Joy. "Why dying at home is not all it's cracked up to be." The Caregiver Space, 20 July 2015, viewed 10 Oct 2019, https://thecaregiverspace.org/dying-home-not-cracked/.

Kennard, Christine. "Famous people With Alzheimer's Disease and Other Types of Dementia." Verywellhealth, 30 Nov 2019, viewed 15 Jan 2020, https://www.verywellhealth.com/famous-people-with-alzheimers-98082?print.

Kerr, Mandi. "Famous people Who You Probably Didn't Know Had Dementia." Showbiz CheatSheet, 15 Jan 2018, viewed 29 Jan 2020, https://www.cheatsheet.com/health-fitness/famous-people-who-you-probably-didnt-know-had-dementia.html/.

"Lack of Sleep May be Linked to Risk Factor for Alzheimer's Disease." *National Institutes of Health… Turning Discovery Into*

Health, NIH Research Matters, Office of Communications and Public Liaison in the NIH Office of the Director, 13 April 2018, https://www.nih.gov/news-events/lack-sleep-may-be-linked-risk-factor-alzheimers-disease.

LeBlanc, Gary Joseph and Lisa Rodrigues, CDP. *Managing Alzheimer's and Dementia Behaviors (Health Care Edition).* Denver: Outskirtspress, 2016.

Liu, Yan, He-Long Zhang, Jia-Zhuan Mei, Yan-Wei Guo, Rui-Jun Li, Si-Dong Wei, Fu Tian, Lu Yang, and Hui Wang. "Primary mucinous adenocarcinoma of the lung: A case report and review of the literature." *Oncology Letters,* Spandidos Publications, 20 July 2017, viewed October 14 2019, https://www.ncbi.nlm.nih.gov/pmc/articles/PMC5587939/.

Mace, Nancy L., MA, and Peter V. Rabins, MD, MPH. *The 36-Hour Day, A Family Guide to Caring for people Who Have Alzheimer's Disease, Related Dementias, and Memory Loss.* 1981. 5th ed. Grand Central Life & Style, 2011.

McKeehan, Nick. "Avoid Risks, Sleep and Alzheimer's Disease: More Evidence on Their Relationship." *Cognitive Vitality,* Alzheimer's Drug Discovery Foundation, 6 February 2019, https://www.alzdiscovery.org/cognitive-vitality/blog/sleep-and-alzheimers-disease-more-evidence-on-their-relationship.

Mayo Clinic Staff. "Alzheimer's Genes: Are you at risk?" Mayo Clinic, 19 April 2019, viewed 26 Dec 2019, https://www.mayoclinic.org/diseases-conditions/alzheimers-disease/in-depth/alzheimers-genes/art-20046552.

Mayo Clinic Staff. "Alzheimer's: Managing sleep problems." Mayo Clinic, 21 Dec 2019, viewed 26 Dec 2019, https://www.mayoclinic.org/healthy-lifestyle/caregivers/in-depth/alzheimers/art-20047832.

Moon, Seok Whan, Si Young Choi, and Mi Hyoung Moon. "Effect of invasive mucinous adenocarcinoma on lung cancer-specific survival after surgical resection: a population-based study." Journal of Thoracic Disease, June 2018, viewed October 14, 2019, https://www.ncbi.nlm.nih.gov/pmc/articles/PMC6051830/.

"More Irish Terms of Endearment." Claddagh Design, 7 May 2019, *Ireland*, viewed 15 Sept 2019, https://www.claddaghdesign.com/ireland/more-irish-terms-of-endearment/.

"My Love (Petula Clark song)" (18 Sept 2019). Wikipedia, viewed 27 Sept 2019, https://en.wikipedia.org/wiki/My_Love_(Petula_Clark_song).

Napoletan, Ann. How Can Pets Benefit Alzheimer's?, Alzheimer's.net, Sept 4, 2017, viewed 21 Sept 2019, https://www.alzheimers.net/2013-05-17/how-can-pets-benefit-alzheimers-patients/.

National Institute on Aging, May 22, 2019, Alzheimer's Disease Fact Sheet, viewed 18 June 2019, https://www.nia.nih.gov/health/alzheimers-disease-fact-sheet.

National Institute on Aging. "Causes of Alzheimer's Disease, Alzheimer's Disease Genetics Fact Sheet" content reviewed 30 Aug 2015, viewed 26 Dec 2019, https://www.nia.nih.gov/health/alzheimers-disease-genetics-fact-sheet#testing.

Paulk, Adina, Fabio Tavora, Allen Burke. "Pulmonary mucinous adenocarcinomas: a clinicopathologic series with emphasis on the prognostic significance of spread through alveolar spaces, and the presence of solid growth component," *Surgical and Experimental Pathology*, vol. 1, no. 1, Gale Academic Onefile, 23 Oct 2018, viewed Jan 13 2020, https://go.gale.com/ps/anonymous?id=-GALE%7CA603082628&sid=googleScholar&v=2.1&it=r&linkaccess=abs&issn=25208454&p=AONE&sw=w.

Rand Corporation. (2014, October 27). Cost of Informal Caregiving for U.S. elderly is $522 Billion Annually [Press Release] Retrieved from https://www.rand.org/news/press/2014/10/27.html.
text: (Rand Corporation, Office of Media Relations, 2014).

"Recognizing Caregiver Burnout." *WebMD*, reviewed by James Beckman, MD, FACC on 1 June 2018, Web MD Medical Reference https://www.webmd.com/healthy-aging/caregiver-recognizing-burnout#1.

Sauer, Alissa. "One Night of Poor Sleep Can Affect Your Alzheimer's Risk." *Alzheimers.net*, A Place for Mom, 24 July 2017, https://www.alzheimers.net/one-night-of-poor-sleep-can-affect-alzheimers-risk/.

Sauer, Alissa. "The Connection Between Sleep Disruption and Alzheimer's." *Alzheimers.net*, A Place for Mom, 26 July 2017, https://www.alzheimers.net/2016-03-09/connection-between-sleep-and-alzheimers/.

"Should You Get the Genetic Test for Alzheimer's Disease Risk?" Cleveland Clinic, 10 July 2019, Brain & Spine, viewed 26 Dec 2019, https://health.clevelandclinic.org/should-you-get-the-genetic-test-for-alzheimers-disease-risk/.

"Sleep Deprivation Increases Alzheimer's Protein." *National Institutes of Health...Turning Discovery Into Health, NIH Research Matters*, Office of Communications and Public Liaison in the NIH Office of the Director, 24 April 2018, https://www.nih.gov/news-events/nih-research-matters/sleep-deprivation-increases-alzheimers-protein.

Small, Barbara. "Caregiver Syndrome," Family Caregivers' Network Society, Family Caregivers of British Columbia, https://

www.familycaregiversbc.ca/wp-content/uploads/2016/03/
Caregiver-Syndrome.pdf.

Tasaki, Susan. "Dementia Assistance Dogs, Expanding the fron-
tiers of the canine capacity to help us carry on." Bark the dog
culture magazine, July 2015, viewed 1 Dec 2019, https://thebark.
com/content/dementia-assistance-dogs.

"The High Cost of Caregiving," American Psychological
Association, 26 June 2006, viewed 15 Jan 2020, https://www.
apa.org/research/action/caregiving.

The Holy Bible, King James Version. Cleveland and New York:
The World Publishing Company, n.d.

Wagley, Ron. *Finding Strength in Tough Times, A Biblical Approach
for Conquering Life's Hardships*. Boise, Idaho: Russell Media, 2012.

Washington University School of Medicine. "Sleep deprivation
accelerates Alzheimer's brain damage." ScienceDaily, 24
January 2019. https://www.sciencedaily.com/releases/2019/
01/190124141536.htm.

"West African Rhinoceros." Wikipedia.26 Dec 2019, viewed 11 Jan
2020. https://en.wikipedia.org/wiki/Western_black_rhinoceros.

Additional Resources

Caregiving

The following is not an all inclusive list of resources. Also check with your local libraries, house of worship, state and local governments in addition to your physician, and social media.

AARP: https://www.aarp.org/caregiving/local/info-2017/important-resources-for-caregivers.html
Membership organization with resources throughout the United States

Alzheimer's Association: http://www.alz.org
24/7 Helpline (365 days a year): 800-272-3900

Alzheimer's Caregiver 24 Hour HELPLINE: 855-476-7600

Alzheimer's Disease Education and Referral Center (ADEAR):
https://www.nia.nih.gov/alzheimers
1-800-438-4380 (Sponsored by the National Institute on Aging)

Alzheimer's Foundation of America: www.alzfdn.org
National Toll-Free Hotline: 866-232-8484

American Society of Aging: https://www.asaging.org/blo
g/25-organizations-take-care-caregivers
Membership organization, based in California, 800-537-9728
(8:30 am–8:30 pm ET)

Association for Fronto-Temporal Degeneration: http://www.
theaftd.org/
1-866-507-7222 (Helpline)

Caregiver Action Network: https://caregiveraction.org/resources/
agencies-and-organizations

Caring.com: https://www.caring.com/
800-973-1540

Eldercare Locator: www.eldercare.gov
1-800-677-1116

Family Caregiver Alliance: http://caregiver.org
California based, information resource

Lewy Body Dementia Association: https://www.lbda.org
1-800-539-9767

National Alliance for Caregiving: https://www.caregiving.org/
202-918-1013

National Parkinson's Foundation: http://www.parkinson.org
1-800-4PD-INFO (Helpline)

Veteran's Administration: https://www.caregiver.va.gov/
844-698-2311

Widowhood

The following represents a sampling of the resources available for widows and widowers. Also check with your local libraries, house of worship, state and local governments. There are private groups in social media you can request membership to as well.

Hope for Widows Foundation: https://hopeforwidows.org/

National Widowers Organization: https://nationalwidowers.org/

Soaring Spirits International: https://www.soaringspirits.org/someone-i-care-about-is-widowed

The Sisterhood of Widows, We Grieve and Heal Together: https://sisterhoodofwidows.com/

Top Fifty Widow Blogs and Websites for Widows and Widowers in 2019: https://blog.feedspot.com/widow_blogs/

Widowed Persons Service, Growing Through Grief: https://www.wpsgr.org/

Women's Institute for Financial Education: https://www.wife.org/widowhood

The Veasey Group

Pointing the Way to Happier Hearts
Alzheimer's   Caregiving   Widowhood

No one but another WIDOW can understand what a widow or widower goes through

And no one but another CAREGIVER knows what a dementia caregiver goes through

VICKI VEASEY

Author ⋅ Advocate ⋅ Speaker
Widow & Caregiving Coach

Take the *Widows and Widowers Happier Heart Assessment* at www.vickiveasey.com to point you in the direction on how to:

» Understand the grieving process
» Become more self-sufficient
» Embrace the new chapter in your life
» Prepare your heart to love again

Vicki is available for:
» Speaking Engagements
» Book Club Webinars
» Educational Workshops
» Live Webinars
» Guest Blog Author

Vicki welcomes the opportunity to participate at your next event and can be contacted at: info@vickiveasey.com

Additional information is available at her website:
www.vickiveasey.com

Take the *Caregivers Happier Heart Assessment* at www.vickiveasey.com to point you in the direction on how to:

» Avoid caregiver burnout
» Refocus your loved one's behavior
» Keep your loved one engaged
» Prepare for the death of your loved one

About the Author

Vicki Veasey is an author, advocate, speaker, and caregiving & widowhood coach who helps others maintain sanity and humor amidst widowhood, caregiving and Alzheimer's. She assists friends to embrace the joy in each new day, providing insight on caring with a loving heart, and guiding the heart in response to a loved one's transition, pointing the way to a happier heart.

Made in the USA
Monee, IL
05 August 2020